Best Wishes.

Mike [illegible]

19.10.04

In loving memory of Sally, 1976 – 1992
Who spent all her short life in The Feldon.

First published in the U.K. in 2004 by A.M.A.Woods BSc. (Agric.)

I wish to thank the following for reading certain chapters and making suggestions for valuable amendments:

F.J.Bennison; Professor A.K.Giles OBE; Mrs. Joan Hughes; M.Hutchings; T.Mahon; B.Rawson MRCVS; C.Reid; the late David Slatter; J,.Walton ARICS; J.Wheeler; M.J.Woods.

Also many others for their help and encouragement in many ways, and those who have provided slides and photographs.

My special thanks to Nick Woods, without whose help this book would never have been published. Also to Emily Mackinnon-Little for drawing the map and to Lesley Shepherd for her tireless support.

Editorial work – Adrian Rawlings of Euronet Associates Ltd.

Printed by Marston Book Services Ltd.

ISBN 1 85580 032 2.

Contents

List of figures

FOREWORD

During the sixty years, or so, between the end of the Second World War and the appearance of this book, change has impacted upon virtually every aspect of British life, including farming, at an unprecedented rate. In *Almost All from Memory,* Mike Woods has recorded, from his personal involvement and observation, the nature and extent of farming change that has occurred in one particular part of the country, South Warwickshire, Shakespeare's countryside.

Much of what he has written, however, tracing the change from the 'dog and stick' days of the 1930s to today's much more specialised and capital intensive methods, typifies what has occurred more universally. He has described what has happened to all of the main agricultural enterprises, as well as some of the newer and lesser ones. With the Vale of Evesham nearby, horticulture has not been left out and, importantly, neither have many socio-economic influences that have changed much of rural life out of all recognition.

A member of the National Agricultural Advisory Service (later ADAS) since its inception in 1946, the author devotes a whole chapter to its continuously changing role in order to meet the needs of an ever-changing industry. He highlights the provision of farm business management advice as the wartime national demand for *food at any cost*, gave way, in the 1950s and 1960s, to the need for farms to be managed in a more business-like manner.

The role of the university-based economists in training NAAS personnel in this discipline is acknowledged, including my own involvement (from Reading) across a large part of Central Southern England. There were no counties in this region, except, perhaps, the trend-setting Gloucestershire, where the whole county staff were as committed as they were in Warwickshire to offering farm business management advice. And there were few on the Warwickshire staff more committed than Mike Woods himself.

It is clear that this approach has influenced all that he has undertaken over the years, which, as the reader will discover, has extended well beyond giving help and guidance to farmers, and well beyond his years of formal employment. Mike Woods has called his book *Almost All from Memory*. Well, if that is so, he has a very long and capacious one! But no doubt helped by the weekly farming column he wrote for nearly forty years for the Stratford *Herald*, copies of every one of which are now, happily, safely lodged in the Archives of the Shakespeare Centre, Stratford-upon-Avon.

For that, as well as for his very informative and readable book, all those who already have, or will have in the future, an interest in South Warwickshire, and its farming, will be grateful to Mike. They will learn that he spurned any attempt to promote himself away from the countryside in which he lived and worked for a lifetime, and which he has written about here, without wearing rose-tinted spectacles, but from his heart as well as with his head.

By Professor A.K. Giles OBE
(Emeritus Professor of Farm Management, University of Reading)

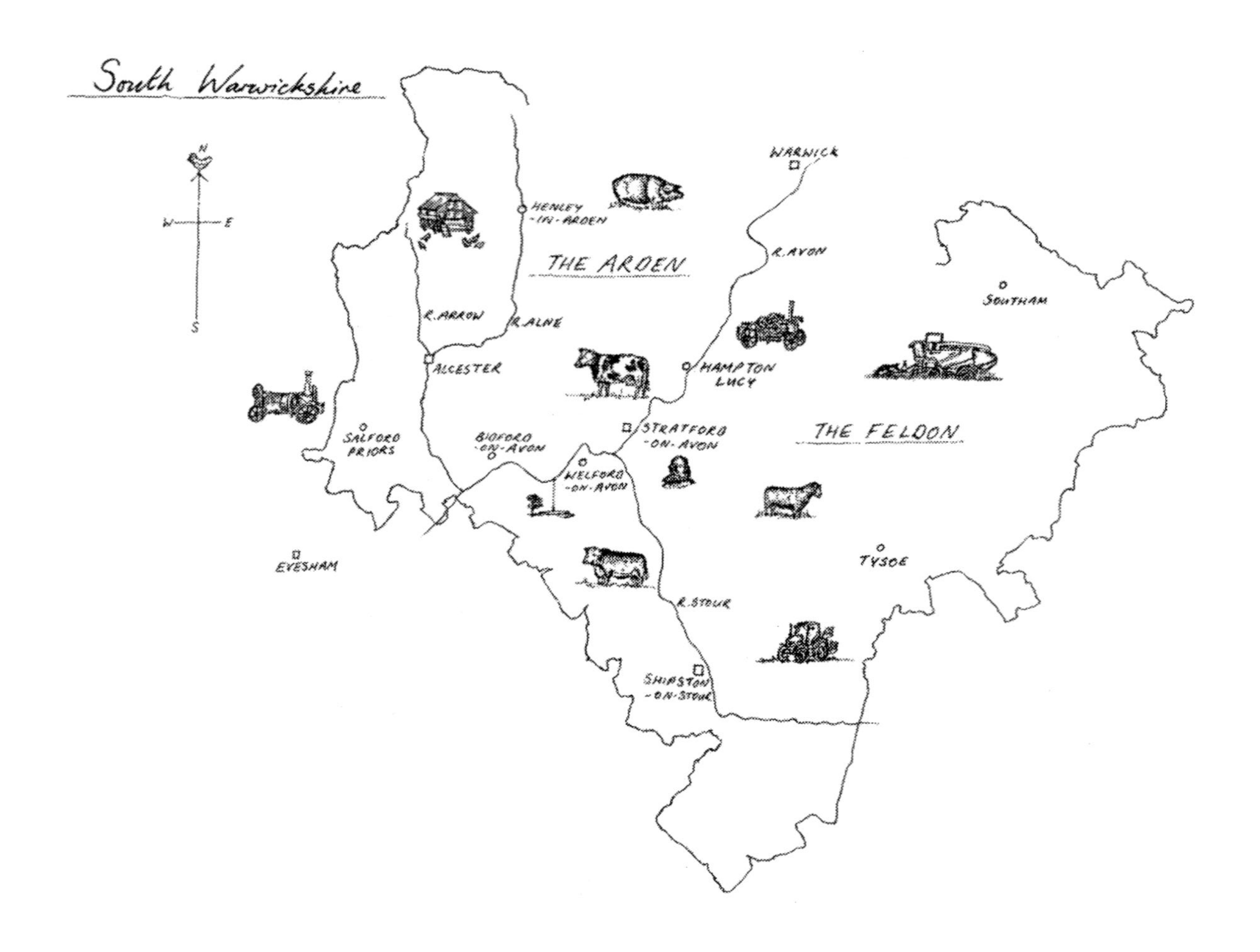
South Warwickshire
N
W
E
S
HENLEY -IN-ARDEN
WARWICK
THE ARDEN
R. AVON
SOUTHAM
R. ARROW
R. ALNE
ALCESTER
HAMPTON LUCY
SALFORD PRIORS
BIDFORD -ON-AVON
STRATFORD -ON-AVON
THE FELDON
WELFORD -ON-AVON
EVESHAM
TYSOE
R. STOUR
SHIPSTON -ON-STOUR

INTRODUCTION

Almost all from memory

Changes in Shakespeare's countryside - a personal view

In December 1943, as part of my official duties, I started the Aston Cantlow Farmers' Discussion Club, meeting in the back room of the King's Head in that village, once a month, during the winter. This flourished, becoming well supported and popular with local farmers. It is, in fact, still in existence today, albeit in a different form and with a different venue.

On the fiftieth anniversary of its founding, Club members asked me to give a talk on what farming was like when the Club first met. Eventually, I published my recollections in a small booklet entitled *Almost All From Memory*. This new, much longer, book takes the story on over the second half of the 20th. century. It's an extension of the same theme, so I have retained the original title.

The onlooker sees most of the game, or so it is said. Thus since 1943 I have been an onlooker of the farming scene in South Warwickshire, first as District Technical Officer employed by the Warwickshire War Agricultural Executive Committee, to give that organisation its full title, but more commonly known as the *War Ag*. Following this, I was a founder member of the National Agricultural Advisory Service which came into being in 1946, where I was a crop husbandry specialist in the West Midlands and, subsequently, District Adviser based in Stratford-upon-Avon, covering at one time or another the whole of South Warwickshire.

Having survived the various re-organisations (an occupational hazard when working in the Ministry of Agriculture), including a change of name to the Agricultural Development and Advisory Service in the early 1970s, and having been careful to avoid promotion, I beavered away happily, and gratefully, in that capacity for thirty three summers.

But for most of those long years I was also in my 'spare' time a visiting lecturer in farm business management and farm records and accounts at the Warwickshire Agricultural College, the Agricultural Departments in the Banbury and Witney Colleges and at Studley College; only two at a time, I would hasten to add. Also, for thirty nine years, I wrote a weekly farming column for the Stratford paper *The Herald*, of which copies of every article are now deposited in the archives of the Shakespeare Centre, Stratford-upon-Avon. While these constitute a week-by-week commentary on current farming affairs with, of course, particular reference to South Warwickshire, this book is an attempt to record all the changes that have taken in the South Warwickshire countryside from the 1940s onwards.

When the time came to retire from ADAS (as early as possible, at the age of sixty), I started afresh, being retained by Sheldon Bosley & Co., a Stratford firm of estate agents. Here, for five years, I was engaged in agricultural consultancy and also carried out those duties normally associated with agricultural land agents.

After my time with this firm, I finally went on my own as an agricultural consultant. As the years slipped by, I gradually reduced my commitments until I ended up spending all my working time helping in the management of a 1,000 acre mixed farm between Stratford and Alcester. To paraphrase an old saying 'Those who can, do, and those who can't, advise.' During this last phase of my working life, my swan song, I think I can claim that I could 'do.'

An uneventful career, if you can call it that. But at least I was able to make some sort of a living without stirring very far from the parish; without having to *fidget about all over the auction* as the country saying goes. And I had the advantage of a front seat from which to watch, at the grass roots and in some detail, the great changes which have taken place in farming and the countryside in the centre of England during the second half of the 20th century. But, of course, such changes have also occurred over this period in many other Midland counties.

The generation to which I belong, and I count myself fortunate to have been born when I was, has seen the main power sources available to farmers, which were the muscles of horse and man, replaced by the diesel engine and mains electricity. The milking parlour, yards and cubicle sheds have replaced the cowpen. The milk churn has gone, so has the self binder and threshing drum, to be replaced by the bulk milk tank and the combine harvester respectively. Fifty years ago, an adequate labour force on a mixed farm in South Warwickshire would have been considered to be three workers on a hundred acres. Today one man on three hundred acres would be nearer the mark, on what might well have become an all-arable holding.

Most farms of one hundred acres, or less, which half a century ago would have supported a man and his family, have disappeared and have been absorbed into broader acres. The number of dairy herds has been much reduced, the survivors increasing greatly in size. Egg, poultry and pig meat production have become concentrated into specialist units, some are still situated on farms, others occupying only a few acres.

In many parts of the country, and certainly in South Warwickshire, village society is no longer primarily agrarian. Villages were populated mainly by those who earned their living from the land – farmers, market gardeners, their families and hired workers – or those who used to provide them with essential services, such as blacksmiths, saddlers, wheelwrights, country millers and merchants, and those that worked for them.

The shop, post office, and even the garage and village school have all closed in many a village. This is certainly the case in many villages in South Warwickshire. And all because the motor car has enabled those who work in towns and cities to live in the countryside and commute.

These now account, along with the retired, for by far the highest proportion of the population in most villages and hamlets. They shop in the nearest supermarket and still, being essentially urban in outlook, look outside the parish for their social and leisure activities. Such people may live in the countryside, but are certainly not of it. Village society as it was fifty years ago is no more. The process of suburbanisation is now complete in many Home Counties and Midland villages, and South Warwickshire is no exception.

From 1939 to 1953 food was rationed. For a further thirty years or so farmers were encouraged to modernise and increase production. But during the last decade all this has changed. EU food surpluses, despite the fact that they represent only some weeks' supply at current rates of consumption, and serve a generation which has never gone shopping with a ration book, have demonstrated only too clearly that full bellies make for empty minds.

The concepts of *environment* and *conservation* have been invented, and modern farming practices are considered to be detrimental to both. Ample supplies of a wide range of foods are now taken for granted by urban dwellers. And since I started writing these pages, the worst agricultural depression for sixty years has hit the farming community. But that's another story.

The effects of the agricultural revolution of the last fifty years have been countrywide. In South Warwickshire these have been profound. Traditionally a county of mixed, or mainly grassland, farms, here one can see the trend towards specialisation at its most pronounced.

All-arable farms, even on the heaviest clayland, are now commonplace. On many holdings where milk is still produced, the other enterprises have been abandoned and the dairy herd expanded. The number of truly mixed farms has much diminished.

Happily, farm workers have shared in the general prosperity of farming, unlike during the comparable period in the 19th century. Their lot, and standard of living, has improved out of all recognition during the period covered by this book, and quite rightly so.

The following pages set out a very personal view of all those changes in crop and livestock husbandry, in management techniques, and in rural society, which have taken place in South Warwickshire during the second half of the 20th century.

1. Setting The Scene

South Warwickshire

Warwickshire – the centre of England – is, in effect, two counties, North and South. The latter, with which we are concerned, is the countryside of Shakespeare – the Forest of Arden and the Feldon. Fifty years ago, this part of the country was mainly rural, with many of those in the villages still earning their living, directly or indirectly, from the land.

The north and central parts of Warwickshire have some very good land and excellent farming but were, and still are, more industrial thanks to domination by Coventry and Birmingham. Atherstone and Nuneaton were formerly centres of coal mining.

Historically, much of Warwickshire was divided into two parts, Arden and Feldon, with the River Avon as the dividing line between them. The Arden, lying to the north of the river, with much of it, but by no means all, in South Warwickshire, was well wooded. This is the Forest of Arden, which has a large proportion of the farmland under pasture, and was enclosed piecemeal as it was reclaimed from woodland and waste. The Feldon, which lies to the south of the Avon, was unenclosed, corn growing country, with the great open fields lying in ridge and furrow, surrounding the villages that contained the church, manor house, farmsteads, cottages and crofts.

Standing on the hill above Long Compton, with the main road Oxford bound, and with the mysterious Rollright Stones nearby, you will see the Feldon spread out like a map below you. Or again on Campden Hill above Ilmington, below the field called Nebsworth with its radio towers, you will be looking across the Feldon countryside with, in the blue distance to the north of Stratford-upon-Avon, the Arden. Or on the Ridgeway, by the hamlet of Weethley, with Ragley Hall and its park below you and behind you, to the west, the county boundary with Worcestershire, you will be looking across the valleys of the Avon, Arrow and Alne with the Feldon beyond and the Arden to the north and north east. This is the South Warwickshire about which I shall be writing.

It is a countryside of river valleys. The Avon, now navigable again as far as Alveston, flows south westerly from Warwick, by Stratford, leaving the county near Salford Priors, on its way to join the Severn. The infant Stour enters the county at Traitors Ford near Brailes, flows west to Mitford Bridge and then north to lose itself in the Avon at Clifford Chambers. The River Alne flows through Arden country, past Aston Cantlow and the ancient dovecot at Kinwarton to its junction with the Arrow at Alcester. The latter passes below Ragley, by Wixford and Broom to join the Avon at the county boundary below Marlciffe.

In addition to the main rivers, South Warwickshire is veined with the little streams, possessing delightful names, that feed them. For example, Nerthercote Brook, Pig Brook, Tus Brook, and Cod Brook are just a few that swell the Stour. Thelsford Brook, Marchfont Brook and the River Dene – the latter being somewhat of a courtesy title; all empty into the Avon, and Ban Brook into the Arrow. And many more besides, all carrying water from field and farmstead by way of ditches and watercourses to join the river flow to its ultimate destination, the sea.

Thus South Warwickshire lies partly in the Feldon and partly in Arden, for the River Avon flows through it from north east to south west. Much of it lies south of the river and is, by definition, Feldon country. But there is an area north of the river, some on clay, some on marl and some on the easier working river valley land, which is, to my mind, more typically Feldon. This area comprises the parishes of Binton, Temple Grafton, Billesley, Haselor, Aston Cantlow & Old Stratford and Drayton, being bounded on the south by the Avon and on the north by its tributary, the Alne. Here the villages resemble those of the Feldon, being nucleated with farmsteads within them, the meadows along the river banks and the old arable fields, now enclosed, radiating away to the parish boundaries. Aston Cantlow is a typical example.

The Feldon

Apart from the lighter soils of the Avon, Stour, Arrow and Alne valleys, those south of a line from Burmington to Brailes and along the county boundary with Oxfordshire, the Feldon is predominantly clayland with pockets of lighter land, the remains of eroded river terraces, on some of the higher ground; Welford and Idlicote are good examples.

Always in need of under-drainage, difficult to cultivate, naturally very deficient in phosphate, essentially autumn drilling land, the Warwickshire clays, derived from the Lower Lias, have in the past always been marginal land in terms of arable cropping. They may well prove to be so again, in spite of a degree of mechanisation undreamt of half a century ago and modern agritechnology (*bag and bottle farming*) in all its aspects.

Not surprisingly, during the agricultural depressions of the last quarter of the 19th century and the inter-war years of the 20th, some of South Warwickshire reverted to poor pasture and even thorn scrub. The cultivation of these clays, at any time in the past and in the present, is made possible only by the fact that they lie in a district of low rainfall, some 24"/year.

Fig. 1 Brailes Church. The Cathedral of the Feldon

Before the Enclosures, which proceeded apace in this district during the last quarter of the 18th century and the first quarter of the 19th, this was open field country with meadow land by the rivers and streams and arable open fields stretching away to the wastes and woodlands on the manor boundaries. Typically there would be three great fields, worked on a rotation of two corn crops followed by a fallow. But there would be many variations locally, with beans sometimes being grown, a traditional heavy land crop. Villagers would hold a number of strips in each field, would have the right to mow an acreage of meadow for hay, rights to pasture cattle on the common and run swine on the wastes and in the woodland.

Oxen were used to cultivate this land and gave rise to the characteristic ridge and furrow, which were always in the shape of an inverted-S. The reason for this was that the plough teams always had to turn to the left on the headland. when drawing out of the work. The mouldboards of the ploughs in those days were straight, not curved as they are today, and made of wood rather than steel, pear wood being preferred as it scoured better in the sticky clay. These mouldboards had to press up on the furrow slice to stop it falling back down the ridge as the plough pulled out. If the teams of probably three, or even four, oxen in line had turned in the opposite direction (*i.e.* to the right) this would certainly have happened.

There was, of course, no under-drainage. Water drained off the ridges and into the furrows which acted as open drains. Channels were dug by hand across the headlands to let the water off into the ditches. Thus the lay-out of ridge and furrow always took into account the lie of the land, so that water could flow in the desired direction.

Digging such channels through the headland ridge was considered essential practice right up to modern times. I can well recall, when he was a *War Ag* district committee member, walking a farm with Mr. Jack Steele of Clifford Chambers. At one point he admonished, in no uncertain terms, a farmer of the younger generation for failing to dig such grips to let water off the winter corn, which was clearly suffering from waterlogging as a consequence.

Each individual strip in these open fields was divided from its neighbour by a narrow grass strip, or balk. Thorns often grew on these, on which sheep, when grazing the stubbles or fallows, left wisps of wool. Arthur Young, the well known writer and commentator on agricultural affairs in the late 18th and early 19th centuries, when describing farming on the Warwickshire clays, noticed this and remarked 'it gave the countryside a somewhat beggarly appearance.' He also observed that the crops were poor and put this down to 'the attempt to farm such land with too little capital.' In other words too few men, oxen or horses, leading to untimely cultivations and late planting.

Caird, author of *English Farming*, writing some fifty years later, makes the same point about farming in the county as a whole. This is something that, in modern times and in terms of sufficient labour and numbers of tractors of adequate power, strikes a familiar note. In passing, one might speculate that a chronic phosphate deficiency could also have been the cause of these poor crops.

Even today, ridge and furrow is a common enough sight in the Feldon, preserved in their original state in fields that have been in permanent pasture since the enclosure of the parish in which they are sited. Many a ridge and furrow appears to go straight through hedges but, of course, these were planted across them when the open fields were enclosed.

Where ridge and furrow was ploughed down during the food production campaign in the 1940s or later, it still leaves a tell-tale mark on the landscape. Tractor ploughs split the ridges to level them, filling the furrows with good topsoil and leaving the tops of the ridges with precious little earth above the yellowish clay subsoil beneath. This caused problems initially and, indeed, for some years after such land was brought into cultivation.

The corn was often poor and starved along the line where the ridges had been, obut tended to lodge in the former furrows where the greatest depth of the best soil lay. Such was the difference between the two that some farmers even went to the extent of broadcasting Sulphate of Ammonia (then the most common form of nitrogenous fertiliser) by hand along the poorest part of the former ridges, where the corn was yellow, thin leaved and looking miserable. Today one still sees the vestiges of the old ridge and furrow in what are now flat, arable fields in the form of alternating strips of light and dark soil curling away from headland to headland, the former marking the line of the former ridges and the latter the furrows.

Fig. 2 Crimscote Downs before reclamation in 1943-44. (Joan Hughes)

Compared to the Arden, Feldon farms and thus post-enclosure fields were much larger. Original holdings in the Feldon, that is those that were immediately post-enclosure, often fell into the acreage range 225 to 275. Some might have been larger and many have been enlarged in the course of time by amalgamation of holdings, by absorbing smaller farms, or by adding acres of bare land. Conversely, and as part and parcel of the same process, other farms have become fragmented, leaving, on occasion just the house, the farm buildings and a few acres to provide 'a place in the country' for an urban incomer.

Typically villages in the Feldon are nucleated, that is to say the farm houses and farm buildings are sited within the boundaries of the village, with possibly only a small amount of land directly adjacent to them, the remainder lying away in what were formerly the open fields.

Farmsteads that lie outside the village, surrounded by their own fields, are often post-enclosure. Crimscote Fields Farm is a classic example. Again, such farmsteads may represent the vestiges of a former, but now deserted, village. Burton Farm, Bishopton and the nearby holdings are good examples, as are Longdon Manor and Compton Scorpion Manor near Shipston-on-Stour.

Mills often had some land going with them, originally probably for the miller's horses. Over the years more acres have been added to make sizeable farms well away from the nearest village. Fell Mill near Honington is one such and there are others.

The fact that so many farmsteads are still located within villages or hamlets has given rise to social problems now that the rural population is no longer predominantly agrarian. In passing, it might be mentioned that the farming

Fig. 3 (upper) House and buildings at Crimscote Fields Farm – an example of a post-enclosure farmstead . (lower) Remains of open fields, with thorns growing along the lines of former balks.

industry is given little credit for releasing substantial numbers of farm houses and cottages to swell the rural housing stock, as farms were amalgamated and the labour force dwindled to a shadow of its former size. Such dwellings are now occupied by incomers from towns and cities, who bring with them urban attitudes and commute daily to their work in offices, factories or wherever. Many villages in South Warwickshire are now completely suburbanised, although the new countrymen would not admit it, with street lighting as the final degradation. Having a farmyard as a neighbour, with the associated smells and noises inseparable from the countryside about its business, can come as a cultural shock to incomers. Of this, more later.

The face of the Feldon was altered, probably for all time, by Dutch Elm Disease. For the elm was by far the most common hedgerow tree in this district, known formerly as the *Warwickshire Weed.* During the war years and just after, one could always tell land which had been taken in hand by the *War Ag.* One of the first things done was to lop all the lower branches of the elms and other hedgerow trees. This was done to allow light and air to accelerate the drying of hay in the swathe, or corn in the stook, lying on the headlands.

Today there are no elms to be seen, except those which manage to grow to no more than fifteen to eighteen feet high before they succumb to the disease. Looking at old colour slides or photographs it comes as something of a shock to realise just how much the appearance of the South Warwickshire countryside has been altered by a natural agent. By contrast human activity seems puny in comparison.

The Arden

In contrast to the Feldon, little of the Arden, or rather that part of it which is situated in South Warwickshire, was never open field country. Heavily wooded, there were settlements which still survive today in names such as Danzey Green, Blunts Green and so on. A *green* is a clearing in the surrounding woodland or forest, with its hamlet or small village and the small fields which sustained it inhabitants. As the need arose, land was cleared from the surrounding woodland or waste – *assarted* as this practice was called – and added to the existing farms or smallholdings.

Typically farms, and thus fields, were smaller than those in the neighbouring Feldon. Moreover, this pattern was laid down well before the industrial revolution and expansion of Birmingham and the Black Country with their burgeoning populations. It was thus a curious quirk of history that the small livestock farms of the Arden became so well suited to supply the needs of the rapidly expanding markets of what was to become the City of Birmingham and its suburbs.

These holdings were on the doorstep of the conurbations, and were very well suited to supply those livestock products that were perishable and thus could not be transported over considerable distances, especially before the coming of the railways. Such produce included milk, eggs, table poultry and pig meat, all of which were traditional small farm products. The smaller farms bought in extra acres by the purchase of feedstuffs for cows, pigs and poultry, especially when formulated compounds became available after the First World War. This is in sharp contrast to the broader acres of the Feldon farms that relied more on beef and lamb, the products of the grazing animal, and on corn growing.

In the case of milk, and long before the existence of the Milk Marketing Board, there was a good trade supplying the liquid market in Birmingham and other urban areas. Fowlers of Earlswood had a number of retail rounds in and around the south of Birmingham. I can well remember seeing a row of horse-drawn milk floats in a field on Forest Farm in the early 1940s, shafts pointing skywards, destined never to be used again.

In the offices of the National Agricultural Advisory Service, then in Guy's Cliffe Avenue, Leamington Spa, there was a large wall map of Warwickshire dotted with round headed pins of many colours. These indicated the location of every dairy herd in the county, the different colours denoting herd size, blue being for the smallest herds of twenty cows or less. There was a dense tightly packed ring of these running around Birmingham and its suburbs, from the south in an arc to the east and north east of the city. Even in the 1950s eggs, table poultry and pigmeat were still the main products of these small farms, as well as milk.

Generally speaking, because farms were typically smaller than those in the Feldon, the farm house and farm buildings were on a like scale. Although there were plenty of fine, spacious farm houses in the Arden, a great many were quite small, in some cases little bigger than cottages. Often these formed one side of a square, with the buildings grouped around the other three.

Fig. 4 A South Warwickshire scene with sheep grazing in Quinton parish before Dutch Elm Disease changed the face of the South Warwickshire countryside. (pre-1970s)

These would consist, usually, of a cowpen, a small brick barn, a stable, an open fronted cattle yard, the odd loose box and a pigsty. All these were fronted by a narrow brick causeway. In the old days one stepped off this at one's peril. In the centre of the square was often a quagmire, and around the sides was the muckheap formed by the simple process of slinging wet straw and dung through the open doorways of the cowpen, stable, loose box etc. Sometimes, and unhappily under or in close proximity to the midden, was situated the farm well that supplied stock and farmhouse alike, not to mention the washing water for the dairy utensils!

Today, many of the small farmsteads have been gentrified, being within easy commuting distance of Birmingham and Coventry. The well-rutted tracks from the public road to the farm have been levelled and surfaced with red tarmac, flanked, as often as not, by the inevitable white painted lamp post, a relic of the original street lighting in some town or city. Needless to say the farmhouse has been converted into a residence, the old stable now houses the daughter's pony and the barn and cowpen have been made into a granny flat.

Farms, hamlets and villages in the Arden are served by narrow, winding lanes, sunk deep between the surrounding fields – a whole maze of them – which take a newcomer many months to find his, or her, way around. This is in sharp contrast to the Feldon, where there are some Roman roads, notably the Fosse and Icknield Street, running more or less in a characteristic straight line. Many more roads were laid down, also as straight as a die, when parishes were enclosed.

These small farms, so typical of The Arden, were worked almost exclusively with family labour with little, if any, outside help. As already mentioned, they were essentially livestock holdings that sent their products to nearby markets. In consequence, and due to the fact that comparatively little paid labour was employed, farming in The Arden appeared to suffer less from the acute depression of the last quarter of the 19th century and the years between the World Wars than the corn, beef and sheep farms of the Feldon. Incidentally, many of these were forced to turn to milk production during these hard times.

This is not to say that, at the beginning of the Second World War, the Arden was a prosperous farming district, far from it. But in 1939, at the outset of the food production campaign, it was significant that there were more farms in the Feldon than in the Arden that were semi-derelict, or completely derelict land, wet, covered with anthills, tussock grass and scrub.

In the former, and on its larger farms, there was no great tradition of dairying, unless for cheese making. *Dog and Stick* farming was the reaction to hard times. This meant that low stocking rates led, inevitably, to the deterioration of the grassland. Another factor was the greater reliance on paid labour on Feldon farms. When the bad times came the first economy to be made was a reduction in the numbers employed. Arable land was allowed to fall down to grass, maintenance work all but ceased with the consequences that were only too obvious when the need to increase food production became urgent.

In the Arden, and elsewhere for that matter, between farm and farm, farmhouse and farmhouse, and farming family and farming family, there were great differences. Some of the holdings were well run. By the standards of the day, the cows were of a good type, yielding well and grazed on grassland that at least saw some lime and basic slag. What little arable there was usually provided kale and mangolds for the cows and a few oats to be fed to the horses and other stock. What went on outside was usually reflected in the farmhouse, all being clean, tidy and well ordered.

As in the Feldon, there were farmers in the Arden of whom this could not be written. In the case of the latter, cows existed during the winter on poor hay, the product of traditional hay meadows, now beloved by some who have never had to make a living from the land, and on purchased cake. The grassland was little more than an exercise ground, except in the height of the grass growing season – poor swards which never saw a bag of basic slag, nor a dressing of lime. The minimum amount of straw was bought and the cattle were sometimes in a sorry plight towards the end of the winter, caked with muck and with none too much dry lying. If there was any arable land, crops were poor and thin, with docks, thistles and other weeds in abundance. Indoors, the state of the farmhouse was, only too often, a reflection of the conditions outdoors.

Both the soils and climate of the Arden are very different from those of the Feldon. Apart from the river valleys of the Arrow and Alne, most of the Arden soils overlie Keuper Marl. The surface texture varies from a marly clay, through marly loams, loams and even light loams. In spite of marl being calcareous, Arden topsoils are often acid, deficient in phosphate and often in potash as well. The poorest land is to be found on the higher ground nearest to Birmingham, above Liveridge Hill on the Stratford road and Gorcott Hill north of Studley.

These two hills also mark the dividing line between the kinder climate of the lower Arden and Feldon, with its comparatively low rainfall, and the wetter, colder weather typical of the plateau near to Birmingham. Those familiar with the district will know, only too well, that on a winter's morning fog and frost will have cleared on the lower ground but will persist well into the late morning, or all day, above Liveridge or Gorcott.

A distinctive feature of the Arden, not to be found in the Feldon, are the marl pits. In the days before lime could be transported any distance, before the use of inorganic fertilisers became common, and when the maintenance of fertility depended upon farmyard manure and folded sheep, marling was a common practice in the Arden, and elsewhere, where the red clay was near enough to the surface. As mentioned above, red marl is calcareous and this, when dug and spread on the overlying acid topsoil, reduces acidity, may provide some potash and improves the texture of the lighter land.

Marl pits, or rather the remains of them, may be little more than a depression in the middle of a field, or a deep pit with sloping sides, too deep to cultivate and by now holding water and tree fringed, an ideal haven for wild life of all kinds. These pits, especially the larger ones, may have been dug where two or more fields meet, so that the marl could be carted over as short a distance as possible.

Arden and Feldon, then, are the two distinct parts of South Warwickshire. They differ substantially in both soils and climate and also in the type of farming, although the latter distinction has become less marked in modern times.

But there is a third division, the river valleys in both areas, where much of the easier working land is found. In days gone by, much of the land in the lower reaches of the Avon and Arrow in particular, was market gardened, constituting a northern extension of the Vale of Evesham. Today, field-scale vegetable growing is carried on in the Avon valley almost as far as Warwick. Where the Avon valley widens in the Barford - Wellesbourne district is found some of the best land in South Warwickshire.

2. Prelude – the 1930s

Those of us born in the 1920s can count ourselves lucky, because we can remember the old farming, always referred to as traditional by those who have never known it, and who view it through the rose coloured spectacles of nostalgia. In fact, for many, if not most, it was a hard life of grinding physical toil in all weathers, while for the weekly wage earners on the land it was, only too often, one of poverty, poor housing and lack of many amenities and, in the mainly arable districts, sometimes winter unemployment as well.

But, by the second half of the 1930s, the worst of the depression, initiated by the repeal of the Corn Production Act in 1921, was over. Its effects had been, and were still, very variable from one part of the country to another. For example, North Norfolk where I spent four long boyhood years at boarding school, was certainly not prospering. In Holt, one could easily pick out the properties which belonged to the public school, Greshams. These had been painted and properly maintained, which was more than could be said of some other houses, shops or other premises. In short, there was a general air of poverty and depression, for, apart from the trade generated by the school, the area was dependent entirely upon agriculture.

Moreover, in the surrounding countryside few farms seemed to be prospering, indeed some were unoccupied. The uncurtained windows of the farmhouse would stare blankly across fields abandoned to gorse and rabbits. Barn doors, on rusty hinges would creak and swing in the wind, as it came sighing across the reed fringed salt marshes from the cold, grey North Sea.

The claylands of the Midlands, including those of South Warwickshire, also felt the effects of poor prices and sluggish demand. These heavy soils were, with horses and with the tractors that were available in the 1920s and 1930s, difficult to cultivate. They were deficient in phosphates, water retentive and always in need of drainage. For some years labour had been cut to the bone, maintenance had, in consequence, been neglected; ditches had become silted up and the outfalls of the original drainage systems blocked. Thus in South Warwickshire there were many hundreds of acres waterlogged for much of the year, sometimes covered with thorn bushes and other scrub or under the poorest of old pasture dotted with anthills and clumps of tor grass with swards consisting of herbage of little agricultural value. On what was really marginal land at that time, *dog and stick* farming was one means of survival.

On the other hand, other parts of the country fared somewhat better. Kent, where I spent a few years as a boy on a fruit and poultry farm, seemed to escape the worst of the depression. Again, talking to a Fenland farmer of the old school many years later, it was clear that the Fens, with their rich soils and diversity of cropping, weathered the years of the depression comparatively well. After the formation of the Milk Marketing Board in 1932, the dairying counties were relatively more prosperous than those where farmers relied mainly on arable cultivation. Needless to say, farmers on the poorer land suffered the most.

But all was not doom and gloom by any manner of means. By the second half of the 1930s competent, hard working men and their families on reasonably good farms at least lived well, although there may not have been much spare cash about. Some, and there were plenty of them in South Warwickshire, farmed very well indeed by the standards of the day.

Others with business flair, a capacity to innovate and with organising ability built up farming empires, taking advantage of the fact that farms and land could be acquired cheaply. A. J. Hosier, for example, invented the milking bail (the precursor of the milking parlour) and produced cheap milk from poor Wiltshire downland. Another such was Patterson who farmed Hampshire downland in a similar fashion.

Webster Cory, at Notgrove in the Cotswolds, adopted the Hosier bail for outdoor milk production, ran a flock of grassland ewes for fat lamb production, the pig unit producing bacon, with some 1,500 laying hens in fold units on grass. All a far cry from the typical Cotswold arable farm.

Coming nearer home, Clyde Higgs of Hatton Rock, Stratford-upon-Avon, was another who built up a large farming enterprise during the inter-war years. He added farm to farm, mainly in the Hampton Lucy, Snitterfield and Norton Lindsey area, and milked a number of herds of Ayrshires in bails. The milk was retailed direct through an extensive network of rounds in Stratford and surrounding districts, this on its own constituting a considerable business.

Market Day

In the 1930s, my recollection is that farmers left their farms, in the course of a week, very much less frequently than is the case today. However, a visit to the local weekly market was normally a matter of routine, being as much a social as a business event. And there are still those amongst us who would never have missed attending the old Stratford market on a Tuesday. Today going to market is much less of a ritual than it was in days gone by, some farmers never going to market from one year's end to the next.

One of the things I was told when I first came to Stratford was that it was a waste of time calling on farmers on Tuesdays as they would be sure to be at the market. But one summer's afternoon, about 6 o'clock, I thought Mr. B. of Admington was sure to be back from Stratford by then. Accordingly, I called on my way home from another job. His wife answered the back door. 'He is back, but you will get no sense out of him; he is market pert.' In other words, he had overdone the liquid refreshment, probably a common occurrence. And so it was, for through the open door I could see him sprawling in an old armchair by the Rayburn, snoring his head off, dead to the world.

My first memory of a market was in Cirencester on the first Monday of the Second World War in early September 1939. A sensation was caused by the sale of one of Lord Bathurst's working oxen. This was a huge beast, weighing, it was said, nearly one ton. It made, for those days, an astonishing price, presumably in anticipation of a meat shortage.

In my pupil days, the boss used to take me every Friday to the market in Chippenham, very often his good friend and neighbour, Tom Rich, coming along as well. One Friday, again in the autumn of 1939, weaner pigs were making the then extraordinary price of £5/head. The following week there were so many entered there were not enough pens for them and some had to be sold direct from the trailers. Needless to say, the price slumped to £1/head, sometimes less.

The *market ordinary* – the market day lunch – could be had in the Angel Hotel in the town's main street. You entered the front door straight from the pavement, went a yard or two down the hall, and then turned right down a few stairs. At the bottom the lady of the house sat at a card table, the felt of which had seen better days. A wooden bowl stood on it into which you paid half a crown (about 13p new money).

You then entered a large, long room, which doubtless served many other purposes during the course of a year. Along its length two long tables stood, covered in white cloths, on which were steaming dishes of potatoes and other vegetables for diners to help themselves, along with jugs of beer, all being continually replenished by the serving girls.

At the far end was a cross table at which stood mine host and on which there were two enormous joints. Always one of beef, pork in season (only eaten in those days when there was an R in the month) or lamb. You took any chair that was vacant and looked expectantly towards the landlord. When you caught his eye, he would point his carving knife at each joint in turn, questioning with his eyebrows. You then pointed to your preference and one of the girls would bring your plate with a very generous portion. You then helped yourself from the nearest vegetable dishes and tucked in. No sweets, of course, but an ample supply of fresh crusty bread, butter and strong Cheddar cheese.

Can one still find an inn that serves a market ordinary? Or are these a thing of the past?

Farmhouses

For the most part, and certainly in South Warwickshire, the farmhouses of the 1930s had been the homes of farming families for several, and often very many, generations. Needless to say, their size reflected the acreage that they served, those on the broader acres being large houses with three, or so, rooms on the ground floor with a large kitchen, larder, dairy and still room in addition. On the first floor, there were maybe four or more bedrooms, with the attics occupied by servants, domestic or farm. On the other hand, houses on the smallest farms were little bigger than cottages. Indeed, today, cottages of some age, now occupied by incomers, were invariably the smaller farmhouses in days gone by.

Many of the bigger farmhouses were enlarged and re-built in the last quarter of the eighteenth century and the early decades of the nineteenth. At least part of the original structure, built in the sixteenth century, or even earlier, was demolished and a new front consisting of a drawing room, dining room, parlour or office built on in the new Georgian style, square fronted, brick built with sash windows, and bedrooms to match on the first floor. Often the older part of the house now became the kitchen, dairy and still room.

There were, of course, many variations on the theme. But the former farmhouse, in which we lived for twenty four years and in which our family grew up, was typical, with one important exception. This was the fact that, instead of the newer part of the house being built in brick, clearly timber from the original house had been used, thus echoing the timber frame with brick in-filling of the original dwelling. Indeed it could clearly be seen, by the pattern of timbering, how the front of the old house had been replaced by the new.

The ceilings in the kitchen, larder and part of one of the front rooms, were much lower than those in the more recent addition. In the kitchen there was a big, open Tudor fireplace in which stood an Aga (in the days before such cookers became status symbols, I might add). The chimney above was vast and in it could still be seen the old hooks and chains on which cooking vessels would have been hung. On the left hand side there had, at one time, been an oven.

The floors in the kitchen and hall were of flagstones and the old backdoor, leading directly into the kitchen, was still there with its original hinges, a wooden-cased lock and a long iron bar on a ring, which swung right across the door, dropping into a hook to give added security.

We know when the house had been re-fashioned, because a local builder had once found a small piece of plank under a floorboard on to which had been burnt 'An old house made new 1820.'

Making new consisted of the addition of two front rooms on the ground floor with two bedrooms above, served by a new hall and landing respectively. There was a fine oak staircase and the new landing floor was also oak. The four new rooms had deal flooring and, as already noted, the ceilings were much higher than in the older part of the house.

In former times, before the advent of fridges and deep freezers, a large, cold larder on the northern side of a farmhouse and a cellar were essentials. Occasionally, and if a suitable source of water was available, an open gully was sometimes laid in the cellar floor along which water could flow, exiting into a drain. This kept the cellar even cooler.

One such arrangement graced the cellar at Barton Farm, Alderminster, which was under the sitting room. One winter's day Ned Hutchings felt the room was exceptionally cold, in spite of making up a good log fire. Eventually it was found that the outlet had become blocked and the cellar had filled with water. No wonder Ned, sitting in his chair with a cellar full of water only a couple of feet below him, felt somewhat chilled.

But back to our farmhouse in Welford-on-Avon where, in the process of making an old house new, a large cellar had been dug under one of the front rooms, needless to say on the north side. A door at the back of the new staircase led down a flight of stone steps. At the bottom on the right and under the hall was a cubby-hole, closed off by a slatted door. It was here that the beer, cider and other drinks could be kept secured by a padlock, as a protection against illicit boozing.

All the cellar walls were lined with Lias limestone, probably from the quarry at nearby Binton. Incidentally most of the timber framed houses, barns or whatever stood on dwarf walls of the same material. The spaces in between the ceiling beams had been plastered, a glazed pig salting trough stood against one wall and two others were lined with wooden shelves.

Our old home had been, in its heyday, a substantial farmhouse on a large farm of some three hundred acres. It was sold off its holding in 1890, to provide funds for the part repayment of a mortgage. Like so many farmhouses in the village, it then became a residence just seventy years after it had been made new. Incidentally, the old house underwent another major re-construction in the early 1930s. Then the stable at the back, which was an integral part of the old structure, was converted into a large room, the hayloft above being turned into a bedroom. In this, one rather unusual window reached from floor level to the eaves, being originally the opening through which hay would have been pitched to be stored and later fed into the hay racks below. This would have been through a gap in the floor, which had not been extended right to the back wall.

In the 1930s in South Warwickshire, no mains water supply was available to many farms and farmhouses. In the case of the latter the supply came from a well, our old home having had one dug immediately adjacent to the kitchen door, lined with the ubiquitous Lias limestone. This was some ten feet deep, the depth of the gravel subsoil before the water-bearing clay was reached. By this decade most farmhouses would have had internal plumbing supplied by a tank in the roof. In the days before mains electricity became available, the tanks would have been filled by a hand pump, or sometimes, perhaps by a pump driven by a stationary petrol engine.

A few farms in South Warwickshire had a more elaborate water supply. A pump driven by a windmill would be located over a well, the water being raised to a reservoir on high ground from which the farmhouse, farm buildings and field troughs would be supplied by gravity. A variation on this arrangement could be that tanks in the roofs of the farmhouse, and possibly some buildings as well, might be fed direct. Ball Bros., the engineering firm in Stratford, installed many of these windmill pumps, with their steel lattice towers topped by metal sheeted sails.

Even in the 1930s, one could find farmhouses without a mains supply of electricity. In these, light was provided by oil lamps and candles, and hurricane lamps around the buildings. Then central heating in farmhouses was almost unknown. But logs for open fires were usually in abundance and cooking was by old fashioned ranges, Rayburns or Agas, all fuelled by coal, coke or anthracite (many in the post-war era being converted to oil). These were often supplemented by oil stoves. One wonders how many of those now advocating a return to the good old days of traditional, sustainable farming (so called), would take kindly to the daily, time-consuming chores of filling oil lamps, trimming wicks, washing and polishing the glass lamp chimneys and shades, sawing and carrying logs and humping coal.

But, of course, all this was to change before the century was much older. By the 1960s most South Warwickshire villages had a mains water supply, followed by main drainage supplanting cess pits and septic tanks. This latter was the kiss-of-death for many South Warwickshire villages, as main sewerage removed the last barrier to suburbanisation.

Similarly mains electricity became the norm for village properties, farmhouses and farmsteads. Farmhouses, and particularly the kitchens, became transformed with all the electrical gadgetry we now all take for granted: cookers, dishwashers, fridges, deep freezers, and so on. Electric irons replaced the flat irons heated on the coal fired ranges, while electric washing machines made the Monday wash day a thing of the past.

This latter could be a performance and I recall being, unintentionally, witness to wash day in a South Warwickshire farmhouse. The farm was run by two bachelor brothers, house being kept for them by their unmarried sister. It was she who presided over the activities of three buxom girls from the nearby village. In the wash-house the copper was steaming away, sheets were being pounded in the dolly tub, shirts on the scrubbing board, while on the washing lines hung an assortment of undergarments from another age.

But one thing remains the same; the kitchen is still the centre of life in the farmhouse. Apart from its obvious function it is the room where visitors are made welcome, where business is contracted, where meals are taken and which serves sometimes as the farm office, although increasingly today this has to have a room to itself to house the mountain of paper work, the filing cabinets, and now the computer.

Farm Cars

In these days when the basic farm transport consists of a reasonably respectable car and a 4x4, van, or pick-up for farm use, it is easy to forget that in the 1930s a few farmers in South Warwickshire did not run a car at all, relying on a pony and trap. But the majority, of course, did have a car which had to be a multi-purpose vehicle.

For transport around the farm itself, a pony or cob in a float was often the order of the day. This was certainly the case on the Cotswold farm where I served my apprenticeship. This particular vehicle had started off life as a milk float, the wooden, iron-tyred wheels being replaced by an old car axle, complete with pneumatic tyres. It was used for every purpose imaginable, transporting fencing materials, hay, straw and other feeds, fetching a calf back inconveniently dropped in a far field followed by its anxious mother, and, on occasion going to the markets in nearby Malmesbury or Tetbury.

In the 1930s and until new cars became freely available, the war having interrupted production, the great majority of farmers bought their cars second-hand, or even third or fourth hand. For instance, it was the proud boast of Arnold Dale of Sheep Leys, Clifford Chambers, that he had never paid more than £5 for a car. He must have struck a hard bargain, because when I first knew him in the 1940s he was driving a very tidy, green Standard, about 1936 vintage. Gordon Davies of Broom Court, Bidford-on-Avon, also ran a Morris Oxford, just as old and in the same excellent condition. But another South Warwickshire farmer, who shall remain nameless, could always be relied upon to reduce even a brand new vehicle into a mobile scrap heap in a matter of a few months.

By no means all farm cars in the 1930s were as smart as Arnold's or Gordon's. The very worst examples had clearly seen better days. Front wings drooping, front bumpers tied to the headlamp stalks with binder twine, running boards clearly suffering from fatigue and due to part any moment from the rest of the body, the underside of which would be well caked with mud and cow muck.

Inside, the back seat would probably be missing. In its place would be a couple of drums of tractor paraffin, or perhaps a calf or two benappied with old sacks secured, again, with binder twine. On the floor could be lying some lengths of wagon rope, a chain with a hook on one end, a mallet and an old tin full of rusty nails and old nuts and bolts.

The front compartment would be in little better shape. It would be carpeted with railway sacks, excellent for the job being close woven and originally intended to hold corn. Any pockets there might be would be stuffed with such vital items as a broken sparking plug, a twelve bore cartridge, a screwdriver with a cracked handle, a rusty tin of sheep ointment and a half empty bottle of cattle drench.

The window on the driver's side would be permanently down, the winder having broken. All the other windows would be permanently up for the same reason, being held in place with a sharpened twig, or a wedge of newspaper. Needless to say, the battery would not have much life in it, so the starting handle would be in a handy position by the driver's seat. The radiator cap would be missing, having been replaced by a Thermos flask cork with a washer of brown paper. Also the petrol cap would consist of a piece of wood roughly shaped to fit the spout, a snugger fit being obtained by the tail of an old shirt. A exaggeration? Those with long enough memories will recall that such vehicles could be found, and without much trouble.

If the farm car of the 1930s had to be a multi-purpose vehicle, its design had certain advantages. With a little practice fencing stakes, slashing hooks, pitchforks, and other agricultural impedimenta could be carried in quantity lashed to the front bumper, or nestling securely in the valleys between the bonnet and front mud wings. There were no boots in cars in those days, but a carrier which let down over the back bumper was superior in many ways. There was, for example, no humping of sacks over the lip of the boot and impaling them on the short rod onto which the lid latched. Moreover, equipment of peculiar and considerable weight could be carried with the aid of some sacks and a plough line: a stationary engine, one of those old mangles with wooden rollers, a small rolling mill, or whatever.

In the second half of the 1940s, all this began to change. Quite soon after the War ended, surplus army vehicles were sold off by auction. These were bought up eagerly by farmers, Jeeps being especially in demand. The vehicle exclusively for farm use had arrived. Later these were followed by Land Rovers, vans and pick-ups. In the days of fuel rationing these all had the advantage of being able to be run on red petrol, forbidden for use in private cars.

And farm workers started to be able to run cars instead of riding bikes. Times had changed, and for the better.

Field and Farmyard

In the 1930s, the main power sources on farms were still what they had always been, the muscles of men and horses. The UK manufacture of tractors in quantity began at Dagenham in the early 1930s, where Fordsons started to be produced. But many a farm still relied exclusively on horses, and combine harvesters in the harvest field in the UK would be numbered in tens rather than hundreds.

Those born in the 1920s can well recall what it was like to work horses. The long hours following the teams, ploughing, cultivating, harrowing rolling and drilling. Or the equally long days sitting on a sack stuffed with hay, the only cushion between the buttocks and the iron seat of a mower, tedder, horse rake or binder. We can well recall the smell of sweating horses and warm leather, the creaking of the heavy wagons making their slow way over hard baked ground at hay making or corn harvest; also the call of 'ol tight,' as the young lad leading the horses warned those on the load that they were about to move on.

One wonders how enthusiastic about the old farming those critics of modern agriculture would continue to be, if they actually had to undertake some of the gut rending and – let's face it – the sometimes tedious and boring manual work which was the lot of those who worked on the land in the old days.

How would the whingeing critics of modern farming face up to mucking out cattle yards and loose boxes by hand at the end of the winter, with straw and dung packed tightly by the treading of cattle over many months, and sodden with urine into the bargain?

How would they fare singling and hand hoeing sugar beet, mangolds and other fodder roots day after day, with the rows seemingly getting longer as the hours went by? In the days before combine harvesters and modern herbicides – the so-called poison sprays – those who regret the passing of the old days might change their minds after a day of stooking sheaves of barley with their fair ration of thistles amongst the straw. Even with sleeves rolled down, the insides of the arms would be raw and red at the end of the day and the hard, sharp, irritating awns of the barley heads would inevitably find their way inside shirts and trousers to add to the general discomfort.

How would those who prattle on about the changing face of the countryside – bigger fields, the loss of traditional hay meadows, and so on – cope with long days pitching hay or sheaves on to wagons with a quick twist of the shaft of the pitchfork which ensured that its load fell away from the prongs?

All these things, and many more besides, were part and parcel of farming before mechanisation, and the use of crop protection chemicals played their part in eliminating so much hand work and hard graft. Only those who never experienced them bemoan the passing of the days of the old farming.

3. THE HUNGRY FORTIES

Preparations for War

By 1935, the writing was on the wall. Hitler was on the march and in that year, the German Government announced the existence of a German airforce and introduced conscription to build up a peace-time army. The following year, the German army re-occupied the Rhineland. All these acts constituted violations of the Versailles Treaty.

Mr. Walter Elliot, then Minister of Agriculture, set up the first committee to review and report on the need for increased home production of food in the event of a Second World War. Two years, and another committee later, a lime subsidy of 50% was introduced, and also one of 25% on basic slag. These measures were designed to help in restoring soil fertility after more than a decade of the neglect of agriculture on the part of Government and the nation.

In April 1939, when war appeared inevitable, the Minister of Agriculture, Sir Reginald Dorman-Smith, asked for authority to stockpile fertilisers, especially phosphates, to buy and store 5,000 tractors and their complementary implements, increase grants for arterial drainage and extend them to field drainage, and introduce a £2/acre grant for the ploughing-out of grassland and cropping, or re-seeding to grass. He was authorised to purchase the tractors and implements and introduce the ploughing-up grant, but was not given authority in respect of the other requests.

Three other measures were put in hand. First, the rate of existing crop deficiency payments was increased and the range extended. Secondly, as conscription had already been introduced, the age for exemption of tractor drivers and farm mechanics was lowered from 25 years to 21, and the call-up of those farm workers reaching the conscription age of 20 before November 1939 was to be postponed until the end of that month. This was a measure to assist the corn harvest, autumn cultivations, drilling, and the lifting of potatoes and sugar beet. Later, of course, the range of exemptions for most farm workers was greatly extended. Finally, and in advance of the outbreak of hostilities, the enrolment for, and training of, the Women's Land Army was to start.

As a matter of principle, it had been decided that, in order to increase food production in the coming war, price incentives alone would not be sufficient. Control of cropping, and the enforcement of the necessary measures, would be essential. Moreover, there would have to be an administrative organisation to allocate scarce resources such as machinery, fertilisers, feedstuffs and, as experience proved, other items as well.

It should be noted that the staff of the Ministry of Agriculture, a comparatively small Ministry, was quite inadequate for this task and few were outstationed in the counties, notably the Livestock Officers and Land Commissioners. Although, of course, the Ministry played a vital and central role in the coming food production campaign.

Thus a scheme for the setting up of county War Agricultural Executive Committees (WAEC) was ready by the end of 1936. These committees were to consist overwhelmingly of practical, working farmers, who, one might add, gave their time without payment, some even not claiming expenses to which they were entitled as a further contribution to the war effort. The Chairmen and paid posts of Executive Officers and Secretaries of the county committees-to-be were selected.

In Warwickshire, Mr. Bert Hughes, a farmer and grower of horticultural crops in the parish of Salford Priors, became chairman of the Warwickshire WAEC in 1941, and served in that capacity for nineteen years.

He was a man of complete probity. He laid it down that no Committee member, at county or district level, could take advantage of his position to further his own interests or, equally important, should be under possible suspicion of doing so.

For instance, there was, in the Stratford district, a farm under supervision because of a poor husbandry record. Without waiting for the inevitable eviction, the owner put the farm on the market. His neighbour was a member of the County Committee of the WAEC, and in a substantial way of business. He asked permission from Bert Hughes to buy the farm – a request that was refused.

The charge has been made that, in some other counties, the same strict rules were not necessarily the order of the day. That, to put it mildly, a certain amount of fixing could take place. I had personal experience of this when in charge of the District Office in Stratford. At this juncture, it should be explained that one of the few ways under the 1948 Agricultural Holdings Act, by which a landlord could regain possession of a farm or land, was to obtain a Certificate of Bad Husbandry from the CAEC, as the County Agricultural Executive Committees became known after the War.

A family trust, based in another county, owned some land in South Warwickshire. The agent for the trust appeared to imagine that he had only to lobby committee members and the county chairman to settle whether or not such a certificate would be granted before formal application was made, the farm inspected and a decision reached in committee. Bert Hughes informed the gentleman concerned, and in no uncertain terms, within my hearing, that whatever he might be used to where he came from, such matters were decided in Warwickshire in a manner that was open, above board, and in accordance with the correct procedure.

For most of the duration of the War, N.E.B.Elgar, a land agent, was Chief Executive Officer in Warwickshire. The Secretary was E.R.Lamburn, who had previously been in the piano business, but who proved to be an efficient and able administrator.

The Stratford-on-Avon District Committee

The members of WAEC District Committees were at the cutting edge of the food production campaign. Each was responsible for a number of parishes and for the farms within them. They would visit them as often as they thought necessary and would carry out a formal survey with a member of staff to grade the holdings A, B or C. In Category A were the best farmers who were left to their own devices except for special reasons e.g. the scheduling of grassland for ploughing, applications to purchase machinery, and so on. Those classified in Category B performed less satisfactorily, while those graded C were kept under fairly close supervision, and were the subject of formal inspections by the district member accompanied by the district chairman and either the district officer or his, or her, assistant. In intractable cases the county committee would inspect and often place the farm under formal supervision, and subject it to a number of Orders to carry out certain work. After twelve months, there might be an improvement, in which case the district member would be asked to visit less frequently. If the reverse was the case, dispossession, the ultimate sanction, might be the last resort.

Until a major re-organisation in 1959, the districts were based on the local authority parishes. South Warwickshire was covered by four Rural District Councils, Alcester, Stratford, Shipston and Southam. From an early stage, for the purposes of the WAEC, Alcester and Stratford were combined, and some years later Shipston and Southam.

Stratford (with Alcester) was the largest district, some 106,000 acres in all, with about 1,300 holdings. But many, if not most, of the smaller farms were in fact market gardens, situated mainly in the parishes of Salford Priors, Bidford-on-Avon, Arrow, Alcester and Welford-on-Avon.

In 1943, my first job after leaving University was District Technical Officer to the Stratford District Committee, and the following description of WAEC district work is based on my own experience there.

The farmer members were as follows: -

Messrs. J.H.Steele (chairman), F.H.Hutsby, E.G.Davies, G.R.Davies, F.M.Walters, G.R.Hammerton, C.H.Whitehead, J.R.Steele, D.Goulbourne, J.K.Hay, W.J.Barnett, and A.Edgar. Later Mr. J.H.Steele was appointed to the County Committee and Mr. Hutsby became chairman at Stratford, followed by

Mr. F.M.Walters at the end of the War. Later some others retired and were replaced by what was then the younger generation: E.R.Bomford, K.L.Smith, F.W.Wiggin and H.Whetter.

As a young man in his first job, I was very fortunate to be in close contact, week after week, with farmers of their calibre. They became, perhaps unknowingly, my mentors and tutors. By accompanying them on farm visits and inspections and listening to them in committee, I learnt a great deal. My debt to them for their kindness, and for what I gained from them, is one that I was never able to repay. In later years, when I was a member of the National Agricultural Advisory Service, I came to realise how fortunate I had been compared to colleagues in their first advisory post, who had never had the advantage of a close working relationship with leading farmers in the district.

While the War was being waged, many farmers who were asked to serve on district committees did so gladly, considering it to be their patriotic duty. But when the Defence Regulations were replaced by the so-called disciplinary clauses of the Agriculture Act 1947, some felt that over-seeing their fellow farmers in peace time was a different matter, and to some, abhorrent.

In passing, it should be mentioned that the principle that lay behind the 1947 Act was briefly as follows. In return for guaranteed prices and assured markets, a reasonable standard of crop and livestock husbandry should be maintained, and it was the function of the peace time CAECs to ensure that this was done. In the event, all this was reinforced by continuing food shortages until the mid-1950s, after which the import -saving role of British agriculture became all important.

Under this peace time regime, farms were still being graded A, B, or C. The latter, the lowest category, were usually placed under Statutory Supervision, a fact that had to be noted in the Land Register. This was then the subject of regular inspections at district level. Incidentally, this could apply to farms, as such, or to bare land. The ultimate sanction, dispossession, was rarely resorted to after 1947. When I took over the Stratford Office in 1949, there were twelve supervision orders in force, most of them for bare land. None of those who farmed these holdings were ever dispossessed..

During the War years W.L. (Taffy) Jones was in charge of the Stratford Office. He had been, I believe, a victim of the inter-war depression, having farmed at one time. By the time I came to Stratford, his knowledge of the district, its farms and farmers, was encyclopaedic. His greeting to anyone he met, young or old, was invariably, 'What have you got to tell me, young man?' He was a competent administrator and had an amazing memory. He would go on a farm inspection with the district member and chairman, after which he would have to write a full report on the condition of the farmstead, the cropping and condition of every field, and the labour and machinery on the farm. This he would do by dictating to Sylvia Hawkins, his secretary, with occasional reference to only the briefest of notes. When he came off the farm, it was all in his head. His great pride and joy was his Rover 10, which was always immaculate. Rovers were much sought after during the War years when no new cars were being made for private purchase, and their possession something of a status symbol. Mrs. Gunston was his assistant. She was a short, sturdy, stump-about sort of person, very efficient at her job. Her old father farmed at Langley, a parish of poor land and, with exceptions, poor farming.

In 1939, many farms in South Warwickshire had insufficient machinery to cope with the increased acreage of arable land for its cultivation and, in some cases, none at all. The Warwickshire Agricultural Executive Committee accordingly set up a contracting service run from machinery depots. In the Stratford District, there were three of these, one at Stratford itself, one at Alcester, and the third at Henley-in-Arden. The Machinery Officers in charge of these were Jack Thomas, Cliff Brice and Bert Wright, respectively, and some characters they were.

Other staff at the Stratford Office included Eric Fairbrother, Horace Kennard (Drainage), and Charlie Stewart (Labour), who also kept The Swan at Alcester. In the office, Sylvia Hawkins was the senior secretary, Rita Jones, Ellice Beesley, whose father farmed at Dovehouse Farm, Temple Grafton, and Eunice Bedford, who lived with her parents at Crimscote, completed the office staff. They were joined later by Barbara Court, who, in the event, was to spend the whole of her working life with MAFF, transferring to the Leamington office when Stratford was closed, and then to the Drayton Experimental Husbandry Farm, just outside Stratford.

During the War years, the Stratford District Office was in the Flowers Brewery Recreation Hall up the Clopton Road. Later, at the end of the War, the office moved to one of the early, 19th. century houses in Bridge Street, which, shamefully, were demolished to make way for what we must now regard as the old Post Office. The next move was to the premises, which had been those of the Auxiliary Fire Service, in the garden of Mason's Croft, off Chestnut Walk. And finally, it moved to another hut beyond the Ministry of Food cold store off the Alcester Road. Both cold store and hut were demolished, eventually, to make way for the Safeway supermarket. By 1956, the wartime district organisation had been virtually dismantled and the Stratford Office, along with the others in the county closed, the staff being transferred to the county office at Leamington. From then on, as the District Adviser, I worked from home for some sixteen years before being given an office at Drayton. This was an ideal arrangement, because I was in close contact with the work going on there and was able to help out on Open Days.

District Committee meetings were held in the former NFU Mutual Insurance Company's offices in Church Street, Stratford-on-Avon, which are now occupied by the Stratford District Council. During the War years, these were marathon affairs starting at 2 p.m. and finishing between 6 and 7 p.m., fortunately with a half hour break for an excellent tea, provided by the canteen.

The meetings were held every other Friday and I never found them boring, in contrast to NAAS and ADAS staff meetings, especially those held at the Worcester Divisional Office.

The Machinery Officers were the first to present their reports, which contained details of the work done during the previous fortnight from the three Depots, any problems encountered and so on. The committee members would then comment and bring forward any complaints or requests for special work. When everyone had had their say, the machinery men took their leave.

Next, it was the turn of Eric Fairbrother, who was responsible for the drainage work being carried out by the drainage machinery and drainage gangs working in the district. He would report on the work carried out since the last meeting, and again members would comment, often passing on requests for visits, or instructions to call on certain farmers who needed drainage work done, but might be reluctant to put the work in hand. He was also responsible for vetting applications for drainage grants for work carried out by farmers themselves, and for certifying payment. He would leave the meeting when his business was completed.

Then W.L. would give his report, which could be very lengthy. In cases where there was a serious problem, a District Inspection would be carried out when he, or Mrs. Gunston, and the District Chairman would accompany the committee member for the parish in which the farm was situated. There could well be two or three of these inspections; the reports were detailed, and could run to many pages of the old foolscap-sized sheets of paper.

After each, there was a discussion on what further action should be taken. This could simply be a request that the committee member concerned should pay particular attention to the farm, visiting more frequently than normal. Eric Fairbrother could be asked to sort out a drainage problem. Or, I might be instructed to take soil samples for analysis and then advise on the types of fertiliser to be used and the rates at which they should be applied.

Where, after a suitable lapse of time, there had been no improvement and, possibly, the man concerned had proved to be unco-operative, or there might be some other reason for lack of progress, the case would be referred to the County Executive Committee for a further inspection by a panel of its members. This might result in the farm being placed under formal supervision, which could mean real trouble for the farmer concerned unless he performed digital extraction [*i.e. pulled his finger out*] and improved his husbandry.

Next it was my turn. As District Technical Officer, I would list the advisory visits I had carried out, the number of soil samples taken etc., the meetings of the Stratford Young Farmers' Club, of which I was Club Leader, farmers' discussion group meetings, the progress of cereal variety demonstration plots and so on. Again, members would ask me to take soil samples for analysis, deal with any cropping problems or crop failures, and possibly request a meeting on a topical subject to be held at a suitable venue in the district.

One such instruction – for that was what it was – sticks in my memory. The artificial insemination (AI) of dairy cows was then, in 1944, something very new. The AI Centre at Bromsgrove had just started up, and a meeting on such a topical, and then controversial, subject was very necessary.

I suggested Reg Kenney as a speaker. He was a senior agricultural lecturer at Reading University and had been my tutor. Early development work had been carried out on the University Farm at Sonning, so Reg was well qualified to talk on the subject as he had had practical experience. Incidentally, he later went on to become Principal at Harper Adams Agricultural College.

He duly agreed to speak, and the meeting was arranged to be held in the White Swan, Henley-in-Arden, because it was central to that part of the district and had the greatest concentration of dairy farms. I reported to the next committee meeting on the arrangements I had made. Mr. Hutsby, by then committee chairman, said, 'Now Mr. Woods, I want you to put up a large notice by the door of the meeting room to point out that ladies and those under the age of eighteen will not be admitted.'

That was certainly a comment on attitudes at that time, which were to change very rapidly, one of the factors being the presence of members of the Women's Land Army on so many farms in the 1940s. Farmers of the generation to which Mr. Hutsby belonged would have always gone to considerable lengths to ensure that wives, daughters and other ladies of the household were not around when the bull was taken out to serve a cow, the stallion called, or a cow was about to calve.

I stayed for the whole length of the meeting. After I had given my report, it was the turn of the committee members. Each reported on the farm visits they had made and the problems they had encountered, and would also ask for ploughing, and other orders, to be served. This was a formality that had to be gone through, even when the man concerned was agreeable to whatever he was being asked to do.

Later, all the orders that had been requested and issued by the county office were confirmed. Crop failures, and their causes, were duly recorded when acreage payments were involved. Then came a host of other matters. Exemptions from military service and Home Guard duty, recommendations for permits to purchase anything from a crawler tractor to a thermos flask, and anything else that was in short supply. And, in spite of everything that had gone before, there were still items under Any Other Business. Small wonder that these meetings went on for four hours, and often longer.

Then there were the minutes to write, inspection and other reports and schedules to be attached before sending onto the county office at Leamington.

When I took over the Stratford District in 1949, this was one of my jobs, but, thankfully, meetings were held only once a month by then.

Reclamation

As already noted, in 1939 there were, as a result of years of agricultural depression, many hundreds of acres of Warwickshire clayland in a derelict condition.

Two contemporary accounts paint a picture that was only too familiar. In June 1940, the Grassland Improvement Station was established on Dodwell and Drayton Farms by the Evesham and Alcester roads, respectively, about two miles outside Stratford. In 1941, Sir George Stapledon, the Director, described the condition of the two farms as follows.

> The lands at Drayton were to all intents and purposes derelict, consisting of fields in bramble and low thorn, uncultivated arable land in foul condition, old tumbledown swards, and a very few poor, young, leys full of weeds. Drayton has no farmhouse, possesses three cottages unfit for habitation, a run of barns and yards in an advanced stage of dilapidation, an unreliable, and insufficient, water supply, and many fields with no watering facilities of any kind. Hedges neglected and overgrown, and water courses clogged.
>
> Dodwell has, indeed, a proper farmhouse, a good run of buildings and two habitable cottages, but no proper sanitation at the farmhouse and no electric light. Much repair work is needed. Again, hedges and ditches are all neglected and many fields need draining. The water supply is inadequate for a fully-stocked farm in a dry year.
>
> When we took over in June 1940, there was only one field on the whole 630 acres that was bounded by absolutely stock-proof hedges or fences. Rabbits abounded everywhere and wood pigeons were in abundance, earth worms and moles at a premium. All this in the very heart of England and on land of high potential.

Dodwell and Drayton were, of course, reclaimed by the Grassland Improvement Station assisted by Nellist Wilkes, a farmer from Worcestershire who had experience of managing heavy land.

The second example was a 250 acre farm, also on clay, which the WWAEC took over and reclaimed in the early days of the War. The farm, and its owner, will remain anonymous, as some of his relatives are still alive in South Warwickshire. The report of inspecting members to the County Executive Committee was as follows.

> The farm is heavy and has evidently been ranched for several years, and is under-stocked. Much of last year's grass is in evidence, and many

> fields are covered with ant banks with thorn beginning to grow in several fields. The land lies wet due to the condition of ditches and drains, but there would appear to be no good reason why the water should not get away from this land.

In addition, it was recorded that the farmhouse was all but derelict, remote and accessible only across a railway level crossing. The buildings were in no better condition.

It was also noted that the owner said he was unable to get labour, or let the farm, due to the remote location of the farmstead. Nevertheless, the owner was instructed to find a tenant by 31st. May 1940 but, in the event, no tenant was found and the WWAEC took possession of the farm, reclaimed it, drained it, and farmed it until just after the War ended.

Without any doubt, one of the outstanding features, and achievements, of wartime farming in South Warwickshire was the reclamation, and bringing into full arable production, of this land in such a short space of time. For example, the Grove Farm, Ettington, and adjoining Knavenhill, near Alderminster, had been reclaimed and cropped for two harvests by 1943. The same could be said of Nardey Bush, Wimpstone. Crimscote Downs, on Crimscote Fields Farm, was being de-bushed in the winter of 1943-44. Hardwick Farm, Pathlow, was one of the last farms to be brought into full cropping, and this by the harvest of 1945, although much of it was carrying crops before that. This were only some of the derelict land reclaimed, albeit a very substantial acreage in all.

The usual method of reclamation was as follows. First, of course, the area had to be cleared of any scrub, some hedges removed and others reduced to their proper width. No nonsense about destruction of wildlife habitat then – life was too serious.

The preferred machine for clearing scrub was the Bomford Bushpusher. This was front-mounted on a crawler tractor. The top arm, which extended well in front of the tractor, pushed against tall thorn and small trees, several feet from ground level, bent them over and put the base under pressure and tension, in precisely the same way as a small bush is bent over by hand before chopping it off at the bottom with a billhook or axe.

The bottom arm was fitted with a blade, to which stout, steel fingers had been welded. This travelled at just below ground level, neatly scooping up the whole bush or tree, free of most of the roots, which were left in the ground to be dealt with later. The uprooted scrub was then pushed up into great heaps to be burnt, but the fires had to be doused every night at dusk because of the black-out.

The whole process was, of course, much quicker than pulling bushes out one by one with a chain and tractor. Also, the Bushpusher made a better, neater job than a bulldozer, which might have to be used for the biggest trees. While all this clearing work was going on, the boundary ditches might well have been re-dug, often by hand, POW labour often being used, in preparation for under-drainage, which was often necessary.

Once the field had been cleared, it would be ploughed, preferably in April, and cross-ploughed a few weeks later. After that, it would be cultivated a number of times, the roots picked, and then carted off after each pass.

Alternatively, a gyro-tiller might be used. This was a massive crawler tractor made by Fowlers. At the rear were mounted two sets of power-driven vertical blades with slightly curved points. When lowered into the ground, they stirred the soil to a depth of eighteen inches, broke up the roots, and brought many to the surface. Gyro-tillers had the advantage of a single operation, although further use of the cultivator to get more roots out was usually necessary. Also, gyro-tillers levelled out ridge and furrow effectively, but they had to be used in late spring or early summer so as to allow the soil to settle before drilling in the autumn, because they left the land in a very loose, puffy, condition.

Whichever method was used, and if all went well, the surface would be relatively even and, hopefully, fairly free of roots to plough depth. Drainage work might be carried out during the second half of the summer and the field ploughed once more, ready for drilling in the autumn.

Needless to say, all this was a very expensive business and farmers and landowners were only too pleased for the WWAEC to take over the land, clear it, and farm it for the duration. Once the land was in full production, it might be let on licence to a neighbouring farmer, a practice that became increasingly common as the CAEC wound down its labour force and machinery operation.

This, then, became the established reclamation routine on the heavy land. Curiously enough, and possibly contrary to expectations, the lighter, acid, land posed a much greater problem, although in terms of acres there was less of it, with a concentration around the Earlswood area, and with one or two isolated patches along the county boundary with Worcestershire, further south.

For, once the clays had been got ready for their first crop, all was plain sailing subject to the ravages of Wheat Bulb Fly and Wireworms, and always providing plenty of phosphatic fertiliser was applied. Not so on light, acid, land. Some such land had a pH below 5, which is very acidic. Lime, as much as you will, plough half the dressing in and put half on top, cultivate as much as you like to get the lime well mixed with the soil, but still the lime would take more than one season to take full effect. Some such land never did crop well, in spite of heavy liming and fertilising. It might have done eventually, if it had been kept in arable cultivation long enough.

These, then, were the methods by which so much derelict land in South Warwickshire, mainly in the Feldon, was cleared, drained and brought into production in the early 1940s. Today, this countryside has never been better farmed. Surveying the Feldon scene early in the 21st century, it is difficult to imagine the state of some of its land just over sixty years ago.

Rationing

A number of things, besides food, were rationed during the 1940s. Among thse were petrol, coal, clothes and, later, soft furnishings and furniture. A whole host of other items were difficult to come by during the war years, and for some time afterwards. But we are, of course, mainly concerned with food and feedstuffs for farm livestock.

Whilst living out of town may have had a few disadvantages, such as not being on the spot to join the queue at the fishmongers when some fish came in, or no factory or office canteen meals, or no British Restaurant, generally speaking country people, and especially farmers, lived well during the years of food rationing compared with townies. Nor did they have to endure nightly bombing, or the threat of it, with long nights in air raid shelters.

Many, if not most, countrymen kept hens, possibly some cockerels for the table, and may well have killed a pig a year for their own consumption – all perfectly legal one might add. There were official rations for up to 25 laying hens, and membership of the village Pig Club entitled one to a monthly ration, usually collected monthly from the club secretary. Household scraps were boiled up to supplement the meal ration. Also, of course, most villagers had a kitchen garden, or allotment, or both, to grow vegetables, soft and top fruit. Waste from these, small potatoes, green stuff etc., also found their way into the rations for pig and poultry. All in all, and providing there was at least one able bodied man (or woman) in the family, most country folk lived reasonably well in times of food rationing.

In passing, it might be mentioned that in the Stratford District Office it was usual to receive, with unfailing regularity, at least two or three anonymous letters every year accusing the local village policemen of receiving illicit pig and poultry feed from local farmers, in the form of barley meal or corn. An accusation that may, or may not, have been justified but certainly a custom which followed a set pattern.

And, of course, none ate better than farmers. In addition to eggs, table poultry, pigmeat and vegetables, they normally had ample supplies of milk. Coal rationing meant nothing to them since they burnt mainly wood as a matter of course. Then there were rabbits, wood pigeons and game to be had for the shooting.

But it should be stressed that, while country people ate comparatively well in wartime, it was really a matter of a considerable degree of self-sufficiency, which in many cases had been the norm for generations, being extended into the hungry forties. For instance, on the Cotswold farm where I was a pupil just before the war, the young woman who helped in the house made the butter every week in a table-top churn – a big glass jar with wooden paddles inside turned by a handle on the top. Doubtless, the practice continued, rationing or no rationing. Indeed, many considered wartime restrictions, particularly the rationing of animal feeds, an interference with their usual way of 'going on.'

Rationing of feedstuffs extended to farm livestock of all kinds. Pigs and poultry came off worst, as these competed directly with humans for scarce cereals. The highest priority was given to milk production, and beef and sheep were expected to be fed mainly off the farm. Self-sufficiency for livestock was a central plank in farming policy. This took the form of increased production from grassland, the growing of fodder roots such as mangolds and kale in the drier districts, of which South Warwickshire was one, and the drilling of acreages of oats, mixed corn and beans to be fed on the farm.

While the life styles of town and country dwellers were very different in the hungry forties, and especially during the war years, they had much in common. Both put up with long hours of work, sometimes at unfamiliar tasks. And after that was done, both had duties in civil defence organisations, the Home Guard, and so on. A common thread that ran through urban and rural communities alike was the continuing nagging anxiety about loved ones away in the Armed Forces. It was not a happy time.

4. Dairying

Dairying has been described as the *sheet anchor of British farming*. Whether this is still true after the collapse of the milk prices in the second half of the 1990s is an open question. But dairying has certainly played an important part in the farming economy of South Warwickshire during the period under review.

As already mentioned, traditionally, the smaller holdings in the Arden, around Henley-in-Arden, across to Studley and up to Earlswood produced milk for the Birmingham market and also elsewhere in the Midland conurbation. However, during the years of depression, many of the larger farms in the Feldon had to turn to milk production for the liquid market, as opposed to cheese and butter making in days gone by, as a means of survival. Much of the milk produced in the area around Shipston-on-Stour went to London via Moreton-in-Marsh station, rather than to Birmingham and Coventry.

The Structure of Dairying

At the outbreak of the Second World War, herds were small by today's standards. Nowhere was this more in evidence than in the Arden district, where many herds were comprised of fewer than twenty milkers, sometimes a lot fewer. Anyone, anywhere in South Warwickshire, milking fifty cows or more would have been considered to be in a big way of business. Mr. Clyde Higgs of Hatton Rock, near Stratford-on-Avon, milked more cows than anyone else in the district. He had a number of Ayrshire herds, milked in outdoor bails, each herd consisting of 60 to 70 cows.

It is a significant indication of the size of so many herds that, when the Small Farms Scheme came into being in 1959, and continued into the 1960s, the usual target for the increase in numbers in the dairy herd was only 30 cows. Very many who entered the Scheme were then milking less than twenty cows. To rely on natural increase to achieve this was far too slow, only a net rise in numbers of some 10%/year. In practice, additional cows or heifers had to be bought in. Regrettably, contagious abortion was introduced with disastrous results in at least two of these small herds in South Warwickshire.

Today, many of the smaller farms under 150 acres have disappeared, sometimes amalgamated with broader acres or becoming residential amenity holdings, with, of course, the dairy herds that they carried with them. Those which were in the Small Farm Scheme and which are still with us, are confined, with one or two exceptions, to County Council holdings but even a number of these have been amalgamated, notably in Ilmington, Long Compton and Cherington.

Dairying in South Warwickshire has followed the national trend in respect of herd size and cow numbers. Herd size has increased and the number of herds has diminished. National figures give an accurate picture of the trend. In the twenty years from 1967 to 1987, the number of dairy holdings had fallen from 132,000 to 50,000, while herd size rose from an average of 24 cows to 60. By 1989, half the nation's milk was being produced from herds of 100 cows or more. This state of affairs was brought about not only by the disappearance of the smaller holdings and their herds, but also by larger farms giving up milk production for one reason or another. These trends have continued during the last decade and there are currently no signs that this will not be the case into the foreseeable future.

The reasons for this were, and are, economic, and dairying was only one sector of British agriculture that exhibited this trend towards larger and larger units. Once food ceased to be rationed, a continuing cost/price squeeze became the order of the day and bigger farms and enterprise units were necessary to obtain the advantages of economy of scale. This was the case both under the Agriculture Act 1947 and under the EU's Common Agricultural Policy (CAP).

The former established a system of guaranteed prices for all the main farm products, although horticulture was not supported in this way. These prices were fixed at the Annual Price Review, held in February each year, for certain periods ahead, depending on the type of product. Each year under this system, usually by the end of December, the economists from the National Farmers' Union and the Ministry of Agriculture had established the facts about farm incomes for the previous twelve months. That is the actual returns from corn, milk, beef, sheep and so on, also the rises in costs which had been incurred.

The unions and the government of the day entered into negotiations to fix the level of farm prices, commodity by commodity, for the following twelve months. This was, of course, influenced by the food supply situation in the early years after the passing of the Act. The most obvious example of this was the 1948 Review, when the NFU got more or less what it asked for following the disastrous harvest of 1947, which had necessitated bread and potato rationing – something that had not occurred during the war years.

But when food rationing ended, it was a different story, although recurring crises in the balance of payments did mean that there was a continuing need for as much food to be produced from British farms as was reasonably possible. During the 1950s, the argument that was put forward each year and was, to some extent, accepted was that milk, along with eggs and pigmeat, should receive special treatment since these were the items upon which the smaller farms depended.

But by 1959, it became apparent that this special treatment in terms of prices could not be maintained. The cost to the Treasury was getting prohibitive and the supply of these small farm commodities began to exceed demand. In that year, Sir John Hare, the Minister of Agriculture, introduced a special scheme to help those on fewer than 100 acres, to expand the size of their businesses to help cope with the cost/price squeeze on those products on which they were so dependent.

In passing, it should be noted that this established the fact that, in the end, the attempt to keep these smaller holdings in business by means of the price mechanism had failed. This was, and still is, the central plank in the EU's Common Agricultural Policy. It is not surprising that the experience of the UK in this respect in the 1950s was repeated in the EU, when the cost of the CAP got out of control and surpluses, notably of milk and milk products and cereals, reached high levels.

Under the scheme for the smaller holdings the policy was usually to increase the dairy herd to at least 30 milkers, to the exclusion of some other enterprises. In the event the scheme proved to be only a palliative, providing a welcome, but temporary, addition to farm income. There was no bucking the trend to larger farms and bigger herds.

Every year from about 1960 onwards, the farming industry was forced at each Annual Price Review to absorb a proportion of the increased costs. The better and more forward looking dairy farms coped with the cost/price squeeze and the effects of inflation by a combination of measures. Amongst these was an increase in cow numbers, which usually meant: abandoning the cowshed and converting to a yard and parlour system; increasing yields by a well-planned breeding policy and other means; better control of disease; improved hygiene to earn bonuses and to escape penalties, and better management. The latter would include: dealing with infertility and a tighter service policy to improve the calving index; milk recording and costing; more accurate feed rationing; more reliance on silage and less on hay and fodder roots, and higher stocking rates made possible by better grassland management. All such measures became commonplace on dairy farms in South Warwickshire.

The fact of the matter was that a stark choice faced milk producers in the 1960s – get on, or get out. In other words to adopt those measures outlined above or go out of milk production altogether. Many chose the latter course. But within two decade or so, history was to repeat itself. Many of the original yards and milking parlours built in the 1960s were, twenty to thirty years later, becoming outmoded and unable to accommodate the ever increasing size of herds, which had become necessary in view of continuing economic pressures.

So, once again, milk producers were faced with the same choice, but with a difference. For the introduction of milk quotas had created, literally at the stroke of a pen, a very valuable capital asset. This, coupled with good cow prices at the time, made retirement from milk production and the adoption of less demanding farm enterprises a very attractive proposition. This was especially so in cases where there was no successor, or where a son, or sons, were not interested in continuing milking – and who could blame them? A number of farming families in South Warwickshire, who were running a milking herd at the time, took advantage of these favourable circumstances while they lasted, sold their quota and herds. No doubt there were many others who wished they had done the same when the milk price collapsed in the late 1990s.

Milk Quotas

The introduction of milk quotas in April 1984 created a valuable capital asset for dairy farmers. But this should not blind us to the devastating effect the sudden imposition of this restraint on milk production had across the dairy sector as a whole, which took place with little warning and handed a slice of the British market for dairy products to foreigners.

For the Government of the day, and particularly the Minister of Agriculture, were guilty of betraying all milk producers in the UK, because they had agreed to a national milk quota substantially below national consumption, including both the liquid and manufacturing markets.

How this state of affairs was ever allowed to arise is beyond comprehension. Common sense, obviously a commodity in short supply, would dictate that the base line for national quotas should be the domestic consumption of each member state in the EU. Those countries producing in excess of this were those that were contributing to the milk surplus and which had become such an embarrassment to the Community's agricultural policy.

But this was not to be and British milk producers lost out in consequence, whereas Italy, of course, steadfastly and successfully ignored the introduction of milk quotas for many years. And when finally brought to heel, Italy had the gall to demand a revised national quota larger than that originally agreed.

Every milk producer in the UK was affected to a greater or lesser degree. Obviously, those dependent entirely upon their milk cheques were placed in the most difficult position. The problem of maintaining income in the face of an enforced lower level of production was at the nub of the matter.

One way forward was to accept a lower yield per cow, placing a greater reliance on grazed and conserved grass, on maize silage and on other fodder crops, thus cutting current concentrate consumption and lowering the cost of production per litre. Others, once the arrangements for transferring quota from farm to farm, either by purchase or leasing, had been put in place, took the latter route. Nevertheless, this was an additional financial burden on a farm business and there was clearly a limit on the total number of litres, as a proportion of the litres already owned, which it was economical to acquire in this way.

Without much doubt, those who were hit worst were those who were in the process of herd expansion, and many, if not most, would have been in the Farm and Horticultural Development Scheme (FHDS). This entailed producing a budget to show that the necessary expenditure on buildings, equipment and stock, would be justified, resulting in increased and more economic production.

The grants under FHDS, needless to say, covered only a part of the necessary new investment, at best 40%, and for many items considerably less than that. Those who had not reached their target production well before the introduction of quotas, were in dire straits. For they had incurred a great deal of expenditure on improvements to buildings and equipment and, possibly, on additional stock as well, only to find that the rug had been pulled from beneath them, as it were, because they were prevented from reaching the increased level of milk production upon which the viability of the exercise depended. No special consideration was given to those who found themselves in this predicament, incredible as it may seem.

Here was a situation in which the Ministry of Agriculture had sanctioned a scheme for expansion and improvement, had undertaken to grant- aid, the necessary investment, and then made it impossible to carry through the approved plan to completion. If the boot had been on the other foot, and a farmer had failed to finish the programme and to carry out his obligations, he would have been in serious trouble in some form or other.

The only redress that those in FHDS had under these circumstances was to appeal to the Milk Quota Tribunal, which had at its disposal a relatively small amount of quota to allocate on grounds of hardship. By this time, I had retired from the Agricultural Development and Advisory Service (as NAAS had become), and was handling the agricultural work for a firm of estate agents in Stratford-upon-Avon. One job I had was to represent a farmer/client at a Tribunal hearing.

It was a pathetic case that involved a hard-working man on a small specialist dairy farm in North Warwickshire, and thus not in my former district. In the first place, it was doubtful whether he should have been encouraged to enter FHDS. He did not own the farm and had borrowed from the Bank on the strength of the FHDS plan. The yield per cow was mediocre and the budget, which had been prepared for him, had assumed an improved performance per cow, always a dangerous thing to do and certainly not good practice. He had done all the improvements to the fixed and other equipment, and had purchased a bunch of heifers, which were now in calf, all of which he had paid for.

I prepared the case, along with all the FHDS documents, and he and I attended the Tribunal at the MAFF Regional Office in Tettenhal. Things appeared to go well, but in due course I had a letter from my client saying that we had been unsuccessful. He thanked me for what I had done, and was kind enough to say that nobody could have dome more, and would I send him my account ? This I kept just as low as I possibly could. How he fared in his unfortunate situation, I never heard. And he was only one; there must have been many others like him for which the imposition of milk quotas had been a disaster.

As the years went by, milk producers learned to live with quotas. Indeed, the more enterprising and able have continued to expand, buying or leasing extra quota as needed. Other gave up dairying, cashing in on the capital value of their quotas, the sum obtained often being in excess of that realised by the sale of the herd.

These then were the economic and political circumstances under which milk producers had to operate during the second half of the 20th. century. By its end, dairy farms in South Warwickshire, and elsewhere for that matter, bore little resemblance to those of fifty years earlier. For milk production during that half century had undergone nothing less than a revolution in housing, milking methods, feeding and so on. The following sections deal with these changes, with special reference to dairying in South Warwickshire.

The Milking Machine

Although the milking machine had made its appearance on the farming scene at least forty years previously, it formed the basis of all the developments that were to follow. The first machines were developed before the First World War, but were unsatisfactory and unreliable. One of the main causes was the fact that the materials available at the time were unable to stand up to the fluctuating vacuums and the cleaning methods then employed.

However, by the winter of 1922-23, machine milking was sufficiently well established for A. J. Hosier to install one in his first milking bail. The vacuum pump was driven by a small petrol engine and the milk conveyed to the cooler by pipeline.

Throughout the two decades between the wars, the milking machine was adopted by owners of many of the larger herds. Good hand milkers were scarce and, by the standards of the day, expensive. Apart from this, fewer men were needed to milk the same number of cows. With hand milking, a man could manage about twelve cows. With a bucket plant in a cowshed this number rose to thirty and, of course, the vast majority of milking machines were installed in cowsheds. Later, bucket plants were supplanted to some extent by milk pipelines and the more sophisticated outfits that incorporated glass jars for weighing the yield from individual cows.

By 1939, it was estimated that there were some 20,000 milking machines in use. This figure had to be read in conjunction with the fact that there were, in the same year, 100,000 producers registered with the Milk Marketing Board. During the war years, 1940 to 1945, the number of milking machines rose by 64%, and at the end of hostilities 50% of the cows in the national herd were being milked by machine.

Hand milking lingered on for many years, especially in the smaller herds where the installation of a machine would have been uneconomical, even if the capital had been available. However, some attempts were made to produce machines suited to the very small herds. But these did not really catch on, possibly because herd size outstripped their development.

Those who served on the WAECs, whether as salaried staff or voluntary farmer members, will recall the old white foolscap Farm Survey forms that had to be completed for every holding during the war years, and for some time after. These all had a box to record whether the herd was hand or machine milked. Silent testimony as to just how long the former practice lingered on was the fact that, even in 1963-64, 3% of the cows in the UK were still hand milked.

Of course, in the 1930s and 1940s, when so many milking machines were being installed, many farms had no electricity. The pumps were driven by small petrol engines, some of which were noted for being reluctant starters, especially on very cold, damp, winter mornings. The late Mr. Righton, who kept one of the garages in Brailes, recalled that on such mornings he was kept busy from first light, or before, rushing from one farm to another in answer to urgent calls for help in starting the engines before milking could begin.

Cowshed to Yard and Parlour

The yard and parlour system did not replace cowsheds overnight, far from it. Indeed, in South Warwickshire at any rate, new cowsheds were being built in the 1950s and even later. To the best of my recollection, the last large cowshed to be put up in this district was on Upper Goldicote Farm, and another big shippon had been constructed in the 1950s on Sweet Knowle Farm, Preston-on-Stour.

The pros and cons of cowsheds and the yard and parlour system were still being argued in the early 1960s. Those who had spent a working lifetime milking in cowsheds were loathe to change. To illustrate this, we go north of The Border to the farm of a client of mine near Dumfries. This was on a large estate, and the Laird had decreed that all tenants who had a milking herd were to be provided with cubicle sheds and milking parlours. When the Laird spoke in that neck of the woods, that was that. However, tenants were allowed to choose their own type of parlour, all opting for herringbones, bar one. Robbie milked in a magnificent cowshed, tying 200 with a slate roof lined with matchboarding. To the amazement of the agent, he said he wanted two twelve-stall, two-level abreast parlours, back to back with a passage in between wide enough for the cows to have access.

When the agent asked Robbie why he wanted such an arrangement, Robbie replied, 'It' s the nearest thing to a shippon I can get.' And there they were installed in the shippon, which was also large enough to house a collecting yard and dairy, and with room for some calf pens.

Efforts were made to modernise cowpens, mainly to save labour. As already mentioned, milk pipelines were introduced, and another innovation was the mechanical cleaning of the dunging gutters. But, in spite of all this, cowsheds were doomed. By the 1960s, the change to the yard and parlour system was in full swing, which was not surprising because the economies of labour were outstanding. Nix quotes 5 Standard Man Days/year/cow for yard/parlour, compared with 8 SMD for cowsheds.

Probably the first milking parlour to be installed, in the 1930s, in South Warwickshire was, judging from a photograph, a single-level twelve-stall abreast layout. This was an Alfa Laval and, according to the caption, was the first of its kind in the country, being built for the late Clyde Higgs of Hatton Rock. But, apparently, the cows were not yarded, being yoked in stalls where they were fed and prepared for milking. The herd then consisted of 120 Ayrshires with an average yield of 800 gallons. This was a very good herd average for its time.

Some twenty five years later, Sam Pritchard put in a similar arrangement at New End Farm, Great Alne. In contrast to Hatton Rock, the cows were yarded. But there was a set of stalls in front of the abreast parlour. In these the cows had their cake, were groomed and their udders washed before going forward into the parlour to be milked. Sam proudly referred to this as his 'lactory.'

A number of single- level abreast parlours were installed on dairy farms in South Warwickshire during the second half of the 1940s and early 1950s. Amongst these were Home Farm, Aston Cantlow for Frank Suffield's Guernsey herd; at Manor Farm, Walcote by K. L. Smith after he moved from his first farm, Bunkers Hill on Alcester Heath; at Preston Pastures by Mr. Gamble; J. Mawle put one in at his Mitford Bridge Farm near Shipston-on-Stour, as did 'Farmer' Slatter at Long Compton.

Before long, other types of parlour became available, some of which were in vogue for only a short time. One of these was the chute type. Cows entered in line-ahead formation, one line each side of the pit, each side being released when all the occupants had been milked. The one advantage of this design was that it could be fitted into a comparatively narrow space, thus making it possible to convert a cowpen without the need for a new building.

A variation of this was the tandem type. Again, cows stood line-ahead, but there was a passage way alongside the milking stalls so that the cows could enter and exit individually. One of these was installed by Col.M.Warriner when he took Pepperwell Farm, Little Wolford, in hand in 1958. Recently, an updated and fully automated version of the Tandem has become available; one was installed at Walcote Manor by Hamish Gray-Cheape in 1997 to replace the abreast parlour, mentioned above, after fifty years service. The big advantage of the tandem over the chute or herringbone was the fact that cows could be treated as individuals and, if necessary, held in their stalls without holding up milking. This was in contrast to the chute or herringbone, where it is a matter of 'all in, then all out.'

By the 1970s and through the 1980s, the herringbone became the standard type, the throughput in terms of cows per hour being swifter than previous types. But other designs came and went during these two decades. In rotary parlours, the cows stood on a revolving platform, moving around the cowman in the pit. With the carousel type, the cows stood with heads inwards, while the platform again revolved, presenting each cow in turn to the operator who stood at a station on the perimeter. These proved to be 'nine days wonders' and, to the best of my knowledge, not one of either type was ever installed on a farm in South Warwickshire. Then there were some variations in pit shapes, one such being built on Ragley Home Farms when the new dairy unit was constructed at Weethley.

Mention must also be made of the use of milking bails – Hosier bails in particular – as static parlours. When commuter traffic made milking the herd at Home Farm, in the centre of the village of Aston Cantlow, impossible, a new unit was constructed by a field barn on the main body of the holding, and a bail was used. Bertie Watts bought a new Hosier bail with cake loft above, the base being stepped to make a two-level abreast parlour, this on Nobbs Farm, Weston-on-Avon. Again, when it was decided to start milking on Ragley Home Farms, a second-hand bail was purchased to keep capital expenditure to a minimum.

Mike Dowler originally milked his herd of Red Polls in a yard in the centre of Ilmington. After some discussion, it was decided to buy a Hosier chute bail and provide it with two concrete bases, one in the yard in the centre of the village and the other on a roadside site next to a Dutch barn on the main body of the farm. The cows were milked in the former when yarded for the winter and in the latter when at pasture during the grazing season. It should be added that the distance from the original cowpen in the yard to the nearest grass field was nearly half a mile, and the bail solution seemed preferable to building a static parlour in the village farmstead.

The milking machine was driven by a Wolsey stationary engine and a small dairy on each site completed the arrangement. This worked well for a number of years. Eventually, however, the village farmstead was sold for development and a new dairy unit established on the field site.

The above were just a few examples of milking bails being used as static parlours; there were others as well as these, in South Warwickshire. The big advantage was that their use avoided the construction of a special building, thus reducing capital costs, and with a little ingenuity the abreast type could be made weatherproof.

There are two other developments associated with milking parlours that are significant. The first proved to be a dead end due to the introduction of the second.

In the second half of the 1950s, direct-to-churn milking was introduced, along with immersion cleaning of the equipment. The idea was to simplify the milking process and also the routine daily cleaning of the equipment, both with a view to saving labour. Special lids for churns were developed into which the clusters delivered the milk direct. When the churn was full it was slid along rails, which were steel pipes half embedded in the concrete floor. They were then lifted onto a platform for in-churn cooling by cold water.

After milking, the clusters and tubing were packed into a stainless steel basket which was lowered into a bucket of the same material. This contained a 2% caustic soda solution into which the basket and its contents were immersed for a period of time before being thoroughly rinsed before the next milking.

This new system had a number of advantages. It eliminated milk pipelines and their cleaning and it reduced the time taken to clean and sterilise the equipment; for example, there was no separate cooler and header tank to scrub and sterilise. But it did necessitate stainless steel throughout and special tubing to resist the corrosive effect of the caustic soda. In spite of these drawbacks, the system was popular for a short time.

Needless to say, in-churn milking was superseded by the second development, bulk milk collection. Bigger herds, and a greater volume of daily production, inevitably meant that a greater number of churns had to be handled, labelled, and often transported, to the milk stand at the end of the farm drive. In hot weather the keeping quality of the milk was not improved by a period standing in churns awaiting collection. Bulk milk collection also meant the end of often frequent and acrimonious arguments with dairies over returning dirty churns!

With bulk collection, the milk was kept in refrigerated tanks in farm dairies until collection by the milk tanker. A great deal of labour was also saved by eliminating the humping and labelling of an (often) steadily increasing number of churns.

Bulk milk collection was introduced into South Warwickshire in December 1960. At least, this is when Blakes of Loxley, who must have collected more milk from South Warwickshire dairy farms than any other haulier, put their first milk tanker on the road. They ceased to collect any churns after October 1973. But Quinneys Dairy, in Redditch, was designated a dairy for residual churn collection, and drew churn milk from a very wide area until bulk tanks became universal.

Thus it is clear that the conversion from churns to bulk tanks was a long drawn out business. To encourage the process, the Milk Marketing Board gave a bonus of so much per gallon for a number of years towards the cost of the milk tank. In addition, it was possible to borrow from the Board to pay for the tank. Thus the exercise could be largely self supporting.

In most cases, some structural alterations were needed to dairy buildings because the tanks were far too large to go through a doorway of normal width. The problem was sometimes overcome on the smaller farms that did not need a very big tank, by erecting a concrete sectional garage, the double doors of which could accommodate the tank. This was the practice on some County Council holdings.

Another matter which sometimes needed attention was access for the tanker lorry and a turning area around the farm dairy. It will be recalled that, when the farm drive was long, the milk stand was situated by the side of the public road, the full churns being taken by tractor and trailer each morning to await collection by lorry. But when the road tanker had to drive to the farm dairy it became obvious that roads which had sufficed for farm traffic were certainly not adequate for wider and heavier vehicles. Thus, in some cases, farm roads had to be improved and even bridges widened and strengthened. There is no doubt that all this added expense gave further impetus to the disappearance of many of the smaller herds. In passing, it should be added that this problem of access was not confined to milk tankers. Merchants' vehicles, and especially grain lorries, were increasing in size and also had to be accommodated.

Cubicles

No account of dairying during this half century would be complete without giving cow cubicles a mention. These consisted of individual lying areas divided by steel tubing or wooden rails. Cows went in head first, the length of the cubicle from front to back being such that the rear ends of the cows projected over a dwarf wall, so that dung and urine was deposited on the concrete passage and did not soil the cubicle bed, which would be covered with chopped straw, sand, shavings or a special mattress.

A variation of the cubicle was the cow kennel, which was simply a double row of cubicles with a roof on. These were usually of wooden construction, in which the back and front upright timbers supporting the dividing rails were extended upwards, and with cross members provided to carry the roof. The rows of kennels flanked a passageway, and sometimes the roof was extended over this, or sometimes gap was left. Cow kennels and cubicle divisions that are made of wood have a serious drawback. They were often a sorry sight by the end of the winter with many broken rails. Whereas the initial costs might have appeared attractive, annual maintenance costs were high.

The main advantage of cubicles was a great saving in the use of straw, especially in those counties which were mainly pastoral and where little straw was produced locally, and where most of it had to be bought and transported from the arable areas in the Midlands and Eastern Counties. Savings of up to 75% could be made in the amount of straw needed per cow during the winter months.

All this made good sense on dairy farms in the West Country, Wales and in some northern areas. However, farming is just as prone to the influence of fashion as women's clothes. Cubicles began to be installed nationwide, even in those areas where considerable acreages of corn were grown. Thus, in South Warwickshire, we had a farcical situation in which cubicles were installed at great expense, while straw was being burnt on neighbouring farms.

The reason for this anomaly was probably a desire to eliminate, or reduce as much as possible, the expense of baling large quantities of straw and, even more important, the labour-consuming chore of carting and stacking.

The advent of the big baler heralded in a different ball game as far as handling straw was concerned, because this could now be completely mechanised. It was significant that new, large, dairy units built in South Warwickshire in the 1970s returned to the traditional loose housing in yards.

Whatever the advantages cubicles might have had, it was certain that the one drawback was that they exacerbated the problem of storing and disposing of the resultant slurry. With herds increasing in size and with the river authorities, now the Environment Agency, making more stringent, and often unreasonable, demands concerning effluent management, any system of housing that produced greater amounts of slurry than was absolutely necessary was obviously undesirable. The fact of the matter is that the cheapest way of storing cow muck and urine is under the cow, mixed with straw. This, in spite of the fact that it is now good practice to clean out such yards two or three times each winter to reduce the risk of high cell and TBC counts.

The demands made by officials in the sacred name of pollution control have necessitated dairy farmers, and others, spending considerable sums to meet their requirements. This is dead money that represents an investment on which there is no return in the form of increased income. Moreover, financial assistance in the form of grant aid had proved to be an inadequate compensation. This was yet another turn of the screw, and made the production of milk from the smaller herds even more difficult and, in many cases just impossible. Many crocodile tears have been shed over the demise of the small family farm, by townies in particular. The fact of the matter is that this has been accelerated, and indeed made inevitable, by bureaucracy in all its forms.

5. MILK PRODUCTION

The last chapter described the economic and political circumstances that milk producers had to endure during the second half of the 20th. century, and the means by which they dealt with these pressures. On the one hand, these included adapting their farm businesses so that they could continue to produce milk at a profit; on the other, giving up milk production either to retire from farming completely, or to continue with less demanding enterprises.

This chapter attempts to record the changes that have taken place in the nitty-gritty of getting milk out of cows in the greatest volume, at the lowest possible cost – the science of milk production.

Breeds

In 1940, in South Warwickshire, the Shorthorn breed dominated the dairying sector, and this continued to be the case into the 1950s. Early in the 1950s, Mr. W.B.Mercer, the West Midlands Provincial Director of the recently formed National Agricultural Advisory Service, stated in a paper, produced as part of a scientific study of the Birmingham district, that Shorthorns were the most numerous breed. Hereford bulls were often used on Shorthorns to produce beef crosses and white faced Hereford x Shorthorn beef stores were a common sight in Stratford market in the 1940s and 1950s.

Within the Shorthorn breed there were two types, the dairy and the beef. One well-known herd in South Warwickshire was kept for milk production but the cattle were more of the beef type. Magnificent looking cows, with great backsides, but with the milking capacity of a high yielding goat. It always seemed somewhat of a mystery to me, and possibly to others as well, that the Warwickshire Farm Institute started with a herd of dairy Shorthorns, and persisted with them for some years, even when the writing was already on the wall.

During the 1940s, there were already a number of Friesian herds in South Warwickshire, which tended to be kept by the more progressive dairy farmers. It should be added that others in the same category were favouring the Ayrshire breed at that time. Among them were Clyde Higgs of Hatton Rock, Bertie Watts of Nobbs Farm (both mentioned earlier), Capt. Dronsfield of Wilmcote Manor, and many others.

Among those with high-yielding Friesian herds were E.G.Davies of Broom Court, Bidford-on-Avon, whose herd was dispersed in the early 1970s;

D.Goulbourne, Haselor Manor Farm, whose sons are still milking the progeny of the original herd, and K.L.Smith of Walcote Manor Farm. This is to mention but a few but, of course, there were a number of milk producers of a similar high calibre who also milked Friesians at that time.

During the 1950s, Shorthorns were losing their dominance, and were replaced by Friesians, Ayrshires and Channel Island breeds. In 1962, I established two Cow Feed Recording Groups – a precursor of the now sophisticated, computerised dairy management schemes – one based at Aston Cantlow and the other at Shipston-on-Stour. Dairy farmers participating in this scheme provided a cross section of milk producers in South Warwickshire.

In September 1963, there were 31 herds in the two groups. Of these, fifteen were pure Friesian herds, three were Ayrshires, six were Jerseys or Guernseys, one was mixed (this contained so many breeds and crosses it was more like a zoo than a herd) and one Red Poll. In addition, there were five herds described as 'Friesian with another breed' which were, in fact, in the process of converting to all Friesians.

During the 1950s, Ayrshires posed a significant challenge to the Friesian breed. The former were, of course, dominant in Scotland. Moreover, in 1948, 29% of herds north of the Border were tuberculosis tested, in comparison with only 7. 3% in England. Already, there were price incentives for producing tuberculin tested milk and the more forward-looking producers were going TT. Thus the easiest, and quickest, way of reaching this goal was to purchase Ayrshire replacements from tuberculosis free herds in Scotland.

Another reason for doing this was the neat, well-formed, and hard-wearing udder that was characteristic of the Ayrshire breed. This was highly inheritable and, in fact, genetically dominant. It was thus good practice – and often given as advice to a young man starting in dairying – to purchase Ayrshire heifers and put them to a Friesian bull for successive generations. Eventually, one ended up with a black and white herd with the higher yields of the Friesians and the harder wearing udder of the Ayrshire. At least, that was the theory. Col. Michael Warriner of Weston Park Estate, near Shipston-on-Stour, established a herd in this way when he took Pepperwell Farm, Little Wolford, in hand, with Frank Bennison as manager, buying fifty Ayrshire bulling heifers from Scotland and putting them to a Friesian bull.

Some idea of the impact of the Ayrshire breed in England can be gleaned from the fact that, in 1955, no less than 18% of dairy herds were composed of Ayrshires, compared with 41% Friesian herds. But later, the influence of the Ayrshire breed waned.

This table below shows the breed figures for Warwickshire in 1969. The dominance of the Friesian breed was well established by that year, especially since many of the herds classified as mixed were in the process of changing to all Friesian. Today, almost all the dairy herds in South Warwickshire are composed entirely of Friesians.

Breed	
Friesians	58%
Ayrshires	5.3%
Shorthorns	2.9%
Channel Island breeds	8.1%
Mixed	25.4%
Red Poll	2%
South Devon	0.1%

Breed figures for Warwickshire, 1969

Feeding the Dairy Cow

In the early 1940s, rations for dairy cows were similar, if not identical, with those fed during the previous two decades. I refer, of course, to what was accepted as the best practice at the time, *Agriculture - The Science and Practice of British Farming* by Watson and Moore, which was the standard text book and the bible for students of my generation. The 1937 edition suggests the following as suitable *maintenance* rations for an 11 cwt. Shorthorn cow, which provides sufficient nourishment to keep the beast alive and in good bodily condition, but makes no contribution to the production of milk; this is the job of the *production* ration

The figure of 20 lb. of good hay was accepted for many years, in practice, as being correct, on the assumption that all hay was considered to be good except that which was obviously of the poorest quality, cut late or badly weathered, or both. In fact, when analysed by a nutrition chemist, few hay samples had a sufficiently high starch equivalent to provide a maintenance ration fed at that rate.

It is, therefore, not surprising that it was part of the received wisdom amongst dairy farmers that winter milk yields were dependent upon the quality of the hay. The fact of the matter was that 20 lb. of hay did not provide an adequate maintenance ration in many, if not most, seasons. Thus a part of the production ration, which consisted of concentrates of one sort or another, had to contribute to the maintenance ration, with yields suffering in consequence.

Maintenance rations listed in Watson and Moore

a. 20 lb. good hay.

b. 40 lb. mangolds with 14 lb. hay.

c. 30 lb. arable silage with 10 lb. hay.

d. 60 lb. swedes, 6 lb. oat straw and 6 lb. hay.

The late 'Bobbie' Boutflour, one-time county adviser in Wiltshire but better known as a Principal of the Royal Agricultural College, Cirencester, always said that feeding roots to cows was an expensive way of providing them with water, which could be supplied more easily and cheaply from a tap! He advised a diet based on hay or silage (very little of this was made in those days) and concentrates fed according to yield. Room in the rumen for the latter should be made by restricting, as far as was possible, the bulky portion of the ration.

By no means all farmers accepted this argument. In fact, when I was a farm pupil on a farm in North Wiltshire, milk producers in that part of the county always maintained that Bobbie Boutflour had killed more cows in Wiltshire than any vet.

In passing, it is interesting to note that his recommendation that bulk feed should be restricted to allow of cake feeding according to yield has, today, been stood on its head. The basis of economical milk production is now maximum reliance on good quality grass and maize silage and other feeds fed outside the parlour, (in some cases even fodder beet) and concentrates fed in the parlour to the highest yielding cows only.

In the early 1940s, and for some time afterwards, cow rations on the best-run dairy farms in South Warwickshire were based on hay and kale, which was fed until Christmas, and mangolds thereafter. Cake was fed in the cowshed, eked out, especially when feedstuffs were rationed, with home-grown oats and beans. Sometimes the roots were chopped or sliced, mixed with chaff, rolled oats, or whatever, and carried in skips to be tipped into the cowshed mangers after milking. Today, this is called *complete diet feeding*!

Kale

The kale crop in the early 1940s was grown in wide rows and chopped out, leaving the plants about 12" apart in the rows. A well-grown and fertilised crop would produce plants with thick stems, which could reach 5' in height. These were cut and loaded by hand onto carts, or tractor trailers, in the autumn. The leaves, which were bunched at the top, held water after rain. This found its way down the neck and into the tops of the wellies. Not a pleasant job on a cold, damp, November morning. Kale was commonly fed out in the field when the herd was let out for exercise in the morning.

A tractor fitted with a cutrake (see Ch. 24) would be driven backwards, at speed, into the kale crop. The plants would fall neatly into the weldmesh cage, packed like daffodils in a box ready for market. The load would be then driven onto to the field where it was to be fed and forked off into rows.

With the coming of the electric fence it was possible to graze kale. This was developed on the Reading University farm at Sonning by a contemporary of mine, Ralph John, when he returned from military service. Kale was then broadcast, instead of being grown in rows, and this resulted in a much shorter and leafier crop. This practice declined as herds got bigger, large numbers of cows tramping about in a wet autumn was not a proposition. In any case the feeding of silage was becoming more common.

Even with modest numbers of cows, poaching could be a problem during a wet period. The herd would come into the cowshed plastered in mud and a great deal of time had to be taken up with udder washing. Moreover, when conditions were really atrocious, cows milked badly on grazed kale because they used up more energy than it provided in getting to and from the field and in grazing the crop.

It was amazing how much kale cows could tuck away when grazing the crop. At Talton Mill, Newbold-on-Stour, Hugh Holberton was milking Jerseys. One day, we were working out the winter rations and decided to find out, as near as we could, how much kale these little cows were eating. We knew by how many yards the fence was moved each day and by weighing sample lengths along the feeding face we could calculate the daily consumption, which worked out at an average of 60 lb./day/cow. This was far more than we had initially assumed and the ration was adjusted accordingly to make the best use of this cheap source of protein.

Latterly, one method used to help overcome poaching was to take a kale crop after grass. This would be burnt off with Gramoxone and the kale drilled directly into the dead sward. The latter went some of the way to reduce the effects of a wet autumn, as poaching was reduced by the remains of the turf.

One rotation that was common for a number of years in South Warwickshire was to alternate kale with two years of Italian Ryegrass for early bite. This would be sown without a cover crop after kale, giving good grazing and, possibly, a crop of silage in the first year. Next year an early bite followed by two cuts for silage. And in the third year grazing in March before being ploughed and sown to kale.

Mangolds

These were, of course, grown in wide rows and singled. Commonly, they would receive a dressing of farmyard manure and a generous application of a compound fertiliser. Done well in this manner, they would be capable of giving very heavy yields per acre.

The crop was pulled, thrown into heaps with a swing of the root with one hand, while cutting off the leaves with a knife held in the other. The leaves served to cover the roots against damage by frost until they were carted off to be clamped. The unforgivable sin was to pierce the skin with a fork, as this led to rotting. It was a laborious, back-breaking business, sometimes carried out in autumn weather that was far from ideal.

The incomparable Sam Pritchard had, of course, to do things differently. He pulled the mangolds and clamped them direct from the field, without cutting off the tops, in a wide clamp made of straw bales. As this was within sight of the road, and it was the talk of the neighbourhood which foretold a clamp of rotten, stinking roots when it came to be opened in the New Year. To the disappointment of the pundits, the mangolds turned out to be perfectly sound when the time came to feed them.

Mangolds had to mature in the clamp, and were fed after Christmas when the kale was finished. Apart from being fed to cattle of all kinds, they were much valued for feeding to ewes in the spring. So much so, in fact, that at least one South Warwickshire farmer used to buy one or two lorry loads every year from the Eastern Counties to feed to his flock.

Silage

In spite of all the wartime propaganda promoting the virtues of silage, in the event little was made until the coming of the buckrake, because the handling of large amounts of fresh, wet, grass proved too much of a gut-rending, mauling job. Plenty had tried it, but usually for only one or two seasons. Again, compared with the feeding of hay, cutting silage out of a stack, or clamp, and carting it to where it was to be fed was heavy work. Also the process of silage making was not always understood resulting in, all too often, silage of poor quality and much waste. In those days, silage was advocated as a substitute for roots, albeit with a higher feeding value. The idea was to cut grass young and produce a silage of 20% dry matter, and 20% protein. Fed at 20 lb./gallon it was supposed to suffice for a gallon of milk. The magic formula 20:20:20.

With the introduction of the buckrake and the pit, the making of silage became more popular. The pit evolved into a clamp above ground, the made silage often being sealed with a layer of ground limestone. But there was still much handwork involved in spreading the grass on the pit or clamp, then cutting it out in the winter and carting to the cows.

Self-feeding Silage

The introduction of the forage harvester, the clamp made with sleeper walls in a Dutch barn, and self-feeding finally put silage at the centre stage in dairying. The Silo Subsidy encouraged the conversion of many a Dutch barn, a common arrangement being to add a lean-to each side for the cows to lie in, a concrete apron along the front, with milking parlour and dairy adjacent.

The full story of making silage will be dealt with in a later chapter. Suffice it to record here that, when self-feeding, some 6" to 9" of silage face per cow were needed. The face could not be more than 6' high, otherwise cows could not reach the top layers, which would have to be cut by hand and thrown down.

It was usual to provide some sort of barrier at the feeding face, often just an electric fence supported on bars driven into the silage. This prevented the cows trampling on silage that had been pulled out and had fallen onto the concrete floor. It was also a means of controlling daily consumption.

One of the disadvantages of self-feeding was that it could be a very inflexible system. Self-fed silage for maintenances and, hopefully, a gallon or so of milk was the order of the day. As NAAS District Adviser in South Warwickshire, much of my time during the winter months was taken up with sampling silage, sending it for analysis and advising on the results.

Very often the silage was of sufficient quality to provide the maintenance ration and a production ration enough for a gallon of milk, then sufficient protein for a further gallon if a starchy food such as rolled barley or oats, or sugar beet pulp was fed in addition. In practice, dairy farmers were very reluctant to make any arrangements to feed such a supplement outside the parlour. It was like banging one's head against a brick wall and much protein must have gone, literally, down the drain.

The breakthrough came with the appointment of George Jackson as Principal of the Warwickshire College of Agriculture at Moreton Morrell. The original dairy unit was by the Teaching Block before the new one was built at Nethermorton. One of the first things George did was to install mangers outside the parlour so that supplementary feeds could be offered when the quality of the silage demanded this. Then all was plain sailing and many milk producers followed suit and, one might add, not before time.

But herd size continued to increase inexorably. Self-feed units became outgrown and the next stage in the silage saga had begun, the feeding of a basic silage mixture, with other ingredients in mangers, feed boxes or behind feed barriers. This was made possible by the introduction of silage grabs and later block cutters, along with forage feed boxes and feeder/mixer wagons. These made possible the extraction of silage from the clamp and feeding in the mangers, or whatever, without leaving the tractor seat.

Dairy units refurbished from the 1970s onwards were laid out, not for self-feeding, but with reliance on manger/bunker feeding with block cutters and feeder wagons.

Bigger herds and the trend towards larger quantities of silage fed per cow meant that silos of greater capacity had to be built, These took the form of big, uncovered, clamps outdoors. The silage could now be sealed with polythene sheets, weighed down with used tyres. Usually the feeding regime was *complete diet feeding*, or a variation of this practice.

Examples of such units in South Warwickshire would include one built at Ragley Home Farms, Weethley, where costs were much reduced by excavating into an earth bank to form the walls, an updated version of the old pit silos. Capt. Hamish Gray-Cheape at Walcote, also built two silos, each containing 700 tons each. These were massive structures with concrete planks for walls and the silage juice collected into an *Eff bag* (silage effluent bag), which was then pumped to tanks in the yard roof and fed back to the cows in troughs.

Complete Diet Feeding

Fig. 5 Complete diet feeding. Feeder wagon being loaded.

Complete diet feeding came onto the farming scene in the mid-1970s. According to an investigation carried out by ADAS, there were about 20 dairy farmers in England and Wales practising complete diet feeding during the winter 1975-76. This figure grew to well over 100 in the following winter, and

Mr. M.Jarvis of Home Farm, Compton Wynyates, was amongst the first in South Warwickshire to adopt this system.

To quote an ADAS booklet on complete diet feeding:

> A complete diet is a uniform mixture of chopped or coarsely milled forage, concentrates, cereals, minerals and other feeds. It is so formulated that, when fed ad lib to cows, it will be eaten in amounts which will meet the cows' nutritional requirements for maintenance, milk production, body weight gain and the growth of the foetus, whilst containing enough fibre to sustain normal rumen function and maintain satisfactory butterfat and solids-not-fat in milk.

So there you have it. Like many other new arrivals on the farming scene, complete diet feeding may not have been adopted widely in its entirety, but adapted so that it is now commonplace in one form or another.

Forage Maize

Maize grown for forage has a somewhat chequered history. It was probably first grown for this purpose for cutting green and feeding during the late summer as an insurance against drought. A small acreage was certainly grown for this purpose on Upper Welford Farm, Welford-on-Avon, on a regular basis in the 1950s. In passing, Bill Craig's Cutrake was tried out successfully there in the maize crop.

Trials were carried out on growing maize for silage at Harper Adams Agricultural College in 1959, with the results published in a leaflet the following year. It was not until the early 1970s that maize silage made its appearance, with a significant acreage being grown. It was at this time that Frank Bennison, manager at Weston Park Estate, Shipston-on-Stour, started growing forage maize silage for feeding, not to the dairy herd, but to beef cattle, and very successfully, too.

Ragley Home Farms are on record as growing forage maize in 1973. In 1974, Lucy and Nephew Ltd., now no longer in existence but at the time a leading agricultural merchant in Stratford-on-Avon, held a conference on growing maize for silage at which Tom Fox of Kirby Farm, Whatcote, gave his experience, in his own inimitable manner, in growing and ensiling the crop in the previous season.

After the mid-1970s, there seemed to be a lull in the popularity of maize silage, although there was a renewed surge in interest ten years later and onwards. One of the reasons for this, apart for the obvious feeding value of maize silage and its ability to complement grass silage, may have been the return to bunker feeding and the mechanisation of the feeding process.

Be that as it may, maize silage is now part and parcel of the dairying scene in South Warwickshire and growing in popularity. In passing, maize is drilled in wide rows; without the introduction of the herbicide Atrazine, amongst others, its cultivation would have been all but impossible under modern conditions. New, earlier and better cobbing varieties have also played an important part in the development of the crop. Those in the district who prefer a contractor to drill and harvest the crop are well served by those operating in South Warwickshire.

Straw

Processing straw into a worthwhile feed can be regarded as the holy grail of British agriculture. The search is endless and, let's face it, never highly successful.

During the Second World War, it was government policy to encourage the treating of straw with caustic soda to improve its nutritional value. Indeed, plants consisting of concrete tanks and draining slabs were provided free to those who would use them. However, soaking the straw, then washing and draining the straw was a labour- and time-consuming business, and never really caught on. In more recent years, attempts have been made to achieve the same result by gas treatment. Again, this has never been practised on a significant scale. All this simply underlines the truth of the old saying 'you can't make a silk purse out of a sow's ear.'

Perhaps the boldest move was by the cake manufacturer BOCM, which introduced the Fodderite system in the 1960s. This was based on feeding barley straw which was described as 'poor but honest' – a phrase that recognised the low feeding value of barley straw, but, at least, it was consistent. Fodderite was a concentrate formulated to be fed with barley straw and provide a maintenance ration for dairy cows. The production part of the ration was to be provided by dairy cake. A feedstuff manufacturer's dream, perhaps, but, again, it was a nine days' wonder.

Sodagrain

Possibly more successful has been the treatment of wheat and barley by pearl caustic soda. This is a process which has been made possible by the mixer wagon. Measured amounts of wheat or barley are loaded in, along with the correct amount of caustic soda and water and mixed thoroughly. The treated grain is unloaded and allowed to stand for some time before feeding. This has proved a good feed, and eliminates the often dusty chore of rolling and conveying to the point of feeding.

Thus, over a period of fifty years, we have seen a revolution in the feeding of the dairy herd here in South Warwickshire, as in the rest of the country. Fifty years ago, the diet of the milking cow was based, at any rate on the better-run holdings, on hay, kale, mangolds, some home-grown oats and beans, and purchased concentrates, sometimes a compound cake, or straights, or a mixture of each.

Today, again on the best-run farms, milkers are fed on grass and maize silage, with brewers grains, sugar beet pulp and other ingredients loaded into a mixer wagon. Unless a complete diet system is followed, the ration fed outside the parlour will be topped up by concentrates fed at milking, the amounts now being controlled by computer in the most up-to-date parlours.

Such a feeding regime is now commonplace in South Warwickshire and the name of the game is to obtain the maintenance ration and as much milk as possible from grass and maize silage and purchased by-products. Some measure of the progress made in reducing the amount of concentrates fed can be gained by recalling that thirty to forty years ago maintenance and 4.5 litres of milk from winter fodder was considered satisfactory. Today that figure could well be of the order of 15-20 litres and sometimes more.

Dairy Cow Feed Recording

In the 1940s, only the most progressive farmers were recording milk production, either officially or otherwise. Official recording was essential for pedigree herds, but commercial herds might not have been in an official scheme. In the case of the latter the object of the exercise was to record the performance of the individual cows, so that passengers could be eliminated and, of course, for the accurate rationing of the concentrate portion, the most expensive part of the total feed.

Towards the end of the 1950s, and as a result of the continuing development of farm business management techniques, various efficiency factors relating to milk production emerged. These included concentrate usage in terms of lb. per gallon, the margin between milk sales and the cost of concentrates, the stocking rate in terms of forage acres per livestock unit and so on. It became clear that something more was needed for the economic management of a dairy herd than the routine recording of individual yields per cow, however essential this might be. Thus the Milk Marketing Board and the National Agricultural Advisory Service started to introduce dairy cow feed recording schemes, which later evolved into full blown dairy herd management exercises.

As NAAS District Adviser for much of South Warwickshire, I started a dairy cow feed recording scheme in 1961. Working from home, a black and white timbered former farm house in Welford-on-Avon, I collected data monthly from those participating, and did all the calculations myself with the aid of a hand-operated calculator. This was a massive machine of limited functions into which one keyed the relevant figures and obtained the answer by cranking a handle at the side. I fondly imagined that I was operating at the very frontier of modern technology, for calculators as we know them today, were a thing for the future.

For the purposes of my feed recording scheme, I had two groups; one was based on Aston Cantlow and the other at Shipston. The recording year was divided into the summer and winter feeding periods. Summaries were produced for each herd and for the group as a whole, and meetings were to held to discuss them. At the end of the winter feeding, period a full annual summary was also produced.

The annual summary for the first full year, that is October 1962 to September 1963 gives a snapshot of dairy farming in South Warwickshire at that time, and is worth quoting in some detail. Whilst, almost by definition, those in the scheme were the more forward-looking milk producers, they nevertheless provided a good cross section.

Herd Size	**Aston Cantlow**	**Shipston**
Under 30 cows	7	5
30 to 50	8	5
Over 50	4	3

Herd sizes in South Warwickshire

It will be noted that there were almost as many herds in the under-30 category as there were in the 30 to 50 group. In the over-50 category only two herds had over 60 cows and these were the largest in the scheme.

Breed	**Aston Cantlow**	**Shipston**
Jersey	4	1
Guernsey		1
Mixed	1	5
Red Poll		1
Friesian	13	4
Ayrshire	2	1

Breeds in South Warwickshire

The number of herds described as 'mixed' might be puzzling at first sight. The majority of these were clearly in the process of changing to all Friesian herds.

Channel Island herds were still represented and their results were included in the group summaries. At this time, the Ayrshires were on their way out.

Fodder	Aston Cantlow	Shipston
Silage	11	8
Kale	8	8
Rye	5	3
Italian Ryegrass	11	7

The transition from feeding with fodder roots to silage

From the above figures it can be seen that fodder feeding was in a state of transition from fodder roots to silage. First of all, five of the silage makers in the Aston Cantlow group and one in the Shipston group were self feeding. Many of the silage makers were still growing kale. In some cases, silage had taken the place of mangolds for hand feeding after the turn of the year. Even those self feeding might still grow kale, often starting to graze rather earlier than had been the practice previously. The emphasis on an early bite provided by rye and then Italian ryegrass was far greater than today.

Concentrate Feeding	Aston Cantlow	Shipston
lb./gallon	2.7	3.0

Concentrate feeding

This was one of the most important efficiency factors in milk production at that time. Incidentally, to convert the above to kg/litre move the decimal point one space to the left! The above figures were for the full twelve months. Bearing in mind that 4lb. of dairy cake produced a gallon of milk, they are a measure of what the grazing and fodder were contributing to maintenance and production.

Two further points of significance emerged from this recording exercise. First, those who used home mixing, as opposed to buying in cake fed, fed concentrates more heavily, especially during the winter when they were shovelling their home mix to the cows at the rate 6 lb./gallon. This was soon reduced once they had been feed recording for a couple of months. Secondly, Silcocks were putting out a 3 lb. cake, fed at that rate per gallon. It was alleged that the extra cost per ton was more than recouped by greater feed economy, but in practice it was not, as the figures illustrated. The discrepancy might have been due to inaccuracy in dispensing, and this left much to be desired. What was planned to be fed could be very different from the weights of concentrates actually given.

Many herds were still milked in cowsheds, the cake being commonly doled out into the mangers using a baler with a handle. Work at Reading showed this to be very inaccurate, the wide surface area allowing a greater or lesser degree of heaping. It was recommended that a cylindrical scoop with a lip and handle be used. Some of these were made up by George Worrall, the farrier and blacksmith of Barford, for the use of my clients who wanted them.

Yields	Aston Cantlow	Shipston
Milk Production/Cow/Year	889 (4041 litres)	908 (4128 litres)

Yield, measured/cow/year

The above figures look abysmal by modern standards but were above average, especially in view of the number of Channel Island herds in the sample. In fact, there were eleven herds in the two groups producing over 1,000 gallons (4546 litres)/cow/year.

Stocking Rates	Aston Cantlow	Shipston
Forage acres/Livestock Unit	1.7	1.5

Forage acres/livestock unit

The figures above were for the farms as a whole and, of course, dairy followers, beef cattle and sheep were all included in the calculation where appropriate. These might be regarded as fairly low by today's standards, but South Warwickshire is a low rainfall area and less nitrogenous fertilisers were used on grassland in those days.

No attempt has been made to quote figures for milk prices or for the cost of concentrates, because these would be meaningless today.

Other District Advisers in Warwickshire followed suit and then the monthly data was processed in the Leamington office. By 1966-67 the cow feed recording scheme had evolved into the Dairy Management (Gross Margin) Scheme, which was also county based.

Over the last thirty years or so, dairy management schemes, now all computerised, have proliferated and are on offer from many commercial firms, consultants and other organisations. On-farm computers also have a wide choice of programs.

All a far cry from cranking the handle of that old mechanical calculator.

6. THE FOOT AND MOUTH DISEASE OUTBREAK 2001

In 2001, this country has experienced the worst outbreak of Foot and Mouth Disease (FMD) in its history, much worse than that of 1967-68. This was exacerbated by gross incompetence on the part of the Labour Government of the day and the Ministry of Agriculture, Fisheries and Food in particular. It was a complete disaster, not only for those farmers directly concerned but also for the whole farming industry, those dependent on it indirectly for a living, the tourist trade in all its aspects, and all those supplying its needs. As the whole story starts to emerge, it is clear that the devastation this outbreak brought to rural areas became far worse than it need have been.

The whole sorry tale began on February 20th, 2001, when pigs delivered to a slaughterhouse in Essex were confirmed as having FMD. Within three days, further outbreaks were confirmed on adjoining farms. The source of the disease was traced to the farm of the Waugh brothers, at Heddon-on-the Wall, Northumberland.

It was thought that the prime cause was the feeding of unboiled swill from schools, army barracks or restaurants, containing infected imported meat. Moreover, it was suspected that the disease had been present on this farm for several weeks, in spite of a recent inspection.

The EU immediately banned the export of livestock from the UK and, after a few critical days delay, during which substantial movements of sheep had taken place, a temporary emergency ban on all livestock movement within the UK was imposed. This is in sharp contrast to the 1967-68 epidemic, when such restrictions were imposed promptly, in some cases in a matter of minutes, after an outbreak was confirmed. The disease then appeared in Hexham sheep market, Northumberland, and in Longtown market, Cumbria. From these markets, sheep were sold and transported all over the country, perfectly legitimately, taking FMD infection with them, before the movement ban was imposed.

Devon was badly hit. Willie Cleave, a farmer and sheep dealer in a very big way of business, had bought sheep at Longtown. Outbreaks were also recorded in Dumfries and Galloway.

In response to this, the countryside was virtually shut down. Footpaths were closed, as was the Dartmoor National Park, National Trust properties, nine RSPB Reserves; horse racing was suspended, deer stalking banned, and so on.

The effect was disastrous on the tourist industry, on hotels, guest houses and farms offering bed and breakfast or self-catering accommodation.

The culling of livestock began on a massive scale; there were six pyres around Longtown alone. By the end of February, 26 cases had been confirmed.

By March, FMD had spread to the Continent with cases being confirmed in France and Holland. The EU suspended all livestock markets for two weeks. In the UK, besides slaughtering infected livestock and known contacts, contiguous and 'firebreak' culls were introduced within a three-mile radius of outbreaks. Huge delays and build-ups of stock awaiting slaughter started to occur. In Cumbria, for example, it was taking ten days from diagnosis to slaughter, and a further seven days for the disposal of the carcasses. David King, the Government's Chief Scientific Adviser, admitted that the disease was now out of control.

The full horror of what was going on in the countryside was brought into almost every home in the land. Every night, the TV showed pictures of piles of cattle, sheep and pigs, their bodies bloated and in the grotesque attitudes of death, awaiting disposal on funeral pyres or to be buried in great pits.

By the end of March, no less than 900 cases had been confirmed.

In April, the Cheltenham Festival was finally cancelled after being postponed owing to an outbreak near the racecourse. William Hague, the then Leader of the Opposition, called for the army to be called in and put in charge. After further delay and dithering, the government did just that.

Of course, all livestock movement was at a standstill. Stock could not be moved, however urgent the need. The TV showed lambs being born in fields which had become nothing less than muddy swamps. Other stock were dying of starvation as keep ran out on the fields in which they were confined. Obtaining permits for animal movements was subject to long delays due to muddle and incompetence in local MAAF offices. Chaos, bringing with it unnecessary animal suffering, was the order of the day, and was recorded on TV screens.

Professor King announced that the epidemic was 'past its worst' and predicted that it would be under control by June. The General Election was, therefore, announced for that month, having been postponed from May.

The number of cases up to the end of April totalled 1,529.

In May, it was announced that rare breeds and hefted sheep were to be exempt from the firebreak cull. Official blood tests showed that nearly a third of stock slaughtered on suspicion of having the disease were incorrectly diagnosed. May 18th was the first day since the epidemic started that there had not been an outbreak.

Farmers were furious at calls for the Government to re-open footpaths in time for the Spring Bank Holiday. There were new outbreaks in Settle, North Yorkshire, sparking off fears that there was to be a resurgence of the disease.

The number of cases at the end of May stood at 1,676.

June saw the Waugh brothers prosecuted under the Animal Health Act and the Protection of Animals Act. Nick Brown, the Agriculture Minister, was demoted in the Cabinet re-shuffle after the General Election. MAFF became the Department of Environment, Food and Rural Affairs, with Margaret Beckett as the Minister in charge. She rejected calls for a full public enquiry into the FMD epidemic. Compensation for farmers reached more than £1 bn.

A public report, published in July, stated that delays on the part of government in dealing with the disease doubled the FMD death toll.

Most footpaths were re-opened in time for the holiday season. DEFRA distinguished itself by miscalculating the cost of cleaning up farms, declaring it was costing £100,000 per farm in England, instead of £36,000 as in Scotland. A reminder that the crisis was far from over came with the news that 4,000 sheep on the Brecon Beacons had to be slaughtered due to positive blood tests.

By the end of July, FMD cases totalled 1,914.

In July, and also in August, a sinister note started to creep in to the FMD saga. Lord Whitty, the food and farming minister, called for an end to compensation and suggested that farmers, in the future, should insure themselves against losses due to FMD, and that farmers should never get so much help again. In passing, it would appear that his lordship lives on another planet. What insurance company would underwrite future risks, when Government control over imports of meat from countries where FMD is endemic is virtually non-existent? Lord Haskins also infuriated farmers by saying 'they have been mollycoddled for too long.'

Some farmers were accused of spreading the disease deliberately. DEFRA released news that 37 farmers had received compensation in excess of £1m each. To the layman, this might seem over generous, as no doubt it was intended to appear, but the better-informed know full well that this is not necessarily so. Large pedigree herds could well be worth this figure and, in some cases, will represent several generations of skilled and careful breeding for which no amount of money represents just compensation.

This, possibly concerted, policy to 'rubbish' the victims of this FMD outbreak might be considered by the cynic, or the realist, to be an attempt to divert attention from the record of appalling incompetence exhibited by those whose duty it was to control this epidemic. In short, a smoke screen.

Mrs. Beckett, returning from holiday, announced that there would be three enquiries into the FMD outbreak, none of them to be held in public. In the ensuing months, every effort was made to force the Government to hold a Public Enquiry. Eventually, the reports of all enquiries that were held, including those instigated by the two County Councils mainly concerned, were critical of the government's handling of the crisis. Moreover, the vice-chairman of an EU committee investigating the affair noted that the manner in which Nick Brown gave evidence 'elevated ambiguity and evasion into an art form.'

A proper Public Enquiry would, of course, have compelled witnesses, politicians, civil servants and others, to attend and give evidence under oath. The government's case against holding one was that it would be expensive and take a considerable time to report. A report which could well coincide to the run-up to the next General Election. In short, the government could not possibly risk the exposure of its incompetence and unpreparedness. This conclusion is inescapable.

During the autumn of 2001, the epidemic gradually petered out, leaving the farming and tourist industries to pick up the pieces and attempt to make a fresh start.

Reading that excellent account of the 1967-68 epidemic, *The Great Cattle Plague* by Ralph Whitlock, one cannot but compare the way in which this was handled by MAFF at that time with the bungling incompetence of 2001. Was it possible that in 1967 there were still some individuals in MAFF who 'knew their farming' and knew what they were doing? Clearly, this was not the case in 2001.

One small point will be noted when reading Ralph Whitlock's account, namely that troops were called in to assist only three weeks after the first case of FMD was confirmed. This in sharp contrast to the delay recorded above.

Following the 1967-68 epidemic, a Committee of Enquiry on Foot and Mouth Disease was set up under the chairmanship of the Duke of Northumberland, and its first meeting was held on March 14th, 1968. It duly reported and made a series of recommendations, amongst which was that the period from diagnosis of the disease to the slaughter and disposal of infected animals should be no more than 24 hours. In 2001, this was anything up to four days, and certainly a lot longer in some instances. Another recommendation was that there should be ongoing planning and liaison between MAFF and army commanders. A layman might be excused for assuming that the Northumberland Report had lain gathering dust on a shelf, unread for thirty three years and certainly not acted upon.

Finally, as a footnote to the 2001 fiasco I cannot do better than quote the two last paragraphs from *The Great Cattle Plague.*

> And on April 16th, 1968, the first cargo of meat from South America was unloaded, to the protests of farmers from all over Britain, in London Docks.
>
> The world goes round again and, without much doubt, in its circling will bring yet another instalment of the Great Cattle Plague.

Nothing has been learnt. Potentially infected meat is still being imported from countries where FMD disease is endemic. And how tragically prophetic were those words written over thirty years ago.

7. BEEF

In days gone by, beef production in the Midlands, including South Warwickshire, was based on the finishing of single-suckled calves and Irish stores, which latterly replaced the Welsh stores. Indeed, the trade in Welsh store cattle is a very ancient one, existing certainly since the 15th. century. It was flourishing in the 18th. century, when it was estimated that some 30,000 Welsh black cattle from the summer and autumn fairs passed through Herefordshire, to be finished in the Midlands and in the southern counties of England.

One of the many old drove roads, the tracks along which these Welsh cattle were driven to their final destination, ran through South Warwickshire. Known along parts of its length as the Welshman's or Welsh Road, it entered the county at Sutton Coldfield, and then went through Coleshill, Stonebridge, Meriden, Berkswell to Kenilworth. It crossed the Avon at Chesford Bridge, where numerous cattle shoes have been found at the adjacent ford. (Cattle were shod to protect their hooves on the long journey). A small stream enters the Avon just downstream from Chesford Bridge, and this is marked on the Ordnance Survey map as *Cattle Brook*, and was possibly a favourite watering place.

The route continued on through the county to Offchurch and then to Southam. On each side of this little town, the road is marked as Welsh Road. Southam has another connection with droving, as the main inn is called The Craven Arms. After the coming of the railways to Wales in the mid-19th. century, the droving trade gradually dwindled away, and by the end of the 1870s was no more.

Breeds

The best beef came, of course, from the pure beef breeds or a cross between them. Equally acceptable was a cross between a beef breed and a beast of a dual-purpose breed. The most popular in South Warwickshire was the Hereford on a Shorthorn cow, and in the 1940s cattle of this sort were sold in Stratford market in great numbers.

The Shorthorn is, as previously mentioned, two breeds: the dairy and beef types, and variations in between. Shorthorn steers of the beefier type were also reared for beef. The Dowlers of Ilmington ran a pedigree Red Poll herd, another dual-purpose breed, although never as popular as the Shorthorn. But Mike Dowler tells me that the bull calves were worth very little, there being no demand, at any rate locally, for rearing them for beef.

Some South Warwickshire farmers used to attend the autumn sales in the West Country to buy Devon stores for finishing. The Passmores of Wormleighton and the Bryans of Fell Mill, Honington, used to follow this practice.

Putting a beef bull onto a cow of a dairy breed, with the exception of the Shorthorn, was not considered likely to produce an acceptable beef beast. This was not particularly surprising in the 1940s, for in those days the Friesian was by no means the dominant breed. In South Warwickshire, there were many Ayrshire herds, a significant number of Channel Island cows and herds that were kindly described as mixed. All too often, these comprised a motley collection of pure bred and cross bred cows of all colours, shapes and sizes. Putting a beef bull onto cows in any of these herds – pure bred or otherwise-would never result in a calf worth rearing for beef.

In passing, it is worth noting that in the 1950s, in order to encourage beef production in the UK, a subsidy was paid on calves which had some, if not very much, beef potential to ensure that they were reared for this purpose.

During the 1950s and 1960s, the march of the Friesians towards becoming the dominant dairying breed was inexorable. With the numbers of Shorthorn cattle dwindling equally rapidly, the Hereford Friesian cross became the most popular beef beast. Joe Spencer, of Whitehill Farm, Alderminster, was one of the first to rear and finish Black Hereford x Friesian beef. But, in passing, it must be noted that it had been the practice for some time to put dairy heifers to an Aberdeen Angus bull to ensure a small first calf and thus ease of calving.

At one time, the criticism was made that Hereford and Aberdeen Angus breeders had been producing bulls that had lacked size. Thus, when Charolais bulls were first imported in the early 1960s, they immediately became popular as terminal sires for beef production. The Limousin followed ten years later; their progeny acquiring a reputation for wildness, deservedly so, or not, as the case may be. Since then, other continental breeds, such as the Blonde D'Aquitaine, have been introduced.

These bulls of foreign breeds have ousted, to some extent at least, the native breeds, especially the Hereford, as the most popular terminal sires for beef production. However, the wheel is now coming in full circle, as it often does in farming, and there is a demand for Hereford x Friesian beef. In late 1998, Meadow Valley Livestock (a farmers' marketing co-operative) was asking members for such cattle, always provided that they had been sired by a registered Hereford bull. MVL had identified a niche market for beef from that cross which it was eager to satisfy and develop.

Beef Production Systems

First, a brief word about finishing weights. Pre-1939, the London market demanded a lighter beast than elsewhere of between 8 - 9 cwt. (400 - 450kg) liveweight. On the other hand, in the industrial and rural areas, heavier weights were the rule, between 10 - 11 cwt. (530 - 580kg)liveweight. This was because these markets wanted a carcass with more fat, but during the war years, and for the duration of meat rationing, it was a case of 'big was beautiful,' and cattle were taken to 14 - 15 cwt. (700 - 760kg) liveweight.. Needless to say, these were some three years old before they were slaughtered.

Single suckler herds comprised cows that produced one calf a year, either sold as a single suckled store or finished on the farm of birth. Production per acre was obviously low, and such herds were sometimes referred to as *gentlemen's cattle*.

Single suckler herds in South Warwickshire were few and far between but, under certain circumstances, they had a place and a valuable part to play in particular farm economies. This was the case when there was a substantial acreage of permanent pasture which, for one reason or another, could not be ploughed. A variation of this practice was to introduce a second calf, which obviously increased the production from what was essentially a low input / low output system.

Two examples in South Warwickshire spring to mind. The late George Wilson ran a single suckler herd at Larkstoke to graze the steep banks, and the late Colonel Michael Warriner, of Weston Park, near Shipston-on-Stour, ran a single suckler herd when Frank Bennison was manager of the farms in hand.

Here, the farming enterprise was mixed with a dairy herd, a flock of breeding ewes, dairy followers, a beef unit and a range of arable crops with cereals predominating. There was a considerable acreage of park-like land which was not ploughed as a matter of policy, and the single suckler herd helped use this grazing, which otherwise would probably have been understocked. There were some 40 Hereford x Friesian cows, the progeny of the dairy herd, which ran with a Limousin bull. The resulting calves were finished on the farm, along with any beef crosses from the dairy herd, on maize silage.

Another example of single suckler herd being successfully integrated into a predominantly arable farm is provided by the herd that was running on parkland attached to a large arable farm in Hertfordshire, on which I was involved as the farm consultant. On taking over the farm on the sudden death of his uncle by marriage, my client inherited a single suckler herd consisting of a number of crosses, some 40 in number, which happily calved down when their time came.

Obviously, the first thing to do was to sort out the calving pattern. This was done by dividing the herd into spring and autumn calvers, and selling those beasts that did not fit. The two herds were then made up to 40 in each by purchasing suitable additional cows.

In the meantime, a small farm had been bought in Suffolk, bordering onto the River Alde, a few miles upstream from the tidal barrier at Snape. This farm consisted of 50 acres of marsh, so-called, which was, in fact, good fattening pasture land, and 100 acres of arable land, mostly blowing sand. On this, winter barley was grown as a break-crop between sugar beet and early potatoes.

The calves from the autumn calving herd were weaned in the spring, taken to Suffolk and turned on to the Alde meadows. Incidentally, the water level in the dykes, and thus the water table, could be regulated by a sluice ensuring an ample bite even in a dry summer. The more forward spring weanlings would finish off grass and the stragglers yarded.

The spring calves were also sent to the Suffolk farm and finished out of yards the following winter. All the yarded cattle were fed on the home grown barley plus a protein supplement, barley straw and sugar beet tops. This system worked well for several years, until the whole farming operation was moved to neighbouring farms in Suffolk.

One advantage of a single suckler herd was purely financial, although the return per acre, or on capital invested, was low. By and large, over the years, with the exception of the last two when there has been a slump in livestock values, the value of cattle has kept pace with inflation. Providing the herd was valued on the herd basis, it could be sold at any time without incurring tax, thus providing a safe haven against inflation. Something which, in the 1970s in particular, had its attractions.

Eighteen to twenty four month beef

This is now the pre-dominant system of beef production in Warwickshire and elsewhere, based on crosses from the dairy herd which are now the main source of calves for beef production. There are, of course, many variations on this theme. In the first place beef calves may be sold from the dairy herd for rearing on by another farmer. He, or she, may then sell them as stores, or finish them. Beasts can, therefore, often pass through three hands, or more, before reaching the butchers block. Alternatively, on a mixed farm, beef cross calves may be finished either off grass, or out of yards, according to the month of birth.

The eighteen month beef system as practised on the NAAS/ADAS Experimental Husbandry Farm at Drayton, near Stratford-on-Avon, is worth noting. Originally, Hereford cross calves were used, with the first batch being bought in the autumn. Once weaned, these would be wintered on silage and some concentrates and turned out to grass the following spring. This was done earlier in the season than was common practice, the idea being that the grass grew to the cattle; the rumen was not overwhelmed by lush grass, and was given a chance to adjust gradually from a dry diet, which avoided the usual check in growth after turn-out. These cattle were at grass all summer and finished out of yards the following winter, again on a ration which was mainly silage with a concentrate supplement.

The second batch of calves was bought in February and, after weaning, was turned out into paddocks which had been grazed by sheep the previous year. These young calves were troughed for a time after turnout, at grass all summer, and then on a store ration of silage alone all winter, and finished off with grass in their second summer. These late winter calves were thus taken to finish on a mainly grass diet, either as grazing or as silage, with a minimum of concentrate feeding.

This system, with many variations, is commonly practised, either with purchased calves, or those born on the holding on which they will be finished. However, the system has been distorted in some instances by the manner in which the Beef Special Premium Scheme: feeders may be inclined to run steer cattle onto 21 months plus, in order to obtain the second premium.

Intensive Beef

This system of beef production became popular in the 1960s and 1970s. Friesian steers or bulls were used, the latter having the advantage of a better feed conversion rate. The beasts were housed throughout their entire life, and were fed on a ration of barley, with a protein supplement, and barley straw. They finished at between 12 and 14 months.

Obviously, the profitability of such an enterprise depended upon the cost of the calf, the value of home-grown barley and the price obtained from the end product. One advantage was that it made no demands upon the grassland on the farm, although ample yarding had to be available.

David Slatter of Lower Clopton, Quinton, was one South Warwickshire farmer who produced beef on this system. He makes the point that for many years it was still possible to use growth promoting hormone implants, now banned. These were a powerful aid in improving growth rates.

Tom Fox started barley beef, as the method was popularly called, when farming at Pebworth, and continued when he moved to Kirby Farm, Oxhill. He was one of the first to adopt the system and since he was a popular and engaging speaker, he was much in demand to talk to farmers' discussion clubs etc. Hamish Gray-Cheape of Lower Barn, Haselor was another barley beef producer, amongst others, in South Warwickshire.

BSE

No short history of beef production can be complete without some reference to BSE and the devastating effect it had on the dairy and beef sectors. The first case was notified in 1985. The official view was that it was caused in the first place by cattle being fed meat and bone meal made from sheep bones and offal.

Scrapie in sheep had, of course, been known for some two hundred years. The brains of cattle infected with BSE had similar lesions to scrapie-infected sheep.

During the 1970s, a change was made in the rendering process, one of the end products of which is meat and bone meal. The batch process was replaced by a continuous flow method which operated at lower temperatures. It was thought that the original process deactivated the BSE agent, whereas its replacement did not. An increase in the sheep population in the 1970s may also have been a factor in increasing the proportion of scrapie infected bone and offal being processed.

The upshot of these theories being adopted as the most likely cause of the BSE epidemic was that a ban was imposed in 1988 on the inclusion of meat and bone meal in ruminant feeds, which was later to be extended to all feeds. From August 1988, all cattle infected with BSE were compulsorily slaughtered. Initially, only 50% of their value was paid in compensation. It was alleged that this gave farmers and incentive to avoid reporting cases, but when the level of compensation was raised to 100%, there was no notable increase in the number of suspected cases being reported, which indicates that there was little or no under-reporting at the 50% level. This is in sharp contrast to other countries within the EU, where there is very definite evidence that cases of BSE are not, in fact, being notified.

In 1989, the Specified Bovine Offal Ban was introduced, which made compulsory the removal of the brain, spinal cord and other organs that were assumed to carry the infective agent. At the enquiry, it became apparent that abattoir workers, in some instances, ignored the ban or, at least, failed to take the matter seriously. Similarly, there is some evidence emerging that the ban on the use of meat and bone meal was not entirely effective. It appeared that this material was fed after the ban because of existing stocks, and there might also have been cross contamination in feed plants while there was no ban on the use of meat and bone meal in pig and poultry rations.

The media made the most of these events, and the suggestion was made on every possible occasion, that there was a link between BSE and CJD, a similar, but very rare, disease in humans. Not surprisingly, demand for beef was much reduced and the final blow came when Stephen Dorrell, Health Secretary, announced in the House of Commons on March 20th, 1996, that he had been advised that there was a possibility that BSE could pass from cattle to humans producing a new form of CJD, referred to as CJDn, which affected younger people.

The evidence for this was by no means conclusive. In spite of this, the announcement was made and the result was catastrophic and beef market collapsed. No lessons had been learnt from the salmonella-in-eggs fiasco. The EU, clearly more for commercial and political reasons than as a result of conclusive scientific evidence (of which there was none), banned the export of beef from the UK. All this while the incidence of BSE in cattle was on the wane, and taking its predicted course towards extinction in a matter of five or six years time.

All cattle over thirty months old had to be slaughtered, but the UK still imported beef from the continent with no reliable guarantee that this was from cattle below this age limit. This was a particularly serious matter in view of the under reporting of the disease in many European countries, and of the strong likelihood that the various measures taken in the UK to prevent infected material entering the food chain were not being applied with the same rigour on the other side of the English Channel. Finally, at the end of 1997, a ban on the sale of beef on the bone was introduced, just to add fuel to the flames.

History may well show that, up to the Specified Bovine Offal ban in 1989, the whole affair had been handled well, given the entire novelty of the situation. After that, and right up to the time of writing (January 1999), it is only too clear that the crisis was worsened by the ineptitude of politicians and fuelled by the media.

BSE in the national herd will probably become a thing of the past; but the legacy lingers on. As the years slip by, those who confidently predicted a massive CJD epidemic have fallen silent, or are making increasingly desperate statements about the length of the incubation period. In the meantime, the whole cattle industry continues to suffer. Milk producers have been badly hit in two ways. First, calf prices, right across the board, have collapsed. Beef cross heifers are worth practically nothing - £15 to £20 at the very best. The calf slaughter scheme, due to end in a few months, has kept some sort of bottom in the calf market. Secondly, the cull cow price under the Over Thirty Month Slaughter Scheme is only a fraction of what it was. In fact, no more than about £290 a head, instead of an average throughout the year of about £430, with big, well fleshed, Friesian culls making over £600. Beef producers, themselves, have taken a very substantial drop in income. Prices have dropped from a level of about 118p/kg liveweight before the BSE crisis, to an average of 88.80p for steers and 86.89p for heifers at the end of 1998; this represents a drop of something of the order of £100 to £150/steer, according to weight and grading.

At present, there are signs of a slight recovery. The worst may well be over, always providing there is no more scaremongering by politicians and others. Beef consumption in the UK is now back at pre-BSE levels. The ban on exports is to be lifted soon, again provided that there is no more heel dragging in Brussels, but it will be a long time before exports reach previous levels, if they ever do.

Finally, the taxpayer has to pick up his, or her, share of the cost of this disaster. It is estimated that the cost of the compulsory slaughter of all cattle over two and a half years old will have cost about £3 bn, and the total cost of the whole fiasco is estimated to reach £5 bn.

8. Dairy Herd Replacements

Calf Rearing

This chapter applies as much to the rearing of calves for beef production as to rearing those for dairy replacements. Without any doubt the most important development in calf rearing during the last fifty years has been the introduction in the 1950s, by BOCM, of the early weaning system. Previous to this, calves had been kept on whole milk at first, and then milk substitute or gruel for a matter of months – a period we would now consider an extraordinary length of time.

The early weaning system allows the calf to be on a diet of dry food entirely by about five to six weeks. The early introduction of concentrates, hay and water at about seven days encourages rumen development. The advantages of early weaning are that concentrates are cheaper than milk substitute and, of course, the labour requirement is considerably less. The vast majority of calves that are reared on the bucket are fed in this way.

Mention has already been made in the previous chapter on beef of single sucklers. Sometimes a second calf is introduced in addition to the cow's own which does improve the economics of this method.

A further development of natural suckling is multiple suckling. This needs a cow with a reasonable milk yield. Each suckling period lasts about ten weeks. In the first ten weeks of lactation four calves are suckled, in the second ten weeks three and then eventually only two. Cows and calves are often separated between feeds.

Multiple suckling has been, and still is, practised in South Warwickshire almost exclusively on farms where the calves are being reared for beef. Possibly the most famous exponent of multiple suckling was the late Wilf Harris of Newnham.

Now Wilf was a character, and is remembered with affection and a chuckle by those who were fortunate enough to know him. He was a regular attender at meetings of the Aston Cantlow Farmers Club, and his somewhat rambling mode of speech belied considerable shrewdness, often not appreciated by those who did not know him. Few club meetings would go by without Wilf getting up to ask a question in his usual roundabout way.. The speaker would get up, full of confidence in his ability to give a straight answer, only to falter when in full voice on realising that there was more to the question than he had at first realised.

One evening the subject turned to calf rearing. Wilf proudly announced that he had a cow which reared many more than the twelve calves, or so, that was considered normal. This fabulous beast was promptly named 'The Newnham Long Teat,' thus passing into South Warwickshire farming legend. 'Mind you,' said Wilf, 'we don't let them suck for too long. When we take 'em off the cow they blart a bit, but we sleep on the other side of the house.'

Dairy Replacements

Rearing one's own dairy replacements is now the usual practice in South Warwickshire. The case for doing so is strong, and during the last fifty years has been reinforced by artificial insemination, which brings the choice of the best bulls within the reach of all dairy farmers. This means that a policy of herd improvement by breeding is possible and your own dairy followers eliminate the risk of buying in disease and are of a known quality.

But in the days when farm size, and thus the size of milk producing farms, was much smaller than at the present time, economists used to argue that the numbers of milking cows should be maximised and that it was not economic to devote scarce acres to rearing dairy followers. It was argued that improvements in general herd health reduced the risk of buying in disease.

However, I can recall two instances in South Warwickshire, in the 1960s, which gave the lie to this contention. Suffice to say here that two herds, both Channel Island, suffered from contagious abortion when additional cows were purchased to meet the requirements of the Small Farm Scheme. In the end both farmers eventually went out of business as a consequence.

Those on the smaller holdings producing milk, and who wished to rear their own heifer replacements, solved the problem of slender acres by taking grass keep as a matter of course, usually for grazing but sometimes for making hay.

Another solution was the contract rearing of heifers, which was in vogue for a short time. This could have attractions for the smaller dairy farmer and also to those on the larger holdings, where there was not a milking herd but which had a large acreage of permanent pasture. This could pose a problem because returns on stocking with beef cattle and sheep were often not exciting. To find enough capital to stock such an acreage adequately could put a strain on financial resources. Further constraints could be lack of yarding for wintering cattle and labour for lambing. Anything which produced a good return without the outlay of capital clearly had its attractions, especially as, on suitable land, the older dairy heifers could be outwintered. Ragley Home Farms, at Weethley, near Alcester, went in for rearing heifers on contract. On these farms, there was a considerable acreage of permanent pasture – parkland, steep banks and river meadows – which could not be ploughed and, thus, had to be stocked.

There were two types of contracts. First, the rearer would buy the calf, stand all the costs of rearing including losses. The dairy man would then have the first choice of buying back the reared heifer. Secondly, the heifer calf would remain the property of the dairyman. The rearer would then be paid a rearing cost per month, at a higher rate from two weeks old to six months and then at a lower rate. A contract would be drawn up in which the rearer supplies transport, pays for veterinary and medical expenses, and stands losses. Provision would also be made for serving the heifers, if this was done on other than their home farm.

Finally, of course, the other way was to buy in replacements from a known source. This has attractions to those, like the Potters of Glebe Farm, Dorsington, who liked to keep their farming system as simple as possible. All cows were run with beef bulls and the resulting calves sold. Downcalving heifers were purchased, Holsteins being imported from Holland, and a secondary business was built up in supplying these and UK-bred heifers to other dairy farmers.

As already mentioned above, one of the problems in breeding one's own dairy replacements is the fact that, on average, only 50% of calves born into any dairy herd will, in fact, be heifers. In some years, if one is lucky this percentage will be greater. But, of course, in others one can be cursed with a run of bull calves. Moreover, today, after the BSE crisis, Friesian or Holstein bull calves are practically worthless.

However, in the closing years of the period with which this book deals, that is the last years of the 20th century, there has been a development which could well revolutionise the practice of rearing dairy replacements and, possibly, eventually the production of bull calves for beef production. It is, of course, the introduction of sexed semen.

Cogent Breeding Ltd. is a subsidiary of Grosvenor Farms Ltd., which, in turn is a subsidiary of Grosvenor Estate Holdings, the corporate arm of Grosvenor Estate, headed by the Duke of Westminster. Grosvenor Farms have 6,000 acres near Chester, run 1,200 cows with 1,500 dairy followers, and grow potatoes and combineable crops.

The UK imports 80% of its dairy semen, more than any other developed nation. In 1995, Cogent started a breeding programme to rectify this, its aim being to provide elite UK Holstein semen at competitive prices to its farmer members. Four years later, in 1999, there were 3,700 of these representing 440,000 dairy cows.

Semen sexing is carried out by cytometry at only two centres: Colorado State University and Cogent. Once trials have been completed, commercial production for use by AI should have started, possibly by the end of 2000.

Conception rates are close to those achieved by conventional semen, with a purity of at least 90%.

Thus the new millennium should see dairy farmers being able to inseminate those cows from which they wish to breed replacements with female semen, with a probability of more than 90% of obtaining heifer calves, and, eventually, serve the others with semen from a beef bull. This makes unwanted, and practically worthless, Holstein bull calves a thing of the past.

9. SHEEP

In days gone by

In medieval times sheep were, without any doubt, the most important farm livestock. In those days, the wealth of England was based on the export of wool to the Continent. The great houses and magnificent churches of the Cotswolds, all built on the proceeds of the wool trade, are silent testimony to the fortunes that this created for some.

The so-called Tudor Enclosures were all about converting arable land to pasture to accommodate the ever increasing numbers of sheep. John Rous, a chantry priest of Guy's Cliffe, Warwick was amongst the first to decry the effects of these enclosures. For many, villages were destroyed, their inhabitants evicted and left to fend for themselves as best as they could, and their open fields turned into sheep runs.

Compton Scorpion and Wormleighton were just two Warwickshire villages to suffer this fate. Perhaps a more famous example was when, in 1614, William Coombe of Stratford-on-Avon attempted to enclose the common fields at Welcombe for this purpose, but was thwarted by direct action and by legal means by the townspeople and the Stratford Corporation.

The later enclosures had, of course, a different purpose, which was to consolidate the holdings of individuals in the open fields, to consolidate their rights to cut hay from the meadows, and to pasture stock on the common land into farms within a ring fence. These enclosures give the countryside of lowland England today's familiar appearance. This led to the introduction of root crops as part and parcel of the Norfolk Four Course Rotation, in which sheep, folded on the roots, played a key role in maintaining fertility.

The agricultural depression, which lasted from about 1880 until 1939, with only a short intermission during and immediately after the First World War, spelt the death knell of the old farming and with it the folded flock. Labour costs were too high and the mutton joints produced were too big and too fat for modern tastes.

In South Warwickshire, much of the heavier land fell down to grass again in the 1920s. The arable land, if any, was confined to a few acres of oats for the horses and, possibly a few mangolds. Figures show that grassland was lightly stocked, 4 to 6 acres per livestock unit, with both sheep and cattle – 'dog and stick' farming, as it was called. It was, in fact, what we would now call a low input /

low output system, well suited to a time when spending as little as possible was about the only way to survive for those farming the most difficult soils.

This philosophy dominated, to some extent, sheep husbandry even when better times returned during the Second World War. Feeding the ewe in the later stages of pregnancy was at a minimal level and only the better farmers were seen to put the hay racks out before Christmas. Sheep were often looked upon as just scavengers, finding what they could and fed at the minimum of expense. One South Warwickshire farmer announced that he did the shepherding during the day and the Almighty took over at night. Needless to say, his lambing percentage was abysmal.

The 1947 Agriculture Act provided a guaranteed price for lamb and wool, but maintained free access for New Zealand lamb into the UK market. These imports really decided the size of the UK sheep sector right up to entry into the EEC in 1973. This is how it all began. I quote from *The Diary of a Victorian Squire* by Dearman Burchall, who had made money in industry and, like many others before and after him, purchased an estate, in this case in the West Country. He was a frequent visitor to London and this entry is for May 27th,1882.

> Lunched on board the Dunedin, a sailing vessel which has just come from New Zealand in 90 to 100 days, which has 500 carcasses of sheep, a few dozen oxen, hares and turkeys. They were all frozen as hard as iron and the lower compartment maintained at 20 degrees of frost all through the voyage, even on the equator. There was also good fresh butter. The mutton tasted very well, but the cooking on board was not calculated to give it a very attractive appearance. ... Some gentlemen from the colonies said they only wanted a regular and assured market to send very large quantities.

The national ewe flock remained static at just over 12 million and this provided between 40% and 50% of the domestic consumption of lamb.

After 1973, when imports of lamb from New Zealand started to be restricted, the fortunes of our sheep industry took a sharp turn for the better. By 1980, ewe numbers had risen to 14.08m and self sufficiency in lamb to 64%. By 1985 ewes numbered 17.2m and self sufficiency rose to 77.2%. By 2000, UK exports of lamb to the continent are a feature of the trade: the volume of New Zealand imports has much diminished, UK production satisfying a high proportion of the domestic market.

Sheep Husbandry

Fig. 6 Lower Farm, Admington. Sheep shearing.

Although there were great changes and developments, during the 1950s, 1960s and early 1970s, in dairying, beef production, arable farming and horticulture, developments in sheep husbandry stagnated by comparison. Nevertheless, advances were made. Amongst these were the more effective control of parasites, better feeding of the in-lamb ewe and the re-introduction of the practice of housing ewes from the beginning of the year until they lambed.

Paddock Grazing was another innovation which proved to be a dead end, which was an attempt to increase the production of grassland stocked with sheep by raising the summer stocking rate. It was yet another aspect of trying to correct the one economic defect of ley farming – the low gross margin per acre from grass stocked with sheep and cattle, other than dairy cows.

Pasture was divided into paddocks with a forward creep area for the lambs. It was an intensive system, requiring a high degree of management and increased rates of fertiliser usage, especially nitrogen. It was expensive in fencing, with the sheep pastures resembling a bird cage. The system also tended to produce a high proportion of store lambs.

Much ink and hot air was expended in promoting the system, but it proved to be an agricultural bandwagon that ran out of steam. It was a bonanza for the purveyors of fencing materials.

In-Wintering

In-wintering of lowland ewes, by contrast with other methods, is a practice which has now come to stay. Indeed it is now almost universal where suitable buildings are available, many of which were erected for this specific purpose.

In-wintering removes the ewe flock from the pastures in winter. This reduces poaching and, because the swards are not stocked in January and February, growth is that much earlier in the spring. Additional benefits are greater ease of shepherding and more control over feeding.

Much experiment and development work on the in-wintering of ewes took place at the Drayton Experimental Husbandry Farm. Ewes were at first housed on slats as well as on straw. However, the slats were found to be unnecessary; those bedded on straw did just as well with no footrot problems, as had once been feared. Slats had other disadvantages, apart from the expense: lambs were inclined to get their legs between the slats, sometimes breaking them, and the wooden slats wore badly in front of the hay racks and troughs. After one or two winters, their use was discontinued.

Ewes were allowed 9-10 square feet of floor space, and there were 30 ewes in each pen. It was found that lambs from in-wintered ewes had a lower birth weight, But this did not affect subsequent growth rates and they finished as quickly as those from ewes that were out-wintered. Later, it was the practice to shear in-wintered ewes and it was found that this increased food intake.

The in-wintering of ewes exploded one farming myth. It had always been held that in-lamb ewes should have plenty of exercise, and it was considered good practice to move them around once a day. In-wintered ewes apparently showed no ill effects from being confined in a comparatively small space for two months in the late winter.

Scanning

A recent development in sheep husbandry has been the scanning of in-lamb ewes. By these means it is possible to ascertain which ewes are carrying twins or triplets, or which have only a single lamb, or are barren. This can ensure the better nutrition of the former, while considerable economies can be made in feeding the latter.

Lambing Percentages

One of the most important factors in determining the profitability, or otherwise, of a flock of breeding ewes is the lambing percentage. A word is necessary here on the method of calculating this. Some, incorrectly, take the number of ewes lambed and the number of live lambs born. The correct way is to take the number of ewes put to the tup and divide into the number of lambs sold.

Looking at the projections given in the Farm Management Pocketbook by John Nix, the progress in this respect, or rather the lack of it, is rather depressing. The ratios were first published in 1966. The table shows that by 1999, there had been a marginal improvement in the lower levels but no progress at all at the higher levels of performance.

Lambs per ewe	**1966**	**1999**
Low	1.2	1.3
Average	1.4	1.45
High	1.6	1.6

Lambing rates

In South Warwickshire, many flock owners will expect to do rather better than Nix's best figure, certainly in a good year. But the results, as we all know, can vary from season to season with the weather having, as usual, an important part to play. Certainly there are one or two individuals who consistently average around two lambs per ewe. But these are invariably on holdings where the ewe flock is the main, or, indeed, the only enterprise.

Breeds

There has been a noticeable change in the breeds found in South Warwickshire over the last half century. In the 1940s and 1950s, Kerry and Clun ewes were dominant. Farmers in this district in those days went on their annual pilgrimage to Craven Arms or Knighton to purchase ewe lambs or theaves. It was common practice to put these to an Oxford or Hampshire tup, although the Suffolk was probably the most popular, even at that time.

The Scotch Halfbred had a period of popularity, followed by the Welsh Halfbred. Then South Warwickshire sheep men travelled to Builth Wells to buy their replacements. Today, the Scottish or North Country Mule is the most common breed and the Suffolk still the preferred ram, although Charolais and Texels are also to be found.

It is probably true to say that South Warwickshire has, over the years, followed the national trend as far as the sheep sector is concerned. Special mention, however, should be made of the part that the Drayton Experimental Husbandry Farm has played in developing and refining the in-wintering of in-lamb ewes. In this respect it has been a trend-setter. At one time Peter Crabtree, the manager of Ragley Home Farms, intensified summer grazing by setting up paddocks with forward creeps for the lambs. This was an attempt to improve returns from the large acreage of unploughable permanent pasture which was such a feature of the farms. Mention must also be made of the outstanding results obtained by Richard Hobbs from his specialised sheep unit on the former Snitterfield aerodrome.

10. PIGS

A Cottage Industry

Although in the 1920s and 1930s large, intensive pig units were by no means unknown, before, during and for some years after the Second World War, pig keeping might almost be termed a cottage industry. A large number of farmers, smallholders and householders kept pigs in small numbers, the latter, of course, mainly for their own consumption. The cottage type pigsty was universal. This consisted of a covered pen with a roof sloping to the back, a small yard in front, complete with trough, and a wooden door giving access. This was the basic design, but the materials used could vary from stone and brick to wood and corrugated steel sheets, often second-hand.

On farms, it was common enough to find a few such sties, part and parcel of the farmstead. But often yards and loose boxes were pressed into service, the latter sometimes being fitted with farrowing rails and used as the maternity suite. It was, at one time, common practice to run a few pigs in yards along with the cattle, the former often scavenging behind the latter.

On the Cotswold farm (Park Farm) where I was a pupil, there was a range of pig sties of the cottage type, giving onto an open yard, the whole being built in local stone. Incidentally, I see that this farmstead has been listed by English Heritage as an example of a model 19th century set of farm buildings.

Wartime Pig Keeping

During the 1940s and early 1950s, domestic pig keeping was encouraged as a part of the food production campaign and to make good use of household swill. Feedstuffs were, of course, rationed and in this respect pigs had a low priority. But by joining a Pig Club one could obtain a ration to supplement the household waste and any potatoes and other vegetable waste which were available from garden or allotment.

The yield of field potatoes can fluctuate widely from season to season. It was, thus, the policy of the Ministry of Food to ensure that a sufficient acreage was planted nationally to meet consumers' needs, assuming a slightly below average yield. In good years, in many years in fact, there was a surplus which was purchased at the guaranteed price, dyed purple to prevent their being used for human consumption and sold at a loss as *pig potatoes.*

I had a smallholding in Welford-on-Avon from 1947 to 1953 and, like many of my neighbours, kept both pigs and poultry. My pigsty had been brick built by the previous owner, a smart affair by the standards of the village, with a built in glazed brick trough which could be filled via a chute through the wall. It was even provided with a concrete pad and its own well and pump!

I bought and finished four weaners a year, two at a time. As a member of the Pig Club, I collected my feed ration once a month from the secretary, Mr. Yates, who lived on the Binton Road. I had a copper built in a large shed and made a ring of sheet steel to sit on top, thus increasing its capacity. The potatoes were well heaped in this and the lot covered with two thick Hudson sacks, the sort that used to be hired and when filled with wheat weighed two and a quarter cwt. The fire was lit to cook enough potatoes to last a week. These were chopped with an edging iron in a big thick steel bucket, the 'official' meal being mixed in, along with any extra barley meal I could scrounge. Most of my fellow smallholders fed their pigs in much the same way, along with garden and allotment waste, and sometimes purchased pig potatoes. This was the pattern of domestic and smallholding pig production.

Many farmers kept a pig for the house during food rationing. Some would keep a sow or two, selling the weaners or finishing a few. But pigs had a low priority for commercial production as far as feedstuffs rations were concerned.

In those days, many pigs, from whatever source, were taken to 10 score (200 lb.) liveweight. Plenty of backfat was considered a virtue, in contrast to modern tastes. Most of us aimed for between seven and eight score. But there was one man in the village, himself over six feet in height and probably weighing twenty stone, who used to take his pigs to the size of a small donkey, certainly well over ten score and probably nearly fifteen. One night his pig, within a few days of slaughter, was stolen. How they ever got it out of the sty and away without awakening the neighbourhood is a mystery. They then left a weaner in its place, a nice touch!

In those days, litters were weaned at eight weeks. Two litters a year was the aim, and if a sow consistently averaged twelve to fourteen weaners a year, one was well satisfied.

By 1954, meat and feedstuff rationing were things of the past. In South Warwickshire, and probably elsewhere, an explosion in the pig(and poultry) population took place. In almost every farmstead you went to there were pigs everywhere. Many kept sows only, producing weaners for those who specialised in finishing for either pork, bacon or heavy hog. The latter was encouraged by Walls who required a hog of not less than 240 lb. liveweight. These were processed into a wide range of products. David Marland and his manager, Peter Ross-Bain producing heavy hogs for Walls on the farm at Idlicote, was just one example in South Warwickshire.

Change

Change was in the air in the pig industry, driven very largely by developments in Denmark. Until the introduction of the Landrace from that country, the most popular breeds had been the Wessex, or Essex Saddleback served by a Large White Boar to produce the *sheeted* weaner; one that appeared to be wearing a pair of grey shorts, for much of the rear end and the back legs were grey in colour. Weaners of this cross always commanded a premium because of their hybrid vigour.

The Landrace was first introduced in 1949. But it was not until 1954 that the breed became well established. The great virtue of this breed was that it produced a long and much leaner carcass, which the urban consumer, in particular, now required. While on the subject of breeding, Walls was the first to initiate a programme of hybrid breeding to be followed later by BOCM and the Pig Improvement Company.

Another import from Denmark was the Danish finishing house. Something similar existed in the pre-war years and was known as the Scandinavian house. The post-war version had a central feeding passage, with rows of pens each side and a dunging passage at the rear. Another innovation from the same country was the farrowing crate.

Another later introduction was the Solari mono-pitch pig house. This was modelled somewhat on the old cottage sty, but, being constructed of wood, was cheaper than a Danish finishing house and came in a range of any required number.

Outdoor Pig Keeping

Outdoor pig keeping had been common enough for years. Sows were often run on waste ground, in scrub woodland or were turned out to scavenge on stubbles. On Park Farm, there was some rough pasture above what had been an old quarry, now worked out. The sows were run out here during the summer and were provided with arks in which to farrow. These were littered with straw, usually supplemented with long, dead, faggy grass that was brought in by the sows themselves. Sometimes they dispensed with the ark and made a nest of such grass, out in the open. They lay in one half, while their piglets occupied the other semicircle. It was noticeable that few, if any, piglets were ever lain on by the sow – a common source of loss in farrowing pens, even when fitted with a farrowing rail.

Later, of course, a lamp with a creep underneath became commonplace with indoor farrowing pens, to be replaced eventually by farrowing crates. Another innovation was stalls for dry sows, now, happily, illegal. The only advantage of these was that sows could be rationed individually according to their stages of pregnancy. Dry sow yards are now standard, in which sows have complete freedom of movement. These can be fitted with individual sow feeders, which, again, can ensure that in-pig sows are fed properly when carrying their litters.

In the post-war years, Richard Roadknight developed an open-air system of pig production which is still popular today. The capital outlay was far less than for indoor systems. Weaners produced per sow per year were only slightly less than indoor farrowing. Foxes could be a source of loss and, of more recent years, rustling has been a problem. Rustling gangs know exactly what they are looking for, and take only the older piglets. This method is still very popular today, especially amongst the enterprising exploiting the gullible who demand 'organic' pigmeat.

The story of the pig sector from the 1960s onwards is one of considerable success in improvements in food conversion, reduced back fat and litter size. Weaning can take place earlier, now down to five to six weeks, instead of eight as formerly, and even in some units to three weeks.

Increased specialisation has been a feature of the 1970s, and onwards, in all branches of farming, and the pig industry is no exception. The small scale production as an enterprise on a mixed farm, so typical at one time in South Warwickshire, gave way to specialised units of, say, fifty breeding sows upwards with the progeny being taken to pork or bacon weights. And as the years have rolled by, the smaller of these units have tended to disappear.

Pigs have traditionally been *copper* or *gold* – a way of describing what is known as the pig cycle; a period of good prices is invariably followed by one in which the returns are much reduced. The root cause of this is that the sow is a quick breeder. When prices are high sow numbers are increased, leading to a glut of pigmeat and lower returns.

During the latter part of the 1990s, the pig sector is passing through a disastrous time, substantial losses being made on every pig produced. Specialisation means that so many producers have no other source of income. Perhaps, after all, there is something to be said for pig production on a mixed farm. At least other enterprises will, one hopes, lessen the financial effects of the troughs in the pig cycle!

11. Poultry

Egg Production

My first experience of poultry keeping was on a fruit farm in Kent, where I spent many a long, happy, holiday in the 1930s. It stood on a southerly slope on the north side of a river valley with the small farmhouse on the highest ground. There was no electricity, so oil lamps were the order of the day. My bedroom lamp would now be a collector's piece, with its brass oil container complete with handle, a slim glass chimney, over which slid a polished, round, metal reflector. During the day, it stood on a table at the bottom of the stairs ready to light my way upstairs and then on a bedside table to give a soft light for a late read.

The little house had an unforgettable aroma all of its own. A blend of the scent of great cherry logs burning on the open fire in the inglenook and the smell of real beeswax polish, along with a hint of paraffin.

In spring time, the orchards on the side of valley running down to the meadows by the river were a sea of blossom. Some 500 Rhode Island Red hens were run on free range amongst the trees and housed either in fold units or houses on those little iron wheels. The breed was noted for large brown eggs, especially so in the second year of laying. The hens were then kept for two years and sold as boiling fowl when they had stopped laying after the second time round.

As some may recall, Rhode Island Reds were noted for their tendency to go broody. This was made full use of, since all the chicks were reared under hens, using whole rows of coops and their runs in early spring – a laborious but otherwise trouble-free method. When old enough, the pullets and cockerels were transferred to rearing arks. The latter were reared and sold to local butchers when they reached about 7 to 8 lb. or more. The pullets, of course, were taken on to the point of lay as flock replacements.

Everything seemed to be fed on wet mash, made with hot water in the winter, and wheat, fed whole. Three times a week two of those old fashioned wooden egg boxes, holding the trays, were put on the 5 p.m. train at the little station on the branch line, arriving at their destinations, two London hotels, in time for breakfast the next morning. A few shops were also supplied and the eggs sold to these, and the hotels, were graded and candled by hand. The surplus went to the packing station as they came from the nesting boxes.

During the school holidays, I worked all day, feeding, cleaning out, collecting eggs, then grading, candling and packing them. In between times, I repaired and creosoted houses, pens, folds etc. There was a large shed which doubled up as a feed store and egg room. The cost of best layers' mash was £7/ton and wheat less than £5/ton. Happy days!

The 1930s

I mention all this not as an autobiographical note, but because this sort of poultry keeping, including the way in which eggs were marketed, was very typical of the years before the Second World War, but with the possible exception that, by then, most would be hatching in incubators and rearing in paraffin brooders. Like pigs, it was almost a cottage industry, although, of course, there were specialist poultry units with larger laying flocks. It was common practice for the farm poultry to be looked after by the farmer's wife and the income from them was her pin money.

The breeds commonly kept, as well as pure Rhode Island Reds, were White Leghorn x Rhode Island Red, and White Wyandotte x Light Sussex or Rhode Island Red. The well known pre-war breeders were Sterlings, Fairburn, Thornbers and Watanabe. Birds for breeding were selected by trap nesting and on conformation. But in the early 1950s, all this went by the board with the introduction of genetics into poultry breeding and the old breeds disappeared.

As on the Kent farm, the vast majority of hens were kept on free range and housed in moveable wooden pens fitted with perches and dropping boards, nest boxes and, in some cases, feed hoppers, or in fold units. Visitors, and even Stratfordians, are unlikely to associate the old tramway wagon standing on the tramway bridge over the Avon with poultry keeping. However, the fact is that it served as a poultry pen on Barton Farm, Alderminster, for many years. Somebody got to hear of this, I think it was Dr. Levi Fox, and approached Mr. Hutchings senior with a view to purchase and restoration.

When asked how much he wanted for the old wagon cum poultry shed, Mr. Hutchings replied, 'Just a new free range house to take its place.' This was duly delivered and much impressed young Ned, as this was about the first brand new item of equipment to appear on the farm during those difficult times that he had ever seen! The undercarriage of this shed, complete with its little iron wheels, is still at Barton Farm in some grass by the farmstead.

There were, of course, some specialist poultry units in the 1930s, some on mixed farms and others on a few acres of land. These were often with static houses giving onto grass runs, usually two to a pen so that one could be rested. A prime example of a large poultry unit on a mixed holding was on Webster Cory's farm in the Cotswolds. He was a very successful farmer at the time, laying a typical 1,000 acre Cotswold arable farm down to grass, milking some 200 cows in Hosier bails, finishing pigs for bacon, running an ewe flock for fat lamb production and three large poultry units for egg production.

Each unit was housed in folds, 60 birds to each, containing in all 1,500 laying hens, all in charge of one man. An ideal system on the free draining Cotswold land but, of course, labour intensive by modern standards. The folds had slatted floors, nest boxes and feed and water hoppers. They were moved daily, in theory, which gave some protection against the weather and vermin.

With almost all layers kept out of doors, artificial lighting was impossible. Thus egg production was highly seasonal; it was at its peak in the spring and early summer and at its lowest during the short winter days. Thus prices also fluctuated, 6d to 1/- (2.5p to 5p)/dozen when at their cheapest in the spring, rising to at least 2/6d (12.5p) and, even on occasion, a lot more in the winter months. Prudent housewives purchased many dozens of eggs when at their cheapest, storing them in water glass in a special tall, large, bucket with a lid. The eggs were loaded into a cage which was then lowered into the liquid preservative.

Some eggs were marketed through a packing station as well as being sold direct to shops and individual customers, and there were egg packing stations in Stratford and Henley-in-Arden. The latter was a co-operative venture run in association with the market. In post-war years the Stratford station was taken over by the one at Henley, which itself ceased to function some years ago. There was also a privately run egg packing station at Wixford when Mr. David Greig, the grocer, owned Oversley Castle Farm. Today, the larger producers grade, candle and pack their eggs themselves or sell to egg packers. Those with flocks numbered in tens or hundreds sell at the back door, through farm shops, or other local retail outlets.

The 1940s

With the outbreak of war in 1939, the poultry industry was hit hard by feed rationing. The ration was sufficient only for one-sixth of pre-war numbers. However, by various means, two-thirds of pre-war numbers were actually sustained. On farms, of course, feeding the laying flock was less of a problem than in the case of specialist units. There was always grain in plenty, and ways and means of making up a farm mixed ration with the official ration and other ingredients.

Domestic poultry keeping was encouraged, as was the case with pigs. Up to 25 birds could be kept and received an official ration of 20 lb. of layers' meal per month, which was supplemented with household scraps and garden and allotment waste. I have already mentioned that I ran a smallholding for six years in the village of Welford-on-Avon, where I have lived for over fifty years. In those days, Welford had yet to become almost completely suburbanised. It was still mainly a village of market gardeners and smallholders, some full-time and others, like myself, part-time. By contrast with today, when village streets are a racetrack for commuters and a menace to the very young, very old, or unwary, the Welford natives conducted their affairs by bike, the riding of which had been developed to a fine art. For there was often a hoe tied onto the cross bar, a bucket on each handle bar, jacket pockets full of seed, topped off by a hand seed drill slung over one shoulder. Thus encumbered, the only greeting possible when meeting a friend or neighbour was the countryman's quick backward tilt of the head with the mouth open.

I have already described their pig-keeping activities, but the vast majority also had a pen of laying hens. My smallholding was fairly typical with three houses with large grass runs enclosed with wire netting. Two runs held thirty layers each, while the third was rested from September until May and then used for the replacement pullets.

There was always a good demand for eight-week old pullets. I had a rearing shed and started in February with one batch and another in April, some of which I kept for myself. From then on, I reared several batches of cockerels, most of which I sold. As I got the chicks for nothing from a poultry breeder after sexing on hatching, this was a nice little earner.

I sold most of the eggs to friends and sent some to the packing station as a gesture, as at the time eggs were still on ration. In passing, it has always seemed a little peculiar to me that the virtues of the free market are extolled when supply exceeds demand. But when the reverse is the case and demand exceeds supply leading to rationing, the free market is always referred to as the black market. Eventually, egg rationing became a farce as more eggs were being sold on the free market than were going through the packing stations and into the rationing system.

The 1950s Onwards

With the end of feed rationing in the early 1950s, the poultry industry took off. On farms in South Warwickshire, keeping laying hens on deep litter became the rage. While many on mixed farms invested in purpose-built deep litter houses, many others pressed what spare buildings they had into housing hens in this way. Old granaries, barns and the covered parts of cattle yards were converted, at very little expense, into deep litter pens. Many a South Warwickshire farmstead was bursting at the seams with laying hens and pigs. In addition, there were, of course, some specialist units which adopted this new style of housing.

New deep litter pens developed in design. Nesting boxes were often at one end and the eggs could be collected without going into the pen itself. Controlled ventilation and mechanical feeding were installed in the bigger units, but the management of the litter posed problems. Too high a stocking rate and the litter, straw or wood shavings, got wet. Too low a stocking rate and the house was too cold in the winter. But, of course, artificial lighting was now possible, in contrast to free range or fold units, and evened out the seasonal fluctuations in production.

By the early 1960s, batteries began to replace deep litter houses; the writing was on the wall. As with pigs, egg production became concentrated into large, specialised units consisting of many thousands of birds. The figures speak for themselves. In 1994, there were 10,000 holdings on which laying hens were kept, of which 200 accounted for 74% of the total number of layers. In 1996, the figures for the throughput of eggs tells the same story. No less than 85.6% of total production came from intensive systems; 1.3% from free range and 3% from perchery or barn and others.

Today, the housewife must be increasingly baffled by the number of types of eggs to be found on the supermarket shelves. For there are battery eggs, free range eggs, barn eggs, columbus eggs, four grain eggs and organic eggs. To counter the prejudice against keeping hens in battery cages and to avoid the hassle, disease risk and expense associated with free range eggs, the concept of the barn egg was hatched.

But this, in turn, turned out to have serious disadvantages. To maximise the number of layers in a barn house, the nest boxes have to be arranged in tiers. This had its hazards with birds flying around when the attendants were checking the boxes; sometimes it was necessary to provide these workers with face masks. I have been in barn houses, or percheries as they are called in the USA, and I have been appalled. Many birds had been the victims of feather pecking, or worse. There was dust everywhere and the slats were filthy. How anyone can imagine that this type of housing was an improvement on batteries, is beyond belief. One can only conclude that the so-called animal welfare activists, and other critics, have never been inside a barn house. But, perhaps, the barn houses that I have seen have not been typical. Be that as it may, one experienced poultryman has expressed the view to me that it will become increasingly difficult to get competent staff to work in barn houses.

The majority of so-called free range eggs are produced in large units. Big static houses are stocked with many thousands of layers. These are free range only in the sense that the birds have access to grassland. But the poaching round the popholes and general contamination of the ground near these houses, pose serious health problems. Not to mention the fact that many birds never venture out, very sensibly preferring the indoor environment!

Most of the larger units have become, in common with other branches of agriculture, victims of a burgeoning bureaucracy created in the names of animal welfare and traceability. In the first place, the packer who is buying the eggs (now the normal method of marketing for units of any size) will want to inspect the unit, or units. Secondly, the supermarkets, as the main customers, may want to do the same. Freedom Foods, run by the RSPCA, will also want a say. Small wonder that egg producers are finding the demands made upon them by these schemes and their customers increasingly difficult to cope with.

However, in South Warwickshire there are still many small-scale producers selling free range eggs either at the back door (a trade much enhanced by proximity to centres of population – buying eggs gives a purpose for a weekend trip into the country by car) or to local shops. To the best of my knowledge, most of these, if not all, are real free range, that is, housed in traditional free range houses or in fold units.

In passing, it is worth mentioning that tests have shown that there is no difference nutritionally nor in flavour between free range and battery eggs. The same can be said of brown versus white eggs. But customer preference is for the brown egg, preferably from layers on free range. The production of free range eggs and, for that matter, organic foods of every kind is essentially elitist. These all sell at a premium, sometimes a very substantial one. It is only the comparatively affluent who can indulge in such food fads. Those who have to watch the housekeeping money with care, the majority, certainly cannot. However, the writing is on the wall for the large so-called free range units. At certain times, the supply of such eggs exceeds demand. Once the premium over battery eggs disappears, or is much reduced, free range egg production will become uneconomic.

The Future for Egg Production

It is impossible to be optimistic about the future of egg production. In common with the pig sector, egg producers are hedged about with welfare, pollution prevention and environmental regulations with which their overseas competitors do not have to contend. The fact of the matter is that, while rigorously imposing these constraints on UK producers of eggs and pigmeat, imports produced under very much laxer conditions are allowed into the country from units which do not have to bear the costs imposed on domestic units.

In the very near future, both pig and poultry units will be facing further regulations, allegedly imposed on environmental grounds. In addition, egg producers face the prospect of the phasing out of conventional battery units over a period of years. From 2003 onwards, any new units have to be percheries or barns. By 2012, all conventional battery units still in existence will be banned throughout the EU. To what extent the EU's Welfare of Laying Hens Directive, agreed by the Council of Ministers in June 1999, will be enforced in Member States on mainland Europe is anybody's guess. On past form, it could well be that in the UK the new rules will be adhered to by our bureaucracy, but largely ignored in the rest of the EU.

Be that as it may, the National Farmers' Union conducted a survey (1999) of egg producers representing half the national laying flock. Sixty percent fear that they will pull out of production by 2012, unless similar regulations are enforced in third countries exporting to the EU, or their imports banned on hen welfare grounds. The latter is unlikely and the European market, on present indications, is likely to be swamped by cheap imports, particularly from the USA. For battery egg production is a lower cost process than barn production.

Those bold spirits who are prepared to continue in egg production with the new type intensive houses face considerable capital expenditure. To house the same number of birds all will need more houses and, possibly, more land to put them on. Some 80% of those producers surveyed were doubtful of obtaining the necessary planning consent. If this is denied them, we will have the Alice-in-Wonderland situation of a society which insists on the abolition of battery cages on the one hand, but on the other denying producers the means by which they can comply with the new regulations. Full bellies make for empty minds.

Table Poultry

In the 1930s, a roast cockerel weighing some 5 to 7 lb. or more was a luxury and appeared on the table on special occasions only. Those with long enough memories will recall the old-fashioned butchers shops with cockerels and, in season, turkeys and geese, all rough plucked and hanging on rails in front of the shop windows. Today, broiler chickens are about the cheapest meat that one can buy.

It all started with the end of feed rationing in the early 1950s. In 1953, 19m table birds were produced, of which only 5m were broilers. By 1960, 108m were produced, of which no less than 100m were broilers. Thus the production of the heavier, traditional, cockerel fell from 14m a year to 8m. Broiler production had increased twenty fold in seven years. The birds were not processed on the farm or specialist unit. They were transported to efficient, well-run packing stations where they were killed, plucked, dressed and packed ready to market.

Ian and Joan Hughes of Manor Farm, Crimscote, near Stratford-on-Avon, were amongst the pioneers of the broiler sector. They started their broiler enterprise in the mid-1950s and soon found that, among other problems, was that of marketing large numbers of small table chickens when a crop had reached the desired weight.

In 1958 they were instrumental in forming a co-operative, Midland Broiler Producers, which not only marketed the broilers but purchased feed and other inputs in bulk. Group members contracted to supply certain numbers at stated intervals, being paid on grade and weight.

Joan had a special responsibility in the organisation and the running of this co-operative. The broilers were sent to the FMC processing and packing plant at

Brackley. Ian also played an active part in the development of broiler production becoming chairman of FMC Poultry Ltd. and also of the NFU Poultry Committee. Where Ian and Joan led others followed. 'We were young; it was all new and very exciting,' said Joan.

Intensive production of table poultry was not to be confined to broilers. Turkeys were to be next, and Matthews of Norfolk is inevitably linked with this development. Turkeys became not just for Christmas, but available all the year round.

But there was, and still is, a traditional market for the farm reared turkey at Christmas. For some of us, fetching the turkey from the farm on which it was reared, killed, plucked and dressed is still one of the rituals in preparation for Christmas Day. Happily, and in spite of the worst efforts of the Hygiene Police, farm-reared turkeys, numbered in tens and hundreds, rather than thousands are still to be had in South Warwickshire.

Salmonella

Good Lord, give me the grace to keep my mouth shut until I know what I am talking about

At one time, this text hung on the wall of the entrance hall of the Animal Nutrition Unit at Drayton, near Stratford-on-Avon, and, for all I know, it still does. It immediately calls to mind the Salmonella fiasco of the later 1980s and early '90s.

It was on December 3rd 1988 that Edwina Currie, then a Junior Health Minister, appeared on television to announce that, 'We do warn people now that most egg production in this country, sadly, is infected with Salmonella.'

The effect of this devastating remark was almost instantaneous. Within days egg consumption in this country fell, overall, by 50%. Hospitals and schools cut consumption to 10% of what it had been. Nine days later we were treated to the sight on television of 300m eggs being dumped in landfill sites.

One year later egg consumption was still down by 10%.

Many poultry farmers in the UK were put out of business, their livelihoods utterly destroyed. Nor did the damage end there. For ancillary industries, notably the manufacturers of poultry food, were also adversely affected To add insult to injury the inevitable shortfall in UK egg production was made up by eggs imported from the continent, which, when tested, were shown to be infected with Salmonella but, nevertheless, were sold in the shops.

The Government reaction was to instigate the compulsory testing of all laying flocks for Salmonella infection, followed by slaughter if the tests were positive. The cost of the testing was borne by the flock owner and penalised severely those in the smaller way of business. The cost per bird per year in flocks of, say,

100 was £1.60. But for the large egg producer with, for the sake of argument 40,000 laying hens the cost was only £0.002p/bird. In South Warwickshire, many of the smaller flocks were free range, selling their eggs at the back door. Many simply gave up, not being willing to put up with all the hassle of registration and testing, and possibly re-stocking when the farce was over.

The supervision of the regulations and testing was in the hands of the local authority. One story going the rounds, which may or may not have been apocryphal, was that one official visiting holdings where there were poultry in South Warwickshire, was so terrified of farm dogs that he would not get out of his car, blowing his horn to announce his arrival and to gain attention. Once this got around, and it did not take long, his hooting was studiously ignored until he got fed up and went on his way. At least this brought a little hilarity into an otherwise sombre and unhappy situation.

All this might have been worthwhile if it had been proven beyond any reasonable doubt, in the first place, that a hen infected with Salmonella on testing was certain to pass this infection on into the egg. Secondly, that fresh eggs were, in fact a main source of Salmonella poisoning in humans, and that the government's slaughter policy would reduce significantly the incidence of these outbreaks. The evidence for the former is either non-existent or, at best, tenuous or inconclusive. In the latter case, the slaughter policy had not the slightest influence on the number of outbreaks of Salmonella poisoning which continued an inexorable rise. The facts speak for themselves. In 1992, the Farmers Weekly reported that, although 3m hens had been slaughtered under the scheme, 8,131 cases of Salmonella poisoning had been reported up to the end of the first week in June of that year. The comparable figure for 1991 had been 5,153. There had, in fact, been a steady annual rise in such outbreaks since 1988.

The conclusion, then, had to be that fresh, unbroken, eggs were not the main cause of Salmonella poisoning as such. The threat to the consumer came from sloppy, ill-informed food handling practices in the domestic kitchen and, particularly, in catering establishments of all kinds, of broken eggs and, indeed, of food of all sorts.

In short, the slaughter policy had been a very expensive failure, costing egg producers and taxpayers many millions of £s. Eventually, it was abandoned having achieved precisely nothing.

In passing, it is worth noting that the House of Commons Select Committee, studying the Salmonella problem in 1989, had come to the conclusion that the slaughter of flocks which had tested positive for Salmonella would be ineffective on the grounds of immediate re-infection after disinfection and re-stocking.

On the political front, Edwina Currie did resign her post. She did admit, in a television interview eleven months after her first disastrous remark, that she had been wrong in saying that *most* eggs were infected with Salmonella, the implication being that many were. Did she ever show any contrition or express regret for what she had done to the poultry industry, for the livelihoods she had destroyed, for the costs incurred unnecessarily by flock owners and taxpayers alike? And what happened to those officials who had advised Ministers so badly? Promotion?

But the most depressing thing about the Salmonella fiasco is this. When the next great food scare came along, BSE in cattle and a possible link to CJD in humans, it became only too obvious that politicians, and those civil servants and scientists who advised them, had learnt nothing. Absolutely nothing, as we still await the predicted epidemic of CJD. Will the BSE episode, when the full story comes to be written, prove as big a fiasco as the Salmonella one? It has certainly had a more devastating, and expensive, effect on the livestock and meat industries, not to mention the taxpayer. Time will tell.

12. ARABLE FARMING

The Soils of South Warwickshire

The soils of the Feldon are predominantly clays derived from the Lower Lias. There is an area of similar soil north of the Avon in the parishes of Temple Grafton, Binton, Billesley, the eastern part of Aston Cantlow parish around Wilmcote, and Bishopton.

South of the river, the clay starts in part of Bidford parish and Dorsingon and follows the county boundary to Mitford Bridge, where the infant Stour flows under the main road from Stratford to Oxford. However, there are enclaves of much lighter land on and around Meon Hill and in the Ilmington Downs, Foxcote and Nebsworth area, also on the tops of Binton, Welford and Idlicote hills, the remains of eroded river terraces. There is also another, curious, small area of light land at Blackwell, surrounded by clayland and, no doubt, a geologist would have an explanation.

From Mitford Bridge, the boundary of the clay goes northwards, by-passing Brailes and continuing to Radway, Tysoe, Kineton, Fenny Compton and Wormleighton, and then north-eastwards to Rugby. But between the clay and the county boundary with Oxfordshire, there is a strip of a little lighter land, heavy to medium loam.

As already explained, the easier working land in South Warwickshire is to be found in the river valleys of the Avon, Alne and Arrow, the lower reaches of which have traditionally been market garden land. Horticultural crops are still grown on a field scale today, along with potatoes, oilseed rape and cereals.

With the exception mentioned above, the land lying north of Stratford, that is in the Arden, is mostly a medium to heavy loam overlying Keuper Marl. Where this latter comes to the surface the soil is clayey and even more difficult to work than the Lias Clay.

In short, the Feldon is clayland country, with the exception of the Cotswold fringe, other land in the extreme south of the county, and the river valleys, while the Arden, with the exception of the clayland parishes listed above, lies predominantly on the Keuper Marl, which provides a surface texture varying from clay to medium loam.

Farming the Claylands

The Lower Lias formation is highly calcareous and the clays derived from it have a similar nature. It is also naturally very deficient in phosphates and is considered to have ample supplies of potash. Like all other clays they are slow to warm up in the spring, their drainage is impeded and they are difficult and expensive to cultivate.

Their successful cultivation depends upon knowledge and experience. For instance, let the furrow slice dry out after ploughing in late summer or early autumn, and you are in trouble. For then the discs or power harrows will simply produce clods, which are then rattled around from one headland to the other without producing anything resembling a tilth. The furrow slice must be broken by cultivation before drying out and then sun, rain, and wind will play their part until the final seedbed cultivations. Spring crops will always be dependent upon a frost tilth for a really good seedbed.

Autumn drilling of cereals on this land is the norm, and winter wheat is the main cash crop. But the window of opportunity for ploughing, working down, and drilling between the end of harvest and, say, mid-November, when all corn should be drilled at the latest, can be very narrow.

Late summer and autumn weather was even more critical when ploughing, cultivations, and sowing were dependent upon horses and what we would now consider to be low-powered tractors. A late harvest and a wet October and November would usually result in failure to drill the target acreage of winter corn.

The classic season in this respect was 1946, followed by an equally disastrous 1947: two years which will never be forgotten by farmers and other countrymen who lived through them.

In 1946, the corn harvest had been a struggle; of course even then most acres were still cut with a binder. The autumn started with much land sodden, and some waterlogged. In consequence, very little winter corn was drilled on the heavier land.

Usually, such an autumn is followed by a much greater acreage of corn drilled in the spring. But in 1947, not even this was an option. The wet weather of the previous year was followed by a severe winter, setting in during the second half of January with hard frosts and snow covering the land for many weeks. This was followed by high winds, more heavy rain and flooding.

When the ground eventually dried out sufficiently for cultivations to start, most spring corn was drilled late into rough seedbeds, because not even ploughing had been possibly in the previous autumn. To cap it all, this was followed by one of the driest, and hottest, summers for many a year. What corn that had been drilled in the spring yielded very badly. This, along with a much diminished acreage of winter corn, made bread rationing necessary after harvest. Another result was a record acreage of fallow in South Warwickshire in 1947, something which was not to be approached until the original set-aside regulations allowed ploughing at the end of May.

Today, of course, it is a very different story from the situation prevailing in the 1940s. More powerful tractors, the bigger implements to go with them and the partial adoption of minimal cultivations means that more can be accomplished in a shorter time, with all that that means in a difficult season.

Another effect of a wet autumn must be mentioned. The use of the mouldboard plough has, under such conditions, an unavoidable but undesirable effect. When the soil is sodden the furrow slice comes up like liver, which is a sure sign that the sole of the plough is smearing the furrow bottom. This seals the clay soil and creates a temporary pan. Something which Mother Nature will cure in due course when the summer is dry and the clay cracks down to a very considerable depth.

Fifty years ago, it was held that, if ploughing had to be undertaken after harvest under wet conditions, the subsequent crop would be bound to suffer come what may. A wet summer, when the clay never became dry enough to crack, was also viewed with foreboding. In spite of the extension of the practice of sub-soiling in recent times, there is still a grain of truth in all this. The fundamentals never change.

Historically, the Warwickshire clays have been marginal land as far as arable cultivation is concerned; that is the first to go out of cultivation when corn prices fell. What the fate of the heavy land in South Warwickshire will eventually be if the present low prices for cereals continue for any length of time remains to be seen. Today, it is a different ball game from that of the 1880s and 1920s, but so many farms in this district are now entirely dependent upon the viability of growing combineable crops. Only time will tell.

Ley Farming

The ploughing-up campaign of the 1940s completely changed the face of South Warwickshire, especially on the heaviest land. Fields that had been under grass, of a sort, for decades, even generations, were ploughed and cropped.

At this point another characteristic of clayland should be noted. Continued cultivation destroyed the fibrous roots of grasses and clovers, all of which had such a beneficial effect on the workability of these intractable soils. As these root systems, and the fibre of which they were composed, rotted away over a period of, say, four or five seasons, the soil became increasingly difficult to work with the horse and tractor power that was available in the 1940s. The remedy, of course, was to lay land back to grass for a period of recuperation before ploughing out again – ley farming in other words.

Until Sir George Stapledon, with his work at Drayton and Dodwell from 1940 onwards, demonstrated otherwise, the truth of the old saying, 'To break a pasture makes a man, to make a pasture breaks a man,' was generally accepted. Locally, it was felt that whatever the advantages of ley farming on lighter soils, and in districts of greater rainfall might be, such a farming system was not for South Warwickshire. The difficulties of obtaining a good enough tilth on the clays for small seeds to germinate were stressed, as was the low rainfall. Moreover, the basic importance of soluble phosphatic fertilisers was not fully appreciated.

But Sir George altered all that. He laid down, and indeed demonstrated in practice, the golden rules for establishing long leys (as opposed to the one year variety) on the heaviest soils. These were: a fine, firm seedbed, preferably a frost tilth; an application of 18% superphosphate at 3 cwt./acre. Grass and clover seeds in those days were sown into spring barley, and should be cross drilled, rather than broadcast, and then rolled well, and all this immediately after the barley had been drilled. The seeds mixture should consist of bred varieties, the so-called Aberystwyth strains, which Sir George had been so instrumental in breeding and which were superior in leafiness and persistency to the commercial strains then available.

Where a ley was sown at all, in days gone by, it was normally of the one year variety consisting of early Ryegrasses and Red Clover, both tall growing and aggressive. The practice had been to broadcast these after the barley was up, otherwise they would grow up into the barley, making harvest difficult. With the lower growing, improved, and more persistent species this would not happen and thus it was safe to sow at the same time as barley, giving the small seeds a better change of establishment.

Ley farming, the alternation of grass with cereals and sometimes other crops, had a number of advantages. In passing, the ploughing-up grant, which was introduced just before the outbreak of war in 1939, gave a great stimulus to ley farming. It was payable after land had been in ley for three years and this, in practice, became the minimum length of a ley. But, of course, there was nothing to prevent the ley being left down longer if need be, and the composition of a seeds mixture for a 3-, 4- or 5-year ley could be identical in practice.

Thus the most common rotation was a three year ley, followed by two wheat crops and then spring barley undersown. It was the best practice to plough the ley out not later than the beginning of July and then make a half fallow. Given the weather, this helped to control perennial weeds such as squitch, docks and thistles. Indeed, if the ley was foul with such weeds, a good farmer would plough the ley in April, or early May, to make as certain as possible of a good kill. The old saying was 'A fallow is three parts made by the end of May.' Either way, one third of the arable after fallow was ready to drill immediately after harvest, one third was for spring cropping in any case and could be ploughed after drilling, leaving one third only to be ploughed from stubble and sown to winter corn. This was a big advantage when the tractor power available was, by modern standards, limited.

Another advantage of this rotation was that with only two autumn-drilled crops in six years, and these then followed by a spring crop, wild oats, wild onions and blackgrass, which are all weeds associated with runs of autumn drilling, were kept in check.

The ley stored up fertility, especially nitrates, particularly when heavily stocked and this was released slowly after ploughing out. In fact the beneficial effect in this respect, was more pronounced in the second crop as the grass and clover residues were, by then, fully rotted. Moreover, in those days a ley down for three years would be cut twice for hay rather than silage, although the latter had the same effect, but to a lesser degree. Now root growth is in direct proportion to aerial growth; the taller grasses grow, the more root fibre they make. Putting grass up for conservation thus had an excellent effect upon soil structure, important at any time, but especially so when tractor power was limited, and soil workability was an even more important attribute than it is today.

One of Sir George Stapledon's favourite phrases when singing the praises of ley farming was that it 'took the muck cart round the farm.' Referring, of course, to the beneficial effect the ploughed-out ley had on fertility and soil structure, an effect which formerly depended upon heavy dressings of farmyard manure at regular intervals. Those fields furthest from the farmstead tended to see the muck cart least, hence Sir George's reference. In other words, the ploughed-out ley did for the remoter fields something which the muck cart, only too often, did not.

To digress, and to mention one way in which farmers and landowners in former times made provision to take the muck cart to the furthest fields. A feature of many farms in South Warwickshire is the field barn and cattle yard, always sited to serve those fields at the greatest distance from the main farmstead. For instance, stand on the north side of Binton Hill, where the lane falls away to the valley of the River Alne and you will see two prime examples. One just to the North West of Haselor Lodge at the bottom of Redhill on the main Stratford to Alcester road, and the other further away in the distance, lying a field away from Withycombe Wood. Neither is in use today, but both are kept in good repair by the owner as being part and parcel of the farming landscape, which is well worth preserving.

The field barn's function was to store hay and straw, some had a threshing floor, to be fed to cattle in the yard and to provide litter. The resulting farmyard manure was then carted and spread on the fields around, thus ensuring that the fertility of the furthest parts of the farm was maintained.

Ley farming had its disadvantages inasmuch as two pests of cereals could be troublesome. First, wireworms could damage the first crop after grass, and sometimes even the second, more usually after an old pasture, rather than a ley, had been brought into cultivation. Seed dressings became available in due course and were a sure method of control.

More serious, perhaps, was the Wheat Bulb Fly. This laid its eggs in bare ground in late July or early August, just when the land was lying fallow after the ley had been broken out earlier in the summer. These eggs had the rather peculiar habit of hatching our in mid-winter, in January or early February. The grubs found a wheat plant, then ate their way inside, killing the centre shoot and often the whole plant. Late drilling, or an autumn drought which delayed germination, usually produced small, backward wheat plants which would be especially vulnerable to attack by this pest.

Fig. 7 Walcote Manor Farm. Withycombe Field barn and yard.

Incidentally, many wartime failures of wheat crops after grass, which had been even half fallowed after ploughing and were usually attributed to Wireworm, were, in fact, the work of the Wheat Bulb Fly. Early drilling to ensure, as far as possible, a strong, forward plant by mid-winter was the most practical answer, although in later years chemical control became possible.

On the livestock side, the alternation of grass with arable crops presented cattle and sheep with clean pasture with a low burden of parasites. This was particularly important in the case of lambs and especially so in a season when they were not doing as well as they might, very often in a cold, late, wet spring. Under these circumstances, it was very noticeable that lambs on leys did much better than those on old pasture.

The system of ley farming, with many variations, described above was adopted widely in South Warwickshire in the 1940s and persisted into the next two decades. Today, many farms are still run on these lines but the reasons for its partial decline are the subject of a later section.

The sodden '60s

This decade was noted for a run of seasons that were exceptionally wet, especially the years 1968 and 1969. This had long term results, notably the rediscovery of the mystery and art of cultivations, which today is known as *soil management*. Something which can only be learnt in part from books but, ultimately, can only be the result of careful observation and experience.

The then Minister of Agriculture, equating activity with action as is customary amongst politicians, asked the Agricultural Advisory Council to investigate the effects of these wet seasons on soil structure of the heavier soils and make recommendations, of which more later.

Needless to say, a run of wet seasons was disastrous on heavy soils, amongst them, of course, the clays of South Warwickshire. It just so happened that in December 1970, I was at a conference on heavy land farming, organised by Fisons Ltd., and held in Cambridge. There was much chatter about growing potatoes and sugar beet on 'heavy' land, and the adverse effect that harvesting and carting off these crops had on soil structure. This brought home to me very forcibly that the terms 'heavy,' 'medium' and 'light' when applied to soil texture, were purely relative. Clearly, what appeared to be 'heavy' land to some of the speakers, would be described as 'potting soil' by at least one South Warwickshire farmer of my acquaintance!

Be that as it may, the report of a committee appointed by the Agricultural Advisory Council, entitled *Modern Farming and the Soil* (commonly known as the Strutt Report, after the chairman) duly appeared in 1971.

Much of the report would be considered platitudinous by those who had not forgotten their basic husbandry, and so caused a certain amount of hilarity in such circles. One such little gem concerned the Report's comments on grassland, for the members of the committee did not confine themselves to arable problems.

> We have been impressed by the difficulties of high stocking rates on grassland in areas of high rainfall. These lead to structural damage and deterioration of the sward.

There was nothing new in this, as the following quote illustrates:

> If clayland is under grass it cannot be stocked in wet weather as treading *poaches* the surface, prevents the passage of air and moisture and greatly deteriorates the herbage. [From *Agriculture* (1937), by Watson & Moore 4th. Ed.]

Or another quote:

> A further means of deteriorating grassland is the practice of allowing pastures reserved for horned cattle to be overstocked. [From *The Complete Grazier* (1908), Fream]

There is much contained in the report of a similar nature. Perhaps time and ink could have been saved by a study of the farming literature going back over the years.

The Report had one very serious defect. It recommended a return to ley farming on the Midland clays without any regard to the economic and financial factors which were leading to its abandonment in favour of all-arable rotations of combineable crops. These factors will be discussed later, suffice to say that the report made no suggestions as to how their recommendation was to be carried out in practice, which was a very serious omission.

However, the Report was valuable as a restatement of old principles. It undoubtedly drew the attention of arable farmers to the importance of soil management, a lesson which the younger generation took to heart. The importance of sub-soiling was recognised and this spawned a whole new generation of sub-soilers and other ironmongery, some of a rather eccentric design. The importance of good drainage was emphasised and one practical and highly desirable result was a substantial increase in the MAFF grant for land drainage.

Up Corn, Down Horn

The Strutt Report (above) had already noted, in 1970, the swing to all-arable farming on the heavy land in the Midlands, and recommended a return to ley farming.

Now it is commonly supposed, and often repeated parrot fashion by those whose knowledge of agricultural matters is minimal, or non-existent, that the increase in arable acreage, and what they are pleased to call 'intensive farming' is the result of greedy farmers taking advantage of EU subsidies.

Nothing could be further from the truth. The eastern and southern counties with their low rainfalls have always been, and always will be, arable country. Similarly, the wetter western districts are naturally mainly pastoral. In between, the Midlands have traditionally been an area of mixed farming with the emphasis swinging towards arable and back to grazing livestock as economics dictated: '*Up corn, down corn*' as the old saying goes. Since the mid-1960s, and certainly before the UK entered the EU, the pattern of farming in the Midlands, including South Warwickshire, has swung towards a greater acreage of arable land.

The reasons for this were obvious. In those days, those in dairying had to decide between the expansion of their herds, with all that that implied in increased capital expenditure, or getting out of milk production altogether.

Those who opted to sell their milking cows usually, at any rate at first, stocked their grassland, leys and old pastures alike, with beef cattle and sheep. The gross margin per acre from grassland stocked in this way was very much less than that from dairying and, more importantly, from arable crops. This was especially the case on the claylands where the growing of the higher value cash crops, such as potatoes, sugar beet and field scale vegetables, etc., was not an option for obvious reasons. For all practical purposes, arable farming on the clays was confined to combineable crops, including peas and beans for vining.

Even in the 1960s, such arable crops produced much higher gross margins per acre than grassland stocked with beef cattle and sheep. This point can be confirmed by quoting from the first edition of the *Farm Management Pocketbook*, by John Nix, published in 1966.

The gross margin per acre from winter wheat, at 35 cwt./acre, was quoted as £35.60, from barley at 29 cwt./acre, £27.50, and from winter beans at 30 cwt./acre, £28.50.

In the case of 18 month old beef, the gross margin per forage acre was £21.50 to £25.50 and for finished lamb production £12.50/forage acre. With winter wheat as the most important cash crop in terms of acreage on the claylands, it is not surprising that the arable acreage increased at the expense of grassland, and the acreage under leys in particular. The figures speak for themselves.

There were other factors. In the 1960s, a new generation was taking over from fathers, and grandfathers, who had struggled through the lean, inter-war years. The new men were more innovative and could afford to be with guaranteed prices and markets; they had to maximise gross margin incomes. They had greater expectations in terms of standards of living and higher borrowings due to the continued swing towards owner/occupation and the need to fund farm modernisation – new buildings, new machinery, and so on.

The difference in outlook between the old and the new generations towards arable farming is well illustrated by the removal of the ploughing-up grant in 1949. There was an immediate slump in the arable acreage in South Warwickshire, and elsewhere in the Midlands, as those who had farmed in the 1920s and 1930s were only too glad to return to pastoral farming with which they were familiar. A couple of years later the grant was restored in the hope of maintaining, or increasing, the acreage under the plough; food was still rationed and it was still a hungry world.

The many advantages of ley farming have been outlined above. Today, this system of farming would, and is, held up as a prime example of *integrated crop management*, which is the rediscovery of the virtues of the paths of rotational righteousness as preached by LEAF – linking the environment and farming. In Greenspeak, ley farming is *sustainable*.

But where were the Greens in the 1960s, when the trend away from such a desirable farming system was still reversible; did they understand the fundamental economic drawback of ley farming in the absence of a dairy herd, as noted above? If so, why were they not using their considerable lobbying expertise to press for higher prices for beef and lamb to eliminate the gross margin gap between combineable crops and grassland stocked with beef cattle and sheep? The answer, one imagines lies in the fact that the Greens' knowledge of the practicalities of making a living from the land is minimal. Even if they had managed to grasp the facts of the matter, was there a reluctance to do anything that would benefit the farming community, which they obviously disliked and envied? We shall never know, but Greens were certainly conspicuous by their absence, when they could have, for once, had a benign effect.

All-Arable Clayland Farming

Fifty years ago, continuous arable cultivation on clay soils without the intervention of a ley break was thought impossible. It was the received wisdom that clayland so cropped would became more and more intractable as the root fibre was lost, and thus greatly at risk in an adverse season when harvest, autumn cultivations and drilling would be seriously delayed. Then there were the weed problems associated with a long run of winter corn, and spring cropping not a solution since yields were low compared to corn sown in the autumn. If anyone had suggested in the 1950s that many clayland farms would be all arable by the mid-1970s, he, or she, would have been attended upon by two men in white coats!

The economic pressures that led farmers on the heaviest soils to an all-arable have already been described. But the factors which made the continuous growing of combineable crops on South Warwickshire clays a practical proposition must now be stated.

First and foremost was the skill and determination of the farmers concerned. One can name names: the Forsyths out Kineton way, the Mahons of Bishopton Hill, Stratford-upon-Avon, Ted Kerby and his sons of Billesley, to name but a few of the outstandingly successful. They, and those like them, took to heart the more valuable lessons from the Strutt Report and elevated the management of these inherently difficult soils to a fine art.

However, a spirit of innovation would not have been enough on its own; other factors were at work. More and more tractors of greater power were being introduced with the implements to go with them, notably new designs of sub-soilers.

New cultivation techniques, such as direct drilling and minimal cultivations, were developed. Above all, the development of herbicides which would effectively control Wild Oats and Blackgrass, which, along with Wild Onion, had always been the bane of a long run of autumn drilling. Later with the wide adoption of non-plough techniques Bromes, both Sterile and Soft, began to pose a problem, but one which was eventually overcome.

New varieties of winter wheat and winter barley, themselves capable of higher yields, enabled heavier applications of nitrogenous fertilisers to be used. The introduction of fungicides for the control of diseases in cereals in the early 1970s was also a powerful factor in increasing yields. In the 1940s a yield of 30 cwt./acre from winter wheat would have been considered very satisfactory (half as much again as the national average), with anything substantially over this really exceptional. Today in South Warwickshire, one looks for at least double, with a yield below 60 cwt./acre thought to be disappointing.

Straw Disposal

With the coming of the all-arable farm, the problem of the disposal of surplus straw became acute. Gone were the days when wheat straw was needed for litter and barley and oat straw for fodder. All straw on the all-arable holding was a by-product for which there was no use. Perhaps this is not strictly correct, for in this district straw was often sold to livestock farmers in the field, the purchaser baling and carting off.

There were also attempts to make use of surplus straw in other ways. Straw burning furnaces for farmhouse central heating was one development. The simpler, cheaper furnaces were never really very satisfactory. Then there was the expense of baling and carting, not to mention the labour involved. Once the straw was in the barn, the bales still had to be manhandled to the furnace. All very well in theory, but in practice it proved to be something of a nine-day wonder.

The use of straw in the manufacture of paper, cardboard, or building board was another potential outlet. Some success in a small way was achieved. But the great drawback was that straw is bulky in relation to its weight and thus expensive to transport. To ensure an even supply to any manufacturing plant, the production from one harvest had to be stored until the next. All in all, it has to be admitted that these channels for the disposal of surplus had little impact on the overall problem. To the best of my knowledge straw from South Warwickshire was not used to any extent for these purposes.

At first, straw burning was the solution. Not only did this get rid of the straw, but a good burn was an essential preliminary to either direct drilling or minimal cultivations. Even at Drayton, where all the straw was baled for use as litter, the stubbles were burnt.

But this was a practice which did not find favour with the public. Columns of smoke rising high into the summer sky did nothing for farming's image. Nevertheless straw burning continued for many years, over which burning techniques were improved and incorporated into a Code of Practice. Among the items included in this were not burning after dark, ploughing fire breaks along headlands (i.e. the ends of a field) and around buildings etc., having sufficient men on hand should the burning get out of control, and so on.

In spite of this, there were one or two rogue farmers (not in South Warwickshire but elsewhere in the county) who disregarded the Code leaving black acres, burnt hedges and scorched trees as the inevitable outcome of their carelessness, or worse. But with the best will in the world accidents did happen and the result was the same but on a much smaller scale, of course. Moreover, under certain weather conditions, black ash could travel considerable distances falling on towns and villages, something which did not endear farmers to urbanites or their neighbours in the countryside, especially if they had just put the washing out.

But straw and stubble burning continued for many seasons, during which farmers took a pride in achieving a good, clean burn without mishap. However, in the end, straw and stubble burning was banned which was a blessing, for it forced farmers to adopt other methods which were all to the good.

Straw incorporation

Fig. 8 Minimal cultivation at Drayton. (1974)

It is only an impression, but it may be that the demand for straw for litter in South Warwickshire is greater than it was. Be that as it may, there is still a substantial surplus of straw to be dealt with and, with burning now illegal, the only way is to work it into the soil.

Straw incorporation does, over the years, have a beneficial effect upon soil structure. On the heavier land it makes cultivations that much easier, whereas on the lighter land it increases water-holding capacity and thus mitigates the effect of a dry season or drought.

The late Ernest Bomford of Rushford, Salford Priors, realised this in the 1950s. As did Peter Hepworth, that well known and forthright farmer-scribe from Yorkshire, several decades later.

Ernest was an acute observer of the arable scene and, some fifty years ago, set great store on soil condition, thus anticipating the recommendations of the Strutt Report by some twenty years. He farmed a large all-arable holding that straddled what was then the main Alcester to Evesham road. Unlike an all-clay farm, he was able to grow a wide range of crops, amongst them early potatoes, sprouts, spring cabbage, savoys, stick beans, and wheat and barley. Apart from an area of very heavy land on Bevington Waste, most of the farm was a light to medium loam with a patch, here and there, running to marl.

Besides straw incorporation, the growing of herbage seeds was another method by which he improved soil structure. His first venture into this was fifteen acres of Cocksfoot on Bevington Waste. This he promptly christened Woods' Folly, so that I would have to take the blame if things went wrong, as I had suggested he tried this crop which he had not grown before. Within a few years, having mastered the unfamiliar techniques in a very short space of time, the acreage under herbage seeds grew substantially, with Timothy, Ryegrass and some Fescues being added to the repertoire.

Ernest had been incorporating straw for some years prior to this new departure. In those days, there were no such things as straw choppers on the back of the combine, the straw being spread by rotating arms as it came off the walkers. It was, of course, in its original long state, longer, indeed than it would be today as the varieties then grown had longer straw than modern ones.

Over a few seasons, Ernest evolved his own method of straw incorporation. In the first place, he believed that it was essential that the straw started to rot before being ploughed under. For he had observed that if this was not the case, straw was ploughed up the following year in much the same state as it had been when ploughed under, much of it being unrotted.

The first thing he did was to apply 1 cwt./acre of Sulphate of Ammonia (the nitrogenous fertiliser in common use in the 1950s) on to the straw as it lay after combining to assist the rotting process. Then, the straw was mixed with the soil and the resulting mulch allowed to remain on the surface for as long as possible before the field was ploughed. Not only did this start the rotting process but also allowed weed seeds to germinate.

But it was the incorporation of straw with the soil that was the problem initially. Rotovators were tried and found to be too slow and expensive. In an ordinary season, discs made little impression. Finally, two disc ploughs were purchased at the dispersal of farm machinery from the former *War Ag* machinery depots, at sales held on the old aerodrome at Gaydon around 1950. These disc ploughs proved to be the answer; their rate of work was satisfactory and their penetration infinitely superior to the conventional disc harrows available at that time.

Today, straw incorporation is much easier. More powerful tractors, heavier discs and a variety of other ironmongery designed for the purpose and which, in some cases, go a long way to producing a seedbed have all played their part in making straw incorporation a routine practice on many farms.

Minimal Cultivations and Direct Drilling

Work at the Drayton Experimental Husbandry Farm, near Stratford-on-Avon played a significant, indeed the major role, in the development of minimal cultivations. Ralph Bee, the Director at the time, will always be linked with his vigorous advocacy of this novel cultivation practice.

John Whybrew, later to become Deputy Director at Drayton, wrote an article in *Agriculture*, when he was on the staff at Boxworth EHF, near Cambridge, which was entitled *Minimal Cultivations for Cereals. Pipedream or Possibility.* It asked why the slow and laborious business of ploughing had been the prime cultivation in the production of a seedbed for so long. The reasons for ploughing were accepted as being: the inversion of the soil; the breaking up of pans and compacted layers; the control of weeds, the incorporation of farmyard manure, and the only way of breaking out grassland in preparation for arable cropping.

There were but a few soil types on which drilling can follow the plough. On most further cultivations were needed and often a period of weathering in the preparation of a tilth. This all takes time, and a delay in autumn drilling can reduce yields and may even necessitate postponing sowing until the spring.

John went on to point out that the introduction of Paraquat, marketed by ICI under the name Gramoxone, opened up a whole range of possibilities for minimal cultivations, thus eliminating the slow and expensive business of attaining a seedbed after ploughing in the conventional way.

John listed the advantages as: the elimination of delay between ploughing and sowing; crops can then be drilled at the optimum time, which is especially important for autumn sown crops after a late harvest; there was much less moisture loss, and the retention of crop residues in the top layer of the soil had a more beneficial effect than ploughing them under.

He went on to link minimal cultivations with direct drilling as another possibility, and to suggest what is now known as rotational ploughing: minimal cultivations for a run of seasons, and then ploughing for one season to loosen up the soil again. This article was certainly far-sighted and prophetic.

The scene now shifts to Drayton. In 1965, it was observed that a good tilth was left after winter beans had been harvested, so the bean stubble was cultivated with an old Ransome rigid-tined cultivater. This was a clapped out old thing, with one or two tines trailing at an angle, like a bird with broken wings. The field was then drilled to winter wheat after about three passes with the Ransome.

This performance was repeated the following year when winter oats were also drilled into a non-ploughed seedbed. By 1967, a third of the winter corn was sown without ploughing. The following year, 1968, was a notably wet one and saw the end of ploughing at Drayton, all the winter corn being drilled after tining only.

It was first decided to fettle up the old cultivator. However, hydraulic linkage for crawlers had been introduced and a Supeflow chisel plough was bought in 1969, but this brought up raw slivers of clay, no matter how shallow the tines were set to work at the first pass. In 1970, the Flexitine heavy duty spring tine cultivator was purchased and this proved to be the tool for the job.

By 1973, the system had become well established. Three passes, usually all with a Flexitine, became standard practice, but occasionally a pass with discs was introduced when conditions warranted it. The same year direct drilling was tried, but these plots never had as good a plant establishment as those treated in the above manner. The bottoms of the slots produced by the drill coulters smeared. Any unburnt straw produced toxins which killed the seedlings, and slugs could cause havoc. Soil compaction was another drawback. Direct drilling at Drayton was abandoned as a matter of policy, although corn was drilled direct into bean stubbles with a conventional drill as a matter of routine when conditions were good enough.

During the 1970s, the farming world trod a path to Drayton's door to hear Ralph Bee extol, and demonstrate, the virtues of minimal cultivations, particularly on clayland. Some tried it on other soil types in South Warwickshire, but with disastrous results.

But there is no doubt that the Drayton work had a profound influence on arable farming on the heavier, more stable, soils. Minimal cultivations have taken their place in English farming and, with variations, are here to stay.

13. LAND DRAINAGE

When I am living in the Midlands, which are sodden and unkind. – Hilaire Belloc.

A fair description of the claylands of South Warwickshire one would think, indeed of any heavy land elsewhere in the Midland counties. The land drainage in the great, open, ridge-and-furrow fields of the pre-enclosure days consisted of simply letting the water out of the furrows by digging grips across the headland, and allowing it to flow into the nearest ditch. It was not until the old common fields began to be enclosed from the end of the 18th century onwards that under-drainage became commonplace.

Joseph Elkington

The first master drainer was a Warwickshire man, Joseph Elkington, who hailed from Princethorpe. He became proficient in interceptor draining, which involved discovering the source of the water that was causing the problem, and then laying drains to intercept its flow and divert it into the nearest ditch or brook.

So successful was he in applying this technique that his reputation became nationwide. The government of the day even gave him a grant of £1,000, a very considerable sum in 1797, to set out his principles as a guide to others. This exercise turned out to be unsuccessful, however, since everything depended upon his own expertise and powers of observation.

Joseph Elkington was buried in Meriden churchyard. In the early 1960s, it was discovered that his grave had become neglected. It was subsequently restored by the Warwickshire Agricultural Society with funds that became available when it ceased to hold a county show after the Royal Show came to Stoneleigh.

Tile Drains

In those days, under-drainage consisted simply of trenches filled with stones, or even just brushwood. By 1840, tile drains were in common use and the agricultural literature of the 1840s and 1850s devoted a great deal of space to drainage methods which the introduction of tiles had made possible.

The first of these was the horseshoe tile. The name describes its shape and the open bottom was laid on a flat tile. Sometimes each side of the horse-shoe had a lug at the bottom to give greater stability. At first each drain was handmade, but by 1843 John Ainslie had devised a machine which manufactured these as a continuous process. A variation of this was the horse-shoe with a flat bottom, all in one piece. These types of tile drain are turned up in great numbers in South Warwickshire in the course of laying new drains, or other excavation work. It might be added that old stone drains can also still be found, stone slabs being used to make a square or triangular drain.

In the 1840s, developments in the design and manufacture of tile drains followed one upon another with great rapidity. John Reade exhibited various types of tiles at the Royal Show in 1843, amongst them a round one, the shape with which we are familiar today. Two years later Thomas Scragg produced a machine for their manufacture.

Josiah Parkes Esq. , Consulting Engineer to the Royal Agricultural Society, read a paper on drainage to members. This was duly printed in the Society's Journal of 1847. It consisted of twenty three pages of close print, and one just wonders how many members were still awake at the end; there must have been a number of casualties! To underline the very rapid development of drain making machines I quote from his paper,

> ... we have arrived in the short space of three years to that agreeable dilemma which actually renders the selection in our showyard of the most meritorious pipe machine a matter of no little difficulty.

He goes on to record that the production of pipes per day had recently risen from 1,000 to 20,000, due to improved pipe making machines with a greater rate of production.

Drainage Boom

This rate of production meant, of course, that the cost of pipes fell considerably, which, along with the introduction of government loans, gave an enormous stimulus to land drainage in the 19th century, until the agricultural depression of the 1880s onwards brought investment in farm improvements to a halt on many estates.

There are some points concerning some of the 19th century draining practices which are well worth noting. First, backfilling over the pipes was common practice, or at least commonly advocated. Pebbles or broken stone were used, as was brushwood. Today draining clayland without gravel backfill would hardly be contemplated, at any rate in more recent years. Once again, former practices are seen to surface many decades later under the guise of something new.

As a further example of this, modern drainers are, or were, wont to lay out blanket schemes ignoring existing field boundaries and ditches and were under the impression that this was something novel. Not so, and there is evidence in South Warwickshire to prove it. There is an area of land, possibly 80 to 100 acres, between Oversley Wood and the old Alcester road, just before Oversley

Green which was drained in this way, sometime in the 19th century. The large brick encased outlet, with its cast iron flap valve can still be found in the roadside ditch, if you know where to look.

In one respect, the 19th century drainers had the edge on their 20th century successors and that was in the construction of outfalls, which were of brick with elaborate splash plates. The ones on farms on what was the Throckmorton Estate at Coughton spring to mind. Here, the water flowed from the pipe onto a two stage splash plate; first into a V-shaped chamber with its outlet in the angle of the V, which slowed the flow, then into a similar device and finally into the ditch. No chance here of the outfall being undermined and eventually toppling forwards. With the modern pre-cast concrete splash plates, this is all too often what happens after two or three winters.

Mole Drainage

Mole draining, the creation of unlined tunnels in the soil, is possible only on heavy, stone-free land which has an even fall. It is very effective under these conditions, the moles being led into the gravel backfill over a pipe main.

In 1851, John Fowler invented a mole drainer which pulled strings of pipes along the moles. The power source was originally a windlass but very soon to be replaced by the famous Fowler steam engines. The pipes were soon discarded and the modern mole plough came into existence.

Moles will last some five or six years, and even longer. When they cease to function, they can be re-drawn over the original piped main drains. And, of course, it was a far cheaper method of draining than laying a tile drain scheme. Steam tackle was ideal for the task and many tens of thousands of acres were drained in this way in the 19th century and well into the 20th. Latterly, many an old mole plough used with the 'steamers' was converted to be used behind powerful crawler tractors.

In the last fifty years, many mole drain schemes have been laid down on the clays in South Warwickshire. Modern mole ploughs are now fitted direct onto tractors with hydraulic systems.

Laying the Drains

Drain laying in the 19th century and well into the 20th was all hand work. Considering the amount of land drainage done between, say, 1830 and 1880 the amount of labour involved was prodigious.

The first spit was taken out with a common spade, then narrower spades, or draining grafts, were used to dig out the trench to the required depth. Finally when this had been reached, the drain scoop was used to smooth off the bottom of the trench and to remove any loose soil and a drain ladle performed a similar function. A pipe layer enabled the tiles to be laid without a man standing in the trench, or leaning down into it. This was a hook fitted at right angles onto a 6' wooden shaft. The pipes were carted onto the field and laid in rows alongside the trenches. The hook on the pipe layer was used to pick up each pipe, placing it next to its fellow in the trench.

Not surprisingly, various trench digging machines were developed in the 19th century, although without much success, to ease the hand labour involved. One such of these was Paul's rotary drain cutter which appeared in the 1850s. In 1881, a drain cutting and laying machine was exhibited at the Royal Derby Show, made by Messrs. Robson and Hardman, and which bore a striking resemblance to machines in use from the 1940s onwards. Buckets on chains dug the trench, while the pipes were laid by sliding them down a chute.

The more modern versions also had a chain and bucket device which dug the trench, the pipes being fed down the chute by two men, one standing either side, taking the pipes from two cradles, again one on each side.

Plastic Pipes

At first, these were just plastic tubes with slits in them. These were followed by coiled plastic piping which allowed drain laying to be fully mechanised. To the best of my recollection the first plastic drains to be used in South Warwickshire were laid in two fields on Glebe Farm, Dorsington, in 1963, the farm then being in the ownership of Norris Potter.

Derrick Clarke became one of the leading drainage contractors in South Warwickshire, and indeed carried out a great deal of work outside our district. He started on his own in a modest way of business in 1964 and his first machine was a Howard Rotapad, using clay pipes. Jim Wheeler joined Derrick in 1970 and by 1975 the firm was using coiled plastic piping.

The next development in 1978 was the purchase of large, self propelled, trenchless draining machine. This laid 60mm pipes, usually at 20 metre spacings.

In 1980, Aqua Pipes was set up to provide the drainage firm with its own supply of plastic piping. This was manufactured by recycling plastic beer crates. Eventually jumbo rolls of plastic piping were developed, each containing 3200 metres of pipe.

D.W.Clarke Ltd. used gravel backfill from the start, which was carted in self unloading trailers. The cost of this backfill accounted for about half the total cost of any scheme.

Not surprisingly, ways and means of reducing the cost of land drainage, without reducing its effectiveness, were much sought after. Clarkes developed the use of 35mm piping laid at 3 metre spacing, with no backfill, for by this time modern technology had made the actual laying of plastic drains a comparatively cheap operation. These were, in fact, lined moles, being connected to a headland main.

Latterly, Derrick Clarke acquired a pilot's licence and his own 'plane. He used aerial photography in his contract drainage work. Derrick was certainly amongst the most innovative of the master drainers of the second half of the 20th century.

Drainage Boom – 20th Century Version

The drainage boom of the 1840s to the 1870s, or thereabouts, was reflected almost exactly one hundred years later in a similar burst of activity. This was triggered by the wartime production campaign and the accompanying programme of land reclamation. The *War Ag* was directly involved, as might be expected. In Warwickshire it ran a contract drainage service, with prisoners of war being employed in drainage gangs. The Drainage Officers drew up the plans for each scheme and there were foremen to supervise the day-to-day work in the field. Although there was a degree of mechanisation, much of the work, especially in the early days, was done by hand. This included cleaning out watercourses and ditches, pipe laying and the construction of outfalls.

With the running down of the *War Ag* field services, which included agricultural contracting as well as drainage work, in the early 1950s, the field was open for private firms to take over. D.W.Clarke Ltd, already mentioned, Barford Farm Services and B.A.Hull Ltd., were the main players in South Warwickshire, to be joined later by the Moretons. Also, one should not forget Eric Fairbrother who was first employed by the *War Ag* as a Drainage Officer and then, until his retirement, by MAFF. During all those years he was busily employed in drawing up drainage schemes, supervising the grant work and so on. He was not only a colleague of mine, but also a valued friend.

During these decades, drainage work, as in the 19th century, was supported by outside finance, this time by direct grant-aid, instead of loans from the Lands Improvement Company as previously. The rate of these grants for ditching, the provision of guard fences, subsoiling and the laying of pipes and the provision of outfalls was increased to a massive 60% in the early 1970s. This was the only tangible result from the Strutt Report on the state of the soils of the country, which was commissioned after the disastrously wet years of the 1960s.

Maintenance and Rejuvenation

Although it was a condition of the granting of aid for drainage work that the systems, once installed, should be maintained properly, unfortunately this was more honoured in the breach than the observance. To the best of my knowledge, no great attempt was made by MAFF field staff to enforce this condition, to carry out inspections to ensure that ditches were scoured properly, outfalls kept in order and moles re-drawn over piped mains when they had ceased to function.

Once a scheme had been completed, one copy of the relevant plan was retained by the farmer or landowner and another deposited on the file in the local MAFF office. Those in private hands were often mislaid and not always passed on to a new occupier. Moreover, and especially in the case of work done in the early days, the plans which should have been held in the MAFF archives were just not there.

The upshot of all this was that, due to lack of maintenance and, to some extent, the loss of records, many fields drained in the 1940s and 1950s had to be re-drained twenty years later.

In passing, one of the features of drainage work and soil management from about 1970 onwards, was the greater use of the subsoiler, both after the completion of a scheme and at regular intervals thereafter. In my own experience, subsoiling could be effective in getting old drains to run again, as the following tale illustrates.

Some years ago, the late Bob Spencer asked me to look at one of the lower fields on Park Farm, Preston-on-Stour which had been drained in the past, but which now lay wet. I found that the ditch and outfall were both in good order; in fact Bob had rodded out the latter to no effect. I suggested it might be worth getting the field sub-soiled before investigating if the system had collapsed at one or more points and going to any further expense. In the event this worked well, the drains began running and the field was dry once again.

Incidentally, about the same time I was treated to an interesting object lesson on the effectiveness of moling. It was on Longdon Manor, a heavy land farm near Shipston-on-Stour, where I was heavily involved for some years.

A new headland main had been laid along the bottom of a nicely sloping field and, on this particular day, the mole plough had started working at the far end. On my way to another field, I noted that the main had already started to run a strong trickle, although only about half a dozen moles had been drawn. By the time I returned some time later, the mole plough had covered nearly two thirds of the field and the outfall was gushing nearly full bore, a satisfying sight.

In some cases, much can be done by clearing outfalls. Even without a plan, it is often possible to make a good guess as to the whereabouts in the ditch these might be; sometimes assisted by a tell-tale trickle amongst the grass and other rubbish in the ditch bank.

One occasion springs to mind when Don Bradshaw was at Sweet Knowle, now better known as the home of the Telly Tubbies. It rained heavily all morning, and fortunately our business was in the farm office. As the morning wore, on we watched the bottom end of a field, which we could see from the office, gradually fill with water until a sizeable lake was formed. After lunch the weather cleared and we set off with a few rods and a spade to see if we could find the outfall, as Don had an inkling that the field, in common with most on the clay, had been drained at some time in the past. Sure enough we found it. Scholarly application of spade and rod produced a satisfying glug and a main drain spouted full bore. And, as we walked the farm, we repeated the exercise some half a dozen times and when we got back the lake had all but disappeared.

Again, on Home Farm, Aston Cantlow, the bottoms of the fields running up to the bank below Newnham lay very wet. Some years ago, Tony and Chris Suffield and I spent a useful afternoon clearing and rodding out the outfalls, which, when the ditch had been cleared, solved the problem.

In the existing economic climate it is very unlikely that extensive new drainage works will be carried out in the foreseeable future in South Warwickshire, and elsewhere for that matter. Existing drainage systems, whenever they were laid down, represent a substantial capital outlay. The above examples do illustrate that these can be made to function effectively again.

With so much more of the heavier land in South Warwickshire under arable cultivation, and with grassland more heavily stocked than it has ever been, the effective maintenance of drainage systems by ditch cleaning, keeping guard fences in repair, attention to outfalls where necessary and re-moling when the old moles have ceased to function, is now more essential than ever. This is more easily said than done. But the ultimate alternative is a reversion to the state of affairs that existed in 1939 (see Chapter 2 *Prelude – the 1930s*).

Finally, I suppose a generation has grown up to whom the name Bobby Boutflour means nothing. He was an agricultural adviser in Wiltshire and then Principal of the Royal Agricultural College, Cirencester, for many years, and was a legend in the farming world in his own lifetime. Much in demand as a speaker at farmers' meetings throughout the length and breadth of the land, he was never at loss for an answer. On one occasion he was asked 'What is the best crop to plant on wet land ?'

'Drainpipes, you fool' came the reply.

Iron Pans

It hardly needs pointing out that most drainage problems are to be found on the heavier land, where the movement of water through the soil profile is very slow, at its best. But in South Warwickshire there is a problem on the lighter river valley soils which over lie a gravelly subsoil. This is caused by iron pans, formed by chemical action at between about 18" and 30" below ground level. If by chance, in the course of digging a hole for a gate post for instance, one brings out a piece of this pan it looks, for all the world, like a lump of concrete that has fallen off a sea wall. It consists of pebbles and sand cemented together by iron compounds formed naturally in the soil and which has the appearance of rust.

The most obvious signs of trouble occur in a dry spring when, say, winter wheat starts to go off in patches over the field. At first sight this looks like an early attack of Takeall with the plants stunted, shrivelling and, in extreme cases, dying on their feet. But there are no characteristic lesions on the base of the stem and the tell tale 'tink, tink, tink' as the soil auger strikes the pan and confirms its presence.

In a dry time, these symptoms appear in late May or early June and are caused, quite simply, by water stress. The soil moisture above the pan becomes exhausted and the crop plants die from drought, the pan preventing the roots penetrating downwards in search of water. Conversely, in a wet winter, surface ponding can occur because the pan inhibits the drainage. Subsoiling is the answer, but when the pan is thick the going can be tough.

14. FERTILISERS

Those of us who have been around long enough and have good memories will recall that in the 1930s, and even into the 1940s, the use of inorganic fertilisers was the target of as much criticism as is now levelled at crop protection chemicals today. Nor was it confined to *urbans*; prejudice against fertilisers extended into the more backward sectors of the farming community.

This was particularly the case with nitrogenous fertilisers, and Sulphate of Ammonia was the one most commonly used at that time. It was considered that the use of such fertilisers drew the land, in other words left soil fertility in a worse state than before. There was some substance to this view if such applications were not supported by the addition of phosphates and potash, according to soil type and the crop being grown.

In South Warwickshire, there were farmers who would not, under any circumstances, have applied Sulphate of Ammonia to their fields but were more than happy to use fish manure at rates which supplied the same amount of nitrates. Some of this was the genuine stuff; most, one hopes. But at least one manufacturer, whose product was used widely in South Warwickshire, heavily laced fish manure with Sulphate of Ammonia. Indeed, one got the impression, on examining a sample, that just enough fish manure was added to the inorganic fertiliser to give the final product the authentic aroma.

Fertilisers during the War years in the 1940s were rationed. The ration of phosphatic and potassic fertilisers was adjusted to soil type. For instance, those farming the phosphate deficient clays, such as those in South Warwickshire, would receive an extra ration of phosphates, while farmers on chalky, downland soils naturally lacking in potash, would also be favoured with an extra allocation.

Permits were issued to farmers authorising them to purchase their fertiliser allocation. As these were eventually returned to the WAEC via the merchants, it was possible to find out which farmers had not purchased any fertiliser at all. One of my jobs as a District Advisor was to visit such men, or women, to encourage them to buy and apply what fertilisers had been allocated to them.

These were invariably farmers of less than outstanding ability, to put it as kindly as possible, and who conducted their agricultural affairs on a financial shoestring, because they had no choice. A common comment when the matter of fertilisers was raised was, 'You don't want to buy the crop before you have sown it.' An admission, in effect, that they had not the necessary cash and an opinion that, even if they had, no advantage would accrue.

One character, standing in a crop of wheat in full ear, which came to just about his knees, reacted to the suggestion that some fertiliser might have helped by spitting smartly into the wind and pronouncing 'I uses farmyard.' He had, of course, a filthy waistcoat, so this must have been his usual manner of pronouncing himself.

There is now a general appreciation of the importance of fertilisers in crop and grassland production and of the role of the three major plant foods – nitrates, phosphates and potash, also that of the so-called trace elements. All these are discussed in some detail below.

This has resulted in the fact that one of the outstanding features of both grassland and arable farming in the last half century has been the dramatic increase in the use of fertilisers, both straights and mixtures of the main plant food elements or 'compounds.'

This has been one, but not the only one, of the factors responsible for the great increase in yields from crops and grass. To take one example of special importance to farming in South Warwickshire, the yields of winter wheat. In the 1940s, the national average was under 1 ton/acre, possibly a little higher in our district. Today, a yield of less than 3 tons/acre is considered disappointing, an increase by a factor of three in half a century.

Nitrogenous Fertilisers

As already pointed out, Sulphate of Ammonia was the most commonly used nitrogenous fertiliser in the 1940s and for some time after that. Nitro-Chalk was also popular. It had the advantage of being a granular material, of not having the acidifying effect of Sulphate of Ammonia on some soils and it was alleged to be more clover friendly when used on grassland. Nitrate of Soda had been around for very many years and was much valued as a top-dressing for roots, especially mangolds.

Today all these materials are things of the past and the standard nitrogenous fertiliser contains 34.5% N and is marketed under a number of trade names. One of the features of arable and grassland husbandry in the second half of the 20th century has been the very considerable increase in the use of this type of fertiliser. This has been one of the most potent means of raising yields of both crops and grass.

Nitrates in Water Supplies

Although this is not a problem in South Warwickshire, the Leam is the only river in the county where nitrate levels give cause for concern. Mention must be made of the subject, if only because so much misinformation on the matter has been, and still is being, put about by the media.

To put the matter in a nutshell, farmers have been accused of using excessive amounts of nitrogenous fertilisers to boost yields, thus creating unwanted grain mountains, at the same time raising the nitrate content of river water and other sources. This is harmful to human health, so the story runs, because nitrates in excess can cause stomach cancer and blue baby syndrome. These allegations are either absolute untruths or, at best, only half truths. The nonsense is compounded by the fact that the standards for nitrate content in water supplies, as laid down in the relevant EU Directive, are twice as stringent as those accepted by other authorities.

The Standards

In this country the water supply authorities are required by our laws to provide wholesome water to consumers. In the case of nitrate levels, the World Health Organisation Standards, issued in 1977, have been adopted to define what is, and what is not wholesome. These are as follows:

Recommended concentration	50mg/litre
Acceptable concentration	50 to 100 mg/litre
Not recommended	More than 100 mg/litre

Nitrate levels in water (ex World Health Organisation)

These standards were accepted and endorsed by the Department of the Environment/ Department of Health and Social Security Joint Committee on the Medical Aspects of Water Quality, and also by the Royal Commission on Environmental Pollution (Seventh Report Agriculture and Pollution, 1979). Thus, in view of the weight of such authoritative opinion, there can hardly be any doubt that a concentration of 50 to 100 mg/litre of nitrates is acceptable. Yet Brussels insists on a standard which is twice as stringent i.e. 50 mg/litre. The problem, therefore, is the creation of EU bureaucracy because public water supplies in the UK are already within the 50 to 100 mg/litre criterion.

The Nitrate Story

By far the greatest proportion of nitrogenous fertilisers applied to UK farmland is used on cereal crops, both autumn and spring sown. This is spread from about the beginning of March through to mid-May at the very latest. Thus, if high nitrate levels in rivers are due to excessive use of these fertilisers on arable land, one would expect these levels to rise throughout the growing season, possibly reaching a peak in early July. Summer rainfall and high soil temperatures produce soluble nitrates very quickly.

But this is just not so. The nitrate concentration in river water starts to rise in September and continues to do so throughout the autumn until the peak is reached towards the end of the year. Moreover, it is possible to label the nitrogen contained in fertilisers and to monitor its use. It has been found that, providing these fertilisers are applied at the recommended rates, and no farmer is likely to exceed these on the grounds of cost alone, all but 1% of the nitrates applied as fertiliser is utilised by the crop. So where do the nitrates come from that cause the annual autumn rise in concentrations of nitrates in river waters?

The answer is by the natural process of nitrification which takes place in the soil. Microbes are constantly breaking down organic matter that is present after harvest in the form of plant roots, stubble, straw and the remains of grass swards which were ploughed out the previous year, not to mention any slurry, farmyard manure or compost, all much beloved by organic farmers. One of the end points of this process is an ample supply of soil nitrates. As there is no crop on the land at that time to utilise them fully, they find their way into land drains, ditches, watercourses and eventually into rivers. (See *Farming, Fertilisers and the Nitrate Problem*, (1991), Addiscott, Whitmore & Powlson, Rothamsted Experimental Station)

This is all very regrettable. Mother Nature is clearly not conversant with the relevant EU Directive. Even if she was, she might find it difficult to restrain the natural exuberance of soil bacteria, happily pumping nitrates into river water every autumn in defiance of the Brussels bureaucrats.

But these are the facts. The assertion that the excessive use of nitrogenous fertiliser is the direct cause of high concentrations of nitrates in river waters is a fiction. Moreover, concentrations of nitrates in deep aquifers are due to soil nitrates released from grassland ploughed out during the food production campaign of the 1940s, which over the years have percolated through soils, sub-soils and the underlying geological formations to eventually reach the deepest sources of water.

Stomach Cancer

The statement is often made in the press and other media that nitrates in drinking water cause stomach cancer. Often as a throwaway line, the implication being that this is a well known fact that hardly needs repeating. But this hardly fits in with the fact that the incidence of stomach cancer has been falling as the tonnage of nitrogenous fertilisers applied has, until recently, been rising. To be more precise, two studies have shown that if there is any correlation between nitrate levels in water and the incidence of stomach cancer, it is a negative one.

The first was carried out by a group of doctors from the Radcliffe Infirmary, Oxford. Two areas in the UK, in one of which the incidence of stomach cancer was unusually high and the other where the reverse was the case were surveyed.

In the former the incidence of stomach cancer was twice as high as in the latter, a big difference. It was found that in the low risk area the concentration of nitrates in the water supply was twice as high as in the high risk area. Clearly, there was no relationship between the incidence of stomach cancer and the nitrate concentration in water sources.

Another study (Beresford, 1985) involved 229 urban districts during the years 1963 to 1973. The result was the same. If there was any correlation, it was negative one. High risk of stomach cancer, low concentrations of nitrates, and vice versa, were the results.

Thus there is no evidence at all to link the incidence of stomach cancer with high concentrates of nitrates in the water supply – another fiction.

Blue Baby Syndrome

The unqualified statement has been put out by the media on numerous occasions that high nitrate levels are the cause of this disorder. No mention is ever made of the fact that this is a very rare disease. The last death from the condition in the UK occurred in 1950 and the last confirmed case in 1972. Nor that Blue Baby syndrome has always been associated with privately dug wells, which are likely to be already contaminated with bacteria. Indeed, Addiscot, Whitmore and Powlson (*ibid.*), state they have been unable to find any reference to this condition ever being associated with a reliable public water supply.

Since writing the above, the UK Government declared, in the late 1990s and at the behest of the EU, that much of the country should be a Nitrate Vulnerable Zone. This will impose restrictions on the spreading of slurry and farmyard manure, leading to additional costs for storage and may well restrict the rates of application for nitrogenous fertilisers, and thus stocking rates.

There is no scientific nor medical justification for this action, which is based on fiction not fact. In any case, what proportion of water used for domestic and industrial consumption is actually drunk or used in cooking? Even in the home, most water is used for washing, showering, bathing and flushing. We live in an Alice-in-Wonderland world.

Phosphates

This plant food is particularly important in South Warwickshire, especially on the Lias clay. But much of the poorer land in the Arden was also deficient in phosphate at the beginning of the food production campaign in 1939.

The South Warwickshire clays are highly alkaline, usually amply supplied with potash, but in their natural state desperately short of phosphate. The use of soluble phosphatic fertilisers was really the key to successful crops during the ploughing out campaign during the Second World War.

Many, if not most, of the imported corn drills at that time were combine drills, where the fertiliser was put down the same coulter as the seed and, thus, in close proximity to the germinating seed. This saved valuable imported phosphate, since very much less of this fertiliser could be used when the crop was combine drilled, compared with broadcasting. Three cwt./acre of 18% powdered superphosphate or 1 cwt./acre of granular triple superphosphate were the standard dressings.

If, during drilling, one of the fertiliser spouts got blocked there was a tell-tale row of stunted corn from headland to headland. A winter wheat plant starved of phosphate in this way had a characteristic appearance; shorter than its fellows with a spiky, erect form of growth akin to winter oats, and leaves all shades of purple with a tinge of yellow.

While the phosphate status of the Warwickshire clays has improved immeasurably over the years, the process took a long time. Eventually, it was found at the Drayton Experimental Husbandry Farm that a good dressing of phosphatic fertiliser every four years, or so, sufficed to maintain the high status and provide for crop needs.

Today the combine drill has been outmoded as being too slow. Also, with the phosphate status much improved compared to fifty years ago, the need for combine drilling is a thing of the past. With modern fertiliser spreaders and wider drills sowing corn only, and seed and fertiliser coming in half-tonne bags which can be handled mechanically, it is quicker and easier to broadcast fertiliser before drilling.

Basic Slag had been the traditional source of phosphate for many years, but changes in the methods of steel production no longer produce it as a by-product. It was generally accepted and widely used, particularly to improve grassland. Applied at the rate of about half a ton per acre, it had a very beneficial effect on the clover content of a sward. It was, however, considered death to mushrooms which in the 1920s and 1930s were a much valued cash crop on those farms fortunate enough to have mushroom fields.

From time to time in the 1950s, some firms were peddling ground mineral phosphate, as a cheaper source than superphosphate. This former was crude mineral phosphate rock ground to a fine powder. Trials had proved this to be an economical and effective fertiliser on land that was acid and situated in areas of high rainfall. As South Warwickshire has an average rainfall of only 25"/year below the 400' contour, and only 28" above, and as the soils were predominantly alkaline, this material was all but useless. But as a NAAS District Advisor, I got into trouble by writing and saying so publicly.

There was another phosphatic fertiliser that made a brief appearance and was equally ineffective. Again, this was mineral phosphate finely ground and treated in such a way that it was alleged to be converted into a soluble phosphate in the soil. But it did not work as the following story indicates.

A farmer on the clay asked me to investigate a two year ley of red clover and ryegrass, which looked sick to put it mildly. I diagnosed acute phosphate deficiency, the severity of which I had not seen for many a year. This was later confirmed by soil analysis, and also by the fact that part of an adjoining field had been let for growing cauliflowers, the grower having given this piece of ground 2 cwt./acre of triple superphosphate. In the process of turning the distributor, he had given a similar dressing in parts to the adjoining wheat crop, with dramatic results in the improved appearance of the wheat so treated.

Our man was most indignant when I pointed all this out to him. For he had been applying this treated phosphate rock at 5 cwt./acre over much of the farm, at this rate being more expensive than conventional soluble phosphatic fertilisers. In short, it was just as ineffective as ground mineral phosphate, but without the virtue of cheapness.

He was one of those men who never made a mistake, but never. The managing director of the firm which manufactured this product arrived and spun our friend a good yarn, which was apparently accepted. I was considered not to know what I was talking about and complaints were made. The truth can cause trouble. But a year later there were bags of triple superphosphate stacked in the yard and visible from the road. One of life's minor triumphs!

Potash

As already described, clays are normally rich in potash. One exception in South Warwickshire would be river meadows on silty clay which had, over several generations, been cut every year for hay. As they were usually far from the homestead they had had little or no farmyard manure, which, in any case, would normally be reserved for application to the arable land. Many hundreds of soil analyses of such meadows, carried out over a number of years, indicated a shortage of potash. Perhaps, not surprisingly, since hay had been carted off every year without the potash being replaced.

Cereals on clayland did not respond to applications of potash, but there were some indications that field beans did. Dressings of potash were, and are, necessary for potash-loving crops such as potatoes, sugar beet, mangolds and horticultural crops.

In contrast to the Feldon, some soils in the Arden have been found to be potash deficient. With the extended use of compound fertilisers, there may be some possibility that potash is now being applied at luxury levels to many soils and crops.

Lime

Although the Warwickshire clays, being naturally alkaline, are not in need of lime, there are many soils in South Warwickshire which are in need of regular applications. The areas of potentially acid soils lie along the county boundary with Worcestershire from Earlswood, near Birmingham, in the north, to Salford Priors in the south. Again, much land in an arc northwards from Alcester to Claverdon needs liming from time to time.

So great was the need for lime in some of the northern and western parishes in South Warwickshire that in 1944 the Soil Chemistry Department at Harper Adams Agricultural College carried out a programme of soil testing in them, in an attempt to persuade farmers to meet whatever lime requirements might be revealed, follow-up visits being made for this purpose.

At that time, lime was being practically given away with a 75% subsidy on the cost. In the days of transport restrictions in the 1940s, the lime needs in South Warwickshire were supplied from quarries in the Cotswolds. This was yellowish in colour, compared to the white of the Buxton lime, a source more familiar to those who used lime. There was strong prejudice against the Cotswold lime, which was held to be less effective in action to the Buxton variety, something which was not so.

But the lime business had a lighter side, unlikely as this might seem. There was one character who had waste lime delivered free by the British Oxygen Company, presumably being only to glad to dump this waste product somewhere. When passing the farm, one might see great white mounds of the stuff tipped on the roadside verge opposite the buildings. Then one knew a grubby postcard would soon arrive at the Stratford CAEC office demanding the subsidy on a non-existent cost, but which, nevertheless was considered due.

In the 1950s, some reps from these lime supplying companies were, on occasion, none too scrupulous. For it was easy to fake a lime test by surreptitiously dipping a finger in the test fluid, which promptly turned the required orange, indicating a need for lime. No matter how clean one's hands are, there are sweaty residues which are invariably acid. One such sold 600 tons of lime to a farmer on the Lias clay and was duly threatened with court action when the purchaser was made aware of the facts. This never came to court, being settled by the firm concerned to avoid publicity. This sort of misdemeanour was short lived for the word soon got round, as it does in farming circles.

Trace Elements

All crops need an adequate supply of these which include manganese, boron, copper, zinc, iron and molybdenum. In days gone by, basic slag supplied these in quantity. Liming materials also contained trace elements, whereas farmyard manure and slurry re-cycled them.

By far the most common trace element deficiency in South Warwickshire is that caused by the lack of manganese. When winter oats were commonly grown, these were the most susceptible crop on the clayland, manganese deficiency being most common on soils of high alkalinity. In oats this condition is known as Grey Speck.

But winter wheat can often show the symptoms. These are a greying, almost whitening, of the leaves. A weakness occurs about two thirds of the way up the leaf, which often bends over at the tip. The symptoms can be seen at a distance and usually occur after a spell of dry, cold weather when growth is at a standstill. The condition is often transitory and the crop will recover and grow out of it after some warm rain. There are certain roadside fields in the district which, almost invariably show these symptoms in the above conditions. When the condition is severe, the cure is cheap and simple: an application of manganese sulphate.

ADAS experiments have shown that a yield or quantity benefit from the application of trace elements is unlikely unless a specific deficiency has been diagnosed. In other words, blanket applications of a mixture of trace elements would not be worthwhile. This is the view I always took, following the party line, until experience proved otherwise.

For some ten years, I was much involved in the arable management of a 300 acre farm near Loxley. There was one field of some twenty acres which was a problem. It had had the full treatment, drained, sub-soiled, and well fertilised, and then corn drilled into a decent seedbed. Even then winter wheat, or winter barley, never looked right in May, even after good spring weather.

Martin Shaw, one time spray contractor and now an agronomist with the farmers' co-operative, Countrywide, was a keen advocate of routine applications of a cocktail of trace elements. At one of his Open Days, held on this occasion at Barton Farm, Alderminster, he demonstrated very clearly the beneficial effect on root growth that his mixture of trace elements had had. On the field at Loxley there was no doubt that this was exactly what the crop of winter barley needed and the cocktail was duly applied with a miraculous result.

It may well be that the ADAS approach would have achieved the same end. But the cost of the necessary investigation and analyses would not have been trivial, and certainly much more than the cost of the mixture of trace elements.

15. Crop Protection Chemicals

The increased use of herbicides, fungicides and insecticides has been one of the main criticisms of modern agricultural technology during the last fifty years or so. Needless to say, the frequency and volume of complaint is in inverse proportion to knowledge of the subject, to the realities of making a living from the land and to the relationship between yield and economic crop production. For, if food, of any kind, is not produced at a profit, it will not be produced at all. If anyone doubts the truth of that statement, let him or her, enquire as to the state of farming in this country during the last quarter of the 19th century or between the two World Wars.

Farmers are being told on every possible occasion that they must compete, eventually, on the world market. What is not mentioned, or spelt out, is how they are to do this if they are to be denied access to the use of modern crop protection chemicals, used freely by their overseas competitors, or if a pesticide tax, one that their competitors do not have to bear, is imposed on UK farmers.

By constant propaganda, often put out with scant regard to the facts, environmental groups have persuaded sections of the media and some members of the public that many foodstuffs are saturated with chemicals which are injurious to health. This is the basis of the so-called organic movement.

The purchase of organic produce is certainly elitist, in the sense that those who have to watch the housekeeping money cannot afford the luxury of indulging their gullibility. One example will suffice. For instance, recently (autumn 2000) a cauliflower in a Stratford supermarket was priced at 45p. One of precisely the same size, but of inferior appearance, on the organic shelf cost £1 25. In addition it is said that some 75% of organic produce is imported, and, by definition, of doubtful provenance.

It is, of course, unkind to confuse the critics of modern farming with the facts, they are more concerned with the fiction. But the following analyses refer to various foods, all grown in the conventional manner, selected at random from shops.

Batches of fruit were bought over the counter.

Pesticide residues were found in 32 samples (11.07%) only.

In all but 3 samples (1.04%), the amounts detected were within the permitted Maximum Residue Level (MRL), in the determination of which a large safety margin is already built.

Advisory Committee on Pesticides Annual Report, 1997

2187 food samples were tested.

98% of these had residues below the legal maximum.

Of these, 73% had no detectable residues.

26% contained residues below the permitted MRL.

1.3% contained residues above MRL. In particular, imported pears had residues above MRL; the use of the material involved is banned in the U.K.

Working Party on Pesticides Residues Annual Report, 1998

29% of the food samples tested were recorded as having pesticide residues detected in them.

Only 1.6% of these had residues in excess of the MLR.

Working Party on Pesticides Residues Annual Report, 1999

The only significant cases were Methamidor Phos in Spanish sweet peppers and another chemical in pears. Neither of these were considered to pose a health risk.

These results can hardly be taken as painting a picture of a wide range of foods contaminated with the residues of crop protection chemicals, still less of these posing any health problems. Those who are prepared to pay an extra 80p for a cauliflower clearly have more money than sense.

But misinformation and unsubstantiated reports on the use, or alleged misuse, of crop protection chemicals are commonplace. Two examples spring to mind.

At-Risk Rambling?

Some years ago, the Ramblers Association published a cartoon, one side of which depicted ramblers in shorts and shirt sleeves happily walking through the countryside with the sun shining, birds singing, and the rest. The other side showed people dressed in what appeared to be space suits, again walking through a crop, with a plane spraying pesticides from a grey sky. The message conveyed was that those who took their leisure walking in the countryside were clearly at risk from pesticide residues in crops.

A most curious assertion in view of my own lifetime experience and that of several thousands like me, not to mention farmers and those who work for them. For fifty years from 1943 to 1993, or thereabouts, I spent a great deal of my working life not only walking headlands of arable fields but also through the crop itself, often criss-crossing from one headland to the other.

This was in the process of inspecting potatoes, grass and clover, seed crops, and cereals for seed certification. But also, and to a far greater extent, walking into cereal crops throughout the growing season to assess levels of weed, disease and insect infestations. In every case, every crop had been sprayed at least once and many as much as three or four times before I had ventured into them. Only when inspecting herbage seed crops would I have worn wellies and waterproof overtrousers. This for the very good reason that growth stage was all-important in the inspection process and, thus, the schedule tight. One had to keep going whatever the weather in May and June.

Normally the gear would be thin drill trousers, farm boots and shirtsleeves. At the end of many a working day, my trousers would be stained green with the cell sap of corn or potatoes. If anyone should have suffered from the effects of chemical residues in sprayed crops when walking through them, it should have been me and all those engaged in crop inspections over a working lifetime. The contrary is the case, having enjoyed very many years of excellent health. I have never heard of any fellow agronomists suffering any ill effects.

To suggest, in any way, that those who choose to take their leisure walking in the countryside can come to any harm from contact with crops which have been sprayed is nonsense and completely contrary to the facts.

There is also another aspect to this. If a farmer or landowner applies to divert a footpath round the headland, instead of going straight across a field, it is absolutely certain that the local branch of the Ramblers Association will object as a matter of course, irrespective of the merits of the case. This needs some explanation. For if the Ramblers Association really believes that its members are at risk in health terms through contact with sprayed crops, one would have thought that it would have welcomed such diversions, instead of opposing them on principle. For a footpath through a field exposes walkers to contact with the crop on both sides. While walking along a headland contact can be on one side only, halving the imaginary danger!

The case of the blinded hare

The second example is the story (or possibly the myth) of the allegedly blinded hare. Some years ago a report appeared in the Stratford Herald to the effect that a hare had been blinded by sulphuric acid spray which was being used to burn off a potato crop on a farm near Stratford. This statement was made at a meeting entitled *Meet the Farmer*, which was arranged by the Stratford Branch of the National Farmers' Union a week or so previous to the report appearing. The meeting was mainly for the benefit of townspeople, whether or not they lived in the country.

This aroused my interest for two reasons. First, I could well recall when sulphuric acid was used as a herbicide, many hundreds of acres being sprayed annually in South Warwickshire alone, and I had never heard of wildlife of any kind suffering in consequence. Secondly, at the time I was writing a farming column in The Herald, and I was determined to find out the details of the allegation, if, indeed, this was possible.

In the first place, the use of sulphuric acid was, at the time, approved under the *Code of Practice for the Agricultural and Horticultural Use of Pesticides.* Secondly, I enquired of my colleagues in MAFF, and especially from those engaged in the monitoring of the effect of pesticides on wildlife, as to whether they had had reports of harm arising from the use of sulphuric acid as a desiccant from anywhere in the country. My informants were not aware of any problem, which was not surprising. Because if the opposite had been the case, this material would not have been approved for use in this way.

Next I concentrated my enquiries on the origin of this statement which had been made in a public meeting. The information had been volunteered to members of The Friends of the Earth by someone who was thought to be a farm worker and was rumoured (and only rumoured) to have had the sack and was under notice to quit his house. The alleged finding of the blinded hare in, or near, a field which had been sprayed with this acid had taken place in August of the previous year, or just over twelve months previous to the above meeting. As far as I could gather, the hare had never been produced, let alone examined professionally. Finally, the original informant had left the district and could not be traced.

If this farm worker, if indeed he was one, reported this alleged incident under the circumstances he was thought to be in, some will draw their own conclusions as to his motive. The allegation made publicly, and reported in the Press, that a hare had been blinded on a local farm by acid spray more than twelve months previously, could not be substantiated nor confirmed in any way.

This was the fact of the matter, which died quietly without being picked up by the national press. The headlines could be imagined, with every environmental group in full cry. How many stories of a similar kind, which receive a great deal more publicity, have any more substance?

Safety Measures

Of course, no mention is ever made by environmental groups, nor by the media, of the whole raft of measures that are taken as a matter of routine to ensure that the use of crop protection chemicals of every kind is safe, and harmless to wildlife, the environment and the consumer.

In the first place, every pesticide has to be officially approved and listed before its commercial use is allowed. Exhaustive tests are carried out over a period of time in respect of the factors listed above. Indeed, many promising materials are rejected at any stage in their development, however late, if they fail to meet rigid safety criteria.

Once this process has been completed, the chemical is placed on the Approved List and marketed with instructions regulating every aspect of its use, which have to be adhered to.

Next, those involved in the marketing, sale and advising on the use of crop protection chemicals have to be registered under the BASIS scheme as being competent, both technically and as regards the safe environmental use of the materials. This registration is renewed annually, and the individuals concerned have to demonstrate that they have taken all the necessary measures during the previous year to keep themselves up to date with recent developments.

When the product is delivered to the farm, it has to be stored in a building which is secure and suited to the purpose. Again, the specification which an on-farm chemical store has to meet is set out in detail in the appropriate regulations. Next, the farm worker, or farmer, has to pass a proficiency test and hold a certificate of competence before he, or she, is permitted to operate a sprayer. Once a field has been sprayed, a log book has to be entered up detailing time and date, the material used, its concentration, weather conditions, including wind speed and direction. Finally, there are rules and regulations concerning how and where the sprayer can be washed out when the operation has been completed for the day.

In short, any crop protection chemical has to undergo rigorous tests even before it is available commercially. Once on the farm, its storage and use are regulated and recorded in every detail. So much so that I recall a conversation I had with a leading farmer of broad acres in the district, which turned to the subject of spraying. 'We have so-and-so to do all our spraying every year.' I expressed some surprise at this, in view of the arable acreage involved. 'Too much red tape, easier to leave it to the expert,' was the comment.

Herbicides

Prior to the introduction of herbicides for farm crops, land was kept clean by traditional methods. These including adhering to a more or less strict rotation, which included a substantial acreage of spring corn as well as that drilled in the autumn, the growing of root crops which allowed of inter-row cultivations and hand hoeing, a full fallow, a half fallow following the breaking out of a ley, and stale seedbeds. In this day and age, and in view of the economic pressures now exerted on farming by government and consumers, many of these practices would be hopelessly uneconomic. Nor would it be possible to find the labour at agricultural wage rates. Chemical herbicides have come to stay, there can be no going back as some seem to assume.

In the early 1940s, the only herbicide available was sulphuric acid or Brown Oil of Vitriol, to give it its old name. It was unpleasant and dangerous to use, and extremely corrosive. The *War Ag* machinery depots carried out sulphuric acid spraying on a contract basis. The sprayers were converted to tractor use and consisted of a wooden barrel and a pump driven by gearing from one of the wheels. The pumps, spray booms and nozzles did not last long, thanks to the acid. It was not uncommon, towards the end of the season, to be forced to cannibalise two sprayers to make a third one serviceable.

Sulphuric Acid, at a rate of 10 to 12% in 100 gallons of water/acre, was most effective against charlock and its close relative, wild radish. It also had some effect on some other weeds which were normally considered a minor problem. These first two were common enough in the district. For example the fields on Billesley Manor Farm, which butted onto the Stratford-Alcester road, were yellow every year with charlock. The fields on Alveston Hill Farm, along Pimlico Lane, supported a healthy population of wild radish.

Selectivity, that is the ability to kill the weed while leaving the crop unharmed, depended entirely on the physical nature of the leaves. Charlock and Wild Radish had broad, hairy leaves which retained the spray, thus killing the plant, while wheat (the only cereal which could be sprayed) had narrow, shiny leaves which shed the herbicide with only a minimum of scorching.

Dinitro-ortho-cresol (DNOC) became available about 1945 and was used extensively for a number of years. It had the great advantage of being non-corrosive, but it was very poisonous and left a bright yellow stain on skin, clothing etc. Those were the days when regulations regarding the use of sprays were virtually non existent. Certainly, in the early days, its toxicity was not appreciated fully and protective clothing was rarely worn.

In consequence everything was yellow: jackets, shirts, trousers, hands, sandwiches, fags and the dogs. Why there were not more casualties is a mystery. Latterly, safety precautions were taken more seriously. Protective clothing became the norm and those in frequent contact, such as contract sprayers, had to have regular blood tests.

DNOC did give control of a wider range of weeds than sulphuric acid. These included poppies, fathen and the mayweeds to mention a few of the more troublesome ones in corn in South Warwickshire. It would also give some control of cleavers, but only if the plants were young.

MCPA and 2-4-D were the first of the so-called hormone weedkillers, and the forerunners of the host of herbicides in use today. They acted in an entirely different way to acid and DNOC, not burning but interfering with the metabolism of the target weeds, while leaving the cereals unaffected. These first became available as a dust, and then in liquid form a year or two later.

In 1945, limited supplies of powder in paper lined sandbags were made available for trial work on a national scale. Stencilled on these bags were the mysterious letters CLC which, we were told, stood for *Corn Land Cleaner*. To the best of my knowledge, the first field in South Warwickshire to be treated with the new wonder dust was that lying in the angle between the main road from Stratford to Warwick and the lane leading to Hatton Rock on one of the farms belonging to Clyde Higgs.

Corn Buttercup

These materials were effective against all the cruciferous weeds, corn buttercup and cornflower. But several important weed species were resistant. These included the mayweeds, corn marigold, knot-grass, chickweed and, of course, cleavers. Arguably, corn buttercup was the most important additional weed to be controlled on South Warwickshire farms. Sometimes called crowfoot, it could nearly smother young corn if the infestation was exceptionally heavy. But, within a comparatively short time after the introduction of these new herbicides, corn buttercup was eliminated completely from arable land. So much so that in the early 1970s, when walking a field on Longdon Manor, near Shipston-on-Stour, with Anthony Forsyth, we came across an odd plant and Anthony, of all people, asked me what it was. In spite of being one of the leading clayland arable farmers in the district, but of the new generation, he had never seen corn buttercup.

Perennial Weeds

These new herbicides were also useful in suppressing, if not killing, perennial weeds in arable crops. Docks and thistles could, at least be prevented from flowering and were contorted into twisted shapes so that they did not compete with, or grow up into, the crop. On permanent grassland, the continued use of 2-4-D, in particular, for a number of seasons, could give a good control of the creeping thistle.

A welcome side effect of the use of MCPA was a considerable reduction, over South Warwickshire as a whole, of the wild onion. This was a pest of the heavier land, with its high proportion of winter corn. It tainted the threshed corn; the only remedy to get rid of the taint was to leave the sacks open, with a stick stuck into the middle from top to bottom. In grassland, milk would be tainted both by grazing and in hay. Nobody ever claimed that the herbicide would control wild onion, but the fact remains that it became very much less of a problem with the continuing use of MCPA.

Powder v. Liquid

MCPA and 2-4-D are both non-corrosive and non-toxic under conditions of normal, practical use. In dust form, the powder consisted of 99% filler and 1%

active ingredient. The plate and flicker type of fertiliser distributor was best for applying the dust but the weight per acre had to be at least 2 cwt., hence the need for a large proportion of filler. Although their use in the powder form was short lived, the new materials were a great advance in terms of logistics; 2 cwt. per acre, instead of 100 gallons of water/acre. No longer could the *War Ag* sprayers be seen trundling across the Wild Radish infested fields along Pimlico Lane. Instead I have an abiding vision of Mr. Griffiths, who then farmed at Alveston Hill, following a horse drawn plate and flicker distributor, applying the new magic powder.

But it was not long before the dust was superseded by the liquid form. In the first place, the material was cheaper, as less active ingredient per acre was needed. Secondly, a new generation of crop sprayers was in the offing, and several makes became available in the early 1950s, notably the Ransomes Cropguard with its vertical, blue tank, which became a familiar sight in the district. These sprayers could use very much less water per acre, some 30 to 50 gallons, instead of 100 gallons as formerly.

Not surprisingly, MCPA and 2-4-D were rapidly adopted by farmers. So much so, that the 1949 edition of Watson and Moore's *Agriculture* contains reference to these new materials, after only two or three years in commercial use. As a footnote, it can be recorded that of the two, MCPA was the better herbicide, at any rate for cereals. Bad timing, and particularly late application, with 2-4-D could lead to ear distortion. But 2-4-D had the advantage of being cheaper and its use was promoted by one manufacturer/retailer for longer than it should have been.

Continuing Development

From the late 1950s onwards, a range of herbicides was developed which were capable of dealing with almost every weed known to arable farmers, with only a few exceptions.

One landmark was the introduction of CMPP in the early 1950s, which controlled cleavers, for which there had been, up to that time, no really effective material. This was a widespread and pernicious weed, dragging any cereal crop down, making harvesting, whether by binder or combine, a slow, tiresome business. The control by chemical means was a real breakthrough. But CMPP was by no means the end of the story, other even more effective chemicals continued to be developed and marketed.

Wild Oats

With wartime overcropping (in terms of the husbandry practices of the day) wild oats had become an acute problem. The development of a selective herbicide for the control of this weed in cereals seemed a challenge that would be impossible to meet, so closely related were the crop plant and weed. But it was done.

The first spray was incorporated into the seedbed for spring barley, Avadex being one of the chemicals first available commercially. The variety Proctor was susceptible to this herbicide, so others had to be sown. Nor could the crop be undersown if Avadex was used, but there were alternatives.

Fig. 9 Headland spraying against Sterile and Soft Brome. Richard Cripps and adapted sprayer. (1970s)

Suffix, the first wild oat herbicide to be applied into the growing crop was under trial at Drayton in 1972, followed later by Shell's Commando. Again, there has been continuing development of materials for the improving control of wild oats and other grass weeds, notably blackgrass.

The Bromes and Onion Couch

As one problem is solved another appears. Over the passage of years herbicides of all kinds were continually being developed and improved in terms of safety, selectivity, economy and in the range of weeds that each could control. However, the brome grasses and onion couch appeared as serious and comparatively new problems in the 1970s and 1980s.

The brome grasses, both Soft and Sterile, had always been with us but usually as headland grasses, invading the field from the hedge bottoms. When herbage seed inspecting, one had always to have been on the look-out for infestations of this kind. Very often, instructions had to be left to cut and make into hay a headland so many yards wide around a particular field. Certification depending upon this being done.

Fig. 10 Tom Mahon at Portobello Farm. Oilseed rape with headland kept clean by rotavating.

Author's note:- Clean tidy farming (good husbandry) now politically and environmentally incorrect! Sterile and soft bromes, natives of South Warwickshire hedge bottoms, have always been the bane of herbage seed growers and, later, with all arable farms have both become invasive. Prevention is better than cure either by spraying or rotavating a headland strip

But in these decades, patches of brome started to appear in the body of many a field. Undoubtedly this was due to the widespread adoption of minimal cultivation techniques, instead of ploughing, in the preparation of autumn seedbeds.

Why onion couch suddenly reared its ugly head on so many fields is something of a mystery. It was always a difficult weed to control. I well recall seeing Hedley Longford of Alveston Hill, harrowing onion couch out and burning it in a field on his Broad Marston farm one year during the War. Many years later, when John Hutchings and I were judging cereals entered in a crop competition in Oxfordshire, we came across field after field heavily infested with onion couch.

As far as the bromes were concerned, a return to conventional ploughing, possibly combined with a stale seedbed technique was advocated. But eventually chemical control became a possibility. In the case of onion couch, a pre-harvest application of Roundup was effective. This was tried before the practice was approved on a farm in Dorsington parish in 1979 or 1980. Again, more conventional chemical control became common place in later years.

The emphasis in the above has been exclusively on weed control in cereals, the most important cash crops in South Warwickshire. But, of course, equal progress has been made with the chemical control of weeds in other crops such as potatoes, sugar beet and horticultural crops. The first two have always been of minor importance, while the husbandry of the latter is beyond the scope of this book. However, mention must now be made of couch and its chemical control, as well as other materials of general application.

Couch

Couch, or squitch, like the poor, has always been with us. Formerly, control of this perennial weed depended entirely on a full or half fallow, or working to the surface, collecting and burning. Needless to say the hunt for a method of chemical control began in the 1950s.

The first materials to become available included TCA, Aminotriazole and Dalapon. While these were all advances in their own way, they were not entirely satisfactory. But the introduction of Roundup proved to be the answer and to have many other applications in addition. It is no exaggeration to say that it eliminated the full and half fallow as a method of the control of couch and other perennial weeds. It penetrated down to their roots, achieving a complete kill. It also solved the problem of killing off an old sward or a ley, preparatory to re-seeding or cropping. Once some time has elapsed, the residues of Roundup in the soil disappear and the field can be sown in the usual way.

Gramoxone is another herbicide, pre-dating the introduction of Roundup, which would also kill a wide range of weeds and also grass swards. But its effect is confined to top growth and the soil residues are very short lived. It was a great advance when fist available, but it is probably true to say that in many situations it has been superseded by Roundup.

Simazine was instrumental to a very large extent in making field beans a popular crop in South Warwickshire, after its acreage had dwindled to almost nothing. It is, of course, a traditional heavy land crop but a fouling one. Formerly drilling in wide rows and inter-row hoeing was the only method of weed control. Simazine, used mainly as a pre-emergence spray, altered all that, controlling a wide range of weeds.

Atrazine is used as the main ingredient in a pre-emergence or post-emergence herbicide for forage maize. Again, it is doubtful whether or not this very useful crop would have gained its present popularity without the introduction of this herbicide.

A Success Story

The development of chemical weed control over the last fifty years is one of the success stories of UK agriculture. With the traditional methods of keeping land clean becoming impossible on economic grounds, even if it had been possible to retain the necessary labour on farms, it is difficult to see what the alternative would have been. Certainly those who criticise the use of herbicides on the grounds of its effect on wildlife have not come up with any proof.

Farmers, themselves, have been taking measures to mitigate this effect, such as leaving headlands unploughed and so on. But, of course, these efforts receive comparatively little publicity. The above is only the sketchiest outline of the herbicide story over the last fifty years or so, but should serve as a reminder of the great strides that have been made and of the profound influence that these materials have had on crop husbandry.

Fungicides

The first fungicide to be used on a farm crop was Bordeaux mixture, a concoction of copper and quicklime, which was first used in 1885 to control mildew on vines and was developed in France. In 1888 and 1889 the first trials were conducted, using this material to control Blight in potatoes, also in France.

Bordeaux mixture was quickly adopted by potato growers as an effective control of the Blight fungus. In contrast to many modern crop protection chemicals, it continued in use for some sixty years as the standard treatment. The 1924, 1939 and 1949 editions of Watson and Moore's *Agriculture* all list Bordeaux mixture as the only fungicide available for this purpose. Today there is a whole host of chemicals available for the control of potato blight and for the control, or reduction, of other fungal diseases which beset the potato crop.

Until the early 1970s, the control of fungal diseases in cereals relied entirely on sowing varieties resistant to mildew, rust, septoria and a whole number of other fungal diseases both soil-borne and air-borne. There was one exception to this, which was a seed dressing, based on mercury, which was introduced in the early 1930s for the control of bunt in wheat, a disease which affected the grain, replacing it with a mass of black fungal spores.

Calixin was the first fungicide for application to growing crops of cereals to come into common use in the early 1970s. Yellow rust was rampant one year and a substantial acreage of winter wheat was sprayed with this chemical, which proved effective.

Aerial application was frequently used, both by helicopter and fixed wing aircraft. This led to at least two unfortunate incidents in South Warwickshire. At Alderminster, the Meadows family had some spraying done on a field adjoining the main road and opposite Thorpe's garage, an adjacent river meadow being used as a re-fuelling pad. All went well spraying up the bank, but coming down, towards the garage, the pilot misjudged his spray cut-off point and filled the garage with a blue mist which was deposited as blue specks covering everything, cars, tools, benches and the rest. Mr. Thorpe, understandably, was not amused.

The second incident was at Ilmington, when a string of cars halted by the side of the lane to watch the unfamiliar spectacle of a low flying plane spraying a crop of wheat. Needless to say, all the vehicles had their dose of blue spray, which was, of course, the farmer's fault and not the that of the gawping owners.

As with all crop protection chemicals, development of cereal fungicides has been rapid and extensive. New products are added to the Approved List year by year and the control of fungal disease in corn crops has become a study and subject all on its own.

Finally, chocolate spot has been a serious fungal disease of winter beans but is one that can now be controlled with fungicides.

Insecticides

Without much doubt, the most serious pests of cereals have been the soil borne species. Of these, wireworms, in the days before effective seed dressings became available, were the most devastating, especially in the 1940s during the food production campaign of that decade. Crop losses, either in the form of partial or complete failure, were widespread in cereals drilled in the first and second years after breaking out old pastures.

In South Warwickshire at that time, the best practice was to plough out such swards and give them either a full or half fallow. This laid the following wheat crop wide open to the ravages of wheat bulb fly, which lays its eggs in bare ground in late July and in August. I am quite certain that a significant proportion of crop damage attributed, almost as a matter of routine to wireworms, was, in fact caused by wheat bulb fly.

Be that as it may, there is now an efficient seed dressing to protect cereals from the ravages of wireworm. The same can be said of wheat bulb fly, but early drilling is still probably the most effective preventative as far as wheat after half fallow in South Warwickshire is concerned. In passing, one might observe that the use of Roundup has eliminated the need of a half fallow after ley in preparation for drilling wheat, in any case.

While a mixture of Paris Green and bran was the standard remedy against leatherjackets for many years, there are now a number of materials which give greater protection against this pest.

Slugs still pose a problem, and in a season favourable to this pest, can cause a great deal of damage to autumn drilled corn. Damage that is only too often unnoticed until it is too late, as slugs will eat into the softened, germinating seed.

The first indication that anything is amiss is the appearance of bare patches in the field. While efficient slug baits are now available, and have been for some time, their successful use still depends very much on close observation, sometimes supported by trapping.

Aphids are an air-borne insect pest of cereals. Their role as vectors for barley yellow dwarf virus is arguably the most potentially serious threat. They can also pose problems after ear emergence in some seasons. Fortunately, effective insecticides are now in commercial use and have been for a number of years.

Black fly on spring beans can need spraying in some years. Again a suitable material is available today, which was not the case in the past. But very often a contractor with a high clearance sprayer has to be employed to avoid damage to the crop, as this pest does not appear until a late stage.

Flea beetle in kale, when the crop was grown extensively, could cause a complete failure of the young crop. In the old days early drilling was considered the best remedy, while some degree of direct control was attempted by dragging brushwood across the field to create a dust storm, in the hope that this would deter the insect. Today, when kale, or any other brassica, is being grown there is an effective seed treatment.

Plant Growth Regulators

No description of crop protection chemicals and their development over the last sixty years, however brief, would be complete without reference to plant growth regulators, or straw shorteners as they are sometimes called.

Lodging in cereals has been, and still can be, a common cause of loss of yield, grain quality and difficulty in combining. Growth regulators, first introduced in the 1960s, reduce stem growth and thus help to control lodging in winter and spring wheats, winter barley and in winter and spring oats. It is also said that, in addition to improving the standing power of cereals, plant growth regulators stimulate root growth, thus increasing yield independently of any improvement in straw strength.

By far the largest majority of plant growth regulators on the market today are based on Chlormequat, either alone or in combination with some other chemical.

The decision whether or not to include a growth regulator in the spraying programme will depend on several factors among which will be the basic fertility of the field in question, the straw length and strength of the variety, and the level of nitrogenous fertiliser use. Under some circumstances there may well be little gain, in others their use will be essential if full yield potential is to be expressed.

In Conclusion

There have been many advances in pest and disease control during the last sixty years or so, but only crop protection chemicals which are, or have been, of major importance in the district have been described. However, it must be said that subjects such as pest, disease and weed control in potatoes and sugar beet would warrant a book on its own and have only been dealt with in passing.

It is hoped that the above description will, at least, give some idea of the immense strides that have been made in this branch of agritechnology over this period of time.

The accusation is often made that greedy farmers are misusing chemicals, and damaging wild life and the environment in the process, in the pursuit of maximum yields and thus maximum profit. In any other activity the greatest productivity on the part of other entrepreneurs, and thus the maximum profit, is usually applauded as being in the national economic interest. Why the double standard?

No mention is ever made of the benefit to the consumer conferred by crop protection chemicals. Let us refer back to the Stratford Safeway cauliflowers, mentioned above. The specimen on the organic shelves, presumably produced in the old way without chemicals of any kind cost £1.25. The ordinary one, grown with inorganic fertilisers and with the aid of crop protection chemicals cost 45p – a saving of 80p. In passing, battery eggs in our village butcher cost 65p/half dozen, and free range 90p.

In short, inorganic fertilisers, crop protection chemicals and modern methods of livestock production have brought the greatest economic benefit to the consumer, something which is never mentioned by the critics of their use.

16. THE CROPS – WHEAT

During the Hungry Forties, the cropping of South Warwickshire was distorted by the ploughing-up campaign and the need to maximise production for human consumption. The maintenance of farm livestock, too, required a great degree of self-sufficiency.

Wheat, mostly autumn sown but some drilled in the spring, was the main cash crop. Barley in the 1940s, and for some years afterwards, was spring sown. Winter and spring oats were also grown. Mixed corn, or dredge, was extensively grown at that time, the idea being that it would be a nearly balanced ration when ground and fed to cattle. At any rate, that was the theory, but in practice any beans or peas that were included only too often would make little contribution to the final yield. Winter beans, a traditional heavy land crop were also grown, along with a smaller acreage of spring beans.

Potatoes and sugar beet were features of wartime cropping and for some years afterwards. A potato quota for every WAEC district had to be fulfilled. The consequence was that this crop was often grown on land that was unsuitable and by those who had no experience of its husbandry. Only too often, the end results were dirty crops and low yields. The only mitigating factor, as far as the farmer was concerned, was a substantial acreage payment.

To digress, this must have made an impression on a young man. When I went for my second interview for a post in the new National Agricultural Advisory Service in 1946, Professor Sanders (later Sir Harold) was a member of the interviewing panel. When his turn came he asked me, 'Do you consider potatoes a good cleaning crop?.' I replied 'It all depends on who is growing them.' He roared with laughter and said 'That is the best answer I have heard today.'

Mangolds, kale and, to a lesser extent, swedes, were to be found on most farms. The three year ley quickly became established in the 1940s as the pivot of rotations almost universally.

In short, the face of arable farming in South Warwickshire in the 1940s was very different from that of today. Many crops have disappeared from the scene, either completely, or to a very large extent. These include the fodder roots, oats, mixed corn and some seed crops. The acreages of potatoes and sugar beet are much reduced and now confined to those soils suitable for their cultivation.

But other crops have established themselves, notably oilseed rape and linseed. Linseed and flax were grown to a limited degree in the war years and just after.

The Decline of Spring Cropping

At this juncture it is as well to consider the reasons for the decline in spring drilling of cereals in South Warwickshire: barley, oats and wheat. Autumn drilled varieties yield better than those drilled in the spring. Fifty years ago, winter barley was hardly a serious option but today the situation in this respect is very different.

The heavier land which covers so much of South Warwickshire is not really spring drilling country. Having said that, in one season at Dodwell, spring wheat variety trials were drilled into a frost tilth with only a light harrowing first to level the seedbed. But this was exceptional; good spring tilths are not easy to obtain on heavy land, especially in the absence of winter frosts.

By the 1970s, the Forsyths were getting over this problem by ploughing in good time, then killing off any green trash in the spring with Gramoxone and carrying out the shallowest of cultivations prior to drilling. They well knew that cultivating any deeper would result in a cloddy seedbed, prone to dry out and resulting in a poor start for the crop.

Finally, as long as a rotation based on a ley of whatever duration was still almost universal, it was held that drilling into a spring cereal, usually barley but sometimes wheat, was the necessary preliminary to establishing a new ley by undersowing.

Now, of course, it is a different story. With the increase in winter barley, at the expense of spring sown varieties, leys are now drilled into the winter barley stubble, often without ploughing. By the late 1970s, one local merchant told me that two-thirds of ley seeds mixtures he sold were for August drilling. My guess would be that, today in this district, this figure is even higher.

Winter Wheat

In 1943, the national average yield of winter wheat was 18 cwt./acre. As far as our district was concerned, the better farmers on the better land would have achieved rather higher yields than this. Even under these circumstances and at that time, 30 cwt./acre would have been considered an excellent yield, with anything substantially in excess being really exceptional.

But, at the other end of the scale, and particularly on the smaller farms in the Arden, growing wheat only under pressure from the WAEC, and where drilling and harvesting amounted to the sum total of the husbandry involved, yields would barely reach the meagre national average. Needless to say, little or no fertiliser was applied to winter wheat on such farms.

The seedbed application of phosphates has already been described. This would be followed in the spring with 2 cwt./acre of Sulphate of Ammonia as a top-dressing. This might well be dispensed with in the first crop after a ley and even on the second, when even more nitrates would be released from the rotting turf. For with the weak-strawed varieties, the only sort available at that time, nitrates, soil or inorganic, in excess, would give rise to laid (i.e. flattened) crops. These were difficult and expensive to harvest with a binder and even with the combines available at that time.

It might seem sacrilege to the modern cereal grower, but winter wheat was often grazed in the spring of the year providing useful keep for ewes and lambs before grass growth started in earnest. In the 1950s, a question often asked of District Advisors was 'How long can I go on grazing my winter wheat without affecting yield?'

One had to admit there was no real answer, there being no firm information on this. So it was decided that proper trials should be laid down for several seasons in South Warwickshire. The conclusions were that there was no loss of yield, as long as ewes and lambs were turned off by the end of March. But grazing could continue until mid-April, always providing a top-dressing of not less than 40 units N/acre was applied. If winter wheat was grazed after mid-April, yield losses became significant, even when a top-dressing was applied.

Fungicides for application to cereals were, of course, unknown in the 1940s. We had to wait thirty years for these. In the meantime, the incidence of fungal disease was a matter of varietal resistance, if any.

Some varieties were, of course, less resistant than others. Desprez 80, for example, could be relied upon to gather unto itself every fungal disease known to man. I shall never forget being asked to look at a crop of this variety standing in stook on Whitley Hill Farm, near Henley-in-Arden. It had obviously had good potential at one time, but the farmer was naturally concerned because, when picking up a sheaf by the band, the butt went down rather than the head. The crop had been attacked by fungal disease in some form and order; the heads were practically empty of grain, thus the butt of the sheaf was heavier than the head. Moreover, what little corn there was, was thin and shrivelled. To describe it as poultry corn would almost be an exaggeration: any self-respecting hen would have turned up her nose at it! But that was the way things were fifty years ago.

Watson and Moore 's *Agriculture*, the 1937 edition, lists the following winter wheat varieties: Squarehead , Little Joss, Red Marvel, Iron III, Victor, Yeoman, and Rivet. Ian Moore's *Crops and Cropping*, in 1943, adds Yeoman II, Holdfast, Wilhelmina, Wilma, Juliana, Desprez 80 and Warden, but omits Iron III and Red Marvel. Winter wheat variety trials drilled in the autumn of 1947, which included the most promising newcomers at that time, listed two newcomers, Scandia and Bersee. The next year, Redman put in an appearance and the year after that Hybrid 46 and Pilot were added to the trial. All these from my field notebook in which all details of these trials were recorded. Watson and Moore in 1949 adds Jubilegem to its list of winter wheat varieties.

But by far the most remarkable of the post-war wheats was Cappelle. It was first listed in the NIAB Recommended List in 1953 and it dominated the winter wheat scene for some twenty years, accounting, at any rate in South Warwickshire, for by far the greatest acreage of winter wheat grown.

In 1974, it was finally listed as being outclassed. New, higher yielding varieties, such as Huntsman, Nimrod, Champlein, West Desprez, Maris Widgeon, Maris Fundin (the first of the so-called dwarf wheats with very short straw by the standards of that day) and Flanders, amongst others, at last toppled King Cappelle from his throne.

It might be added that none of these new varieties ever accounted for such a high proportion of the acreage, and for so long, as Cappelle. Indeed, there were some spectacular disasters. In 1972, Joss Cambier, a formerly popular variety, succumbed to a new strain of yellow rust and a similar fate was suffered later by Rothwell Perdix. This led to an intensification of research into this fungus and, in due course, a warning about putting too much reliance on one variety and the publishing of tables of varieties to enable growers to select a least risk option.

In passing, one might note that the first recommended list of cereal varieties was published by the National Institute of Agricultural Botany in 1944.

Since the demise of Cappelle, new varieties have come and gone with bewildering rapidity. Taking the 1999 List as an example, the average time between a variety being first listed and then being described as 'outclassed' is five years , in sharp contrast to Cappelle's twenty.

There are, of course, a number of reasons for this. Not least, perhaps, the establishment of plant breeders' rights, which has done so much to stimulate the development of new varieties. Many of the varieties listed above will be completely unknown to the present generation of cereal growers, having long since departed into the mists of agricultural history. It is interesting to speculate how many of the better ones would have fared today, given growth regulators, more generous fertilising and the protection of the modern range of herbicides, fungicides and insecticides.

Today, with fertiliser broadcast, much wider corn drills and seed and fertiliser coming in half-tonne bags which can be handled mechanically, the acreage of corn that can be sown in a working day is unbelievable by old standards. Commonly, a herbicide will be applied in the autumn, and often a second one in the spring, and top-dressing will be a matter of 130 to 140 units N, while two or three passes with a fungicide, according to the incidence of disease and the season, will be common practice. As already mentioned, yields have increased three-fold over fifty years.

The corn harvest has, of course, altered beyond recognition. In the 1940s, the harvest field presented a busy scene on all farms. Men and horses with self-binders, a gang of others following behind stooking the sheaves. When the time came to load the crop, many of the older generation will recall the horses and the smell of sweat and hot leather, the wagons creaking their way over hard ground, two men on the load, two more pitching the sheaves up to them and a boy leading the horse. And woe betide him if he forgot to shout *'ol tight'* to warn those on the load that he was moving on.

When the crop was safely in barn or stack the job was only half done. The threshing drum would duly arrive with two attendants and a whole gang was needed to feed it, see to the sacks of corn, remove the cavings (the worst job) and rick the straw. Coal was provided by the farmer, and water had to be carted.

Today, one man on a monster combine will cut and thresh the crop, gobbling up big acreages in a day. The only others in the field will be the men driving the grain trailers, for corn is now handled in bulk. Later the straw will be baled, usually with a big baler so the process can be completely mechanised, or it will be chopped and worked into the soil. All a far cry from a harvest field and the rickyard full of folk, and the same at threshing time.

Spring Wheat

Although winter wheat is now the most important cash crop in South Warwickshire, spring wheat was extensively grown in the 1940s and 1950s. One of the main reasons for this was the popularity of the variety Atle, a comparatively new introduction. It was of high milling quality, which at that time was of great significance.

In the late 1940s, nationally, combine numbers had overtaken drying and storage capacity. Thus, there was for a number of years a post-harvest glut of wheat trying to find a home. While it was difficult to sell many varieties at that time, Atle would always find a ready market in the early autumn months.

In the *War Ag* days, when I was District Technical Officer at the Stratford office, I laid down variety demonstration plots of winter wheat and oats and spring wheat and oats. My field notebook recording these, and the trials that I also carried out on cereals in later years, lies before me as I write.

The first demonstration plots of spring wheat varieties were drilled in 1944 on the farm of G. R. Hammerton, of Wellesbourne, in a field which is now covered by a post-war housing estate. This was the first time, and as far as I was concerned the last, that plots of any kind were drilled using horses.

The varieties in this demonstration included Red Marvel, Extra Kolben II, Fylgia, Atle and Meteor. It is interesting to note that the 1937 edition of Watson and Moore makes no mention of Atle nor Fylgia. *Crops and Cropping* by Ian Moore (1943) lists these two varieties and an older one, April Bearded.

By the 1950s, Atle and Fylgia were dominating the spring wheat scene, and I spent a considerable amount of time from 1944 until 1955 on trial work on spring wheat, particularly as regards the optimum levels of nitrogenous manuring. It was established that seedbed dressings were preferable to top-dressing when the crop was well up. This was possibly due to the fact that seedbeds were usually moist enough for the fertiliser to act. Top-dressing, on the other hand, depended upon rain, which might be sparse and long delayed in a dry spring.

These trials were laid down on Dodwell Farm, just outside Stratford, then being farmed by the CAEC until the lease, which was held by The Grassland Improvement Station, expired. Needless to say Dodwell was on the clay and hardly spring wheat land. The other trials were put down at Rushford, Salford Priors, courtesy of Ernest Bomford.

There were variety trials at the same sites. At Dodwell, the varieties were Meteor, Atle, Fylgia and Bersee. It must be added that Bersee was really a winter wheat variety, but one which could be safely sown in the spring. The trial at Rushford simply compared Bersee with Atle. It was found that the former would outyield the latter, providing the trial was drilled in early March. Sowing later than this resulted in the reverse being the case.

A lot of work went into these trials, but they did establish important points in the husbandry of spring wheat, then an important crop locally, and about which surprisingly little firm information formerly existed.

First, a seedbed application of 3 cwt./acre of Suphate of Ammonia was the optimum and, of course, phosphate and potash as needed. Secondly, as mentioned above, Bersee outyielded Atle when drilled in early March. In the third place, Fylgia was best for late drilling in the second half of April being a ninety-day wheat. Finally, it was found, more or less accidentally, that 2 cwt./acre was the minimum seed rate. The normal practice had been to drill at winter wheat seed rates which were too low.

17. BARLEY

'In farming, there are three things you should always avoid: spring wheat, winter barley and parson's daughters.' This was the advice given to me by a farmer of the old school soon after I arrived in South Warwickshire. Let me put on record straight away that I never understood the reference to parson's daughters! Spring wheat was held in little regard until the appearance of Atle and Fylgia on the farming scene, and winter barley was certainly the Cinderella of the cereal world. This was to be the case for many years after the end of the Second World War. It is significant that John Nix's *Farm Management Pocketbook* does not distinguish between spring and winter barley until 1980.

Old Varieties

In 1937, Watson and Moore's *Agriculture* lists one six-row variety that was autumn sown. Called Bere, it was weak in the straw, winter hardy, and produced grain of poor quality. It was sometimes drilled in the autumn to provide fodder in the early spring, much as rye was used in later years. The spring barleys listed were the old stalwarts, Spratt Archer and Plumage Archer. The former was considered the choice for the lighter land and the latter for the stronger soils, being somewhat stronger in the straw. Both, under the right conditions, would produce malting samples.

Spring barleys predominated the scene for many years. The above two varieties were joined by Abed Kenia in the 1940s. This was popular in South Warwickshire, for it had a stronger and stiffer straw and was thus well suited to clayland. It had no pretensions as far as malting was concerned.

However, during the war years, country breweries were required to draw their supplies of barley within a certain radius to save on transport. Thus many maltsters had to make do with samples of barley that they would not have contemplated purchasing in happier times.

Conway Rees

Flowers Brewery in Stratford-on-Avon was no exception. There was, in the '40s, a corn trader in Stratford named Conway Rees. I think he had been with Titchmarsh and Hunt, agricultural merchants in the town. Before I knew him, he had started trading corn on his own, having a small office between the Red Horse Hotel (now Marks and Spencers) and the old house which stood below it in Bridge Street, a site now occupied by the Mulberry Centre. In it there was a table, a chair, a telephone and a filing cabinet, and that was it. For the transport of corn he relied upon hauliers and had no office staff until Don joined him after the war. He was held in high repute by the farming community and was kindness itself to me, especially when I first arrived in Stratford in my first job.

Russell Taylor bought the barley for Flowers, and he and Conway Rees were good friends, doing much business together. If Russell Taylor had a car, it had been laid up 'for the duration,' so he relied on Conway Rees to take him around farms barley buying. For a couple of seasons, in the autumn after harvest, Conway Rees not driving in the black-out, used to ring me at the Stratford *War Ag* office in the morning first thing. 'If you are not doing anything this evening, would you drive me and Russell round some farms to look at barley, tea here 4.30 p.m.'

He lived in a large house at the bottom of the Banbury Road. After tea, Russell Taylor arrived on his bike. We then clambered (that was the operative word) into a Vauxhall 25, 1936 vintage, which appeared to me to be a huge vehicle of stately proportions. I took the wheel and the other two were in the back with their sample bags and barley cutters, for corn was bought on sight and smell in those days, And off we set, visiting some half a dozen farms in the course of an evening. What a valuable experience for a young man, who kept his eyes and ears open and his mouth shut! We always ended up at The Bell in Shipston-on-Stour for supper as dusk fell; this was late in the evening, for then we had to suffer Double Summer Time as a wartime measure.

New Varieties

Spring barley varieties started to be introduced in profusion by the 1960s. Proctor was popular as a variety which could be relied upon to produce a malting sample. Others included Maris Badger, Maris Baldrick, Cambrinus, Mosane and so on. Three feed barleys became popular on the heavier land due to their short, stiff straw; these were Rika, Herta and Vada. The latter, if I remember correctly, never made it onto the NIAB List but was widely grown nevertheless. Specially mention must be made of an extraordinary variety of spring barley, Deba Abed. It had a very stiff, short straw, a poor grain sample and a peculiar habit of growth: great, thick, wide leaves lay close to the ground in the early stages of growth, looking for all the world like a winter variety.

Barley Barons

During the 1960s and right up to the present time, spring barley varieties continued to appear, and disappear with bewildering rapidity. The barley acreage, nationally, was also increasing. It had begun to supplant oats as the main feed grain and an increasing acreage was encouraged by Government, as it was policy to be as self sufficient as possible. By 1961, the acreage had increased by 50% since 1952 and stood at 3m acres, an all-time high. The continuous growing of spring barley became commonplace, especially on the Cotswolds, and the barley barons became the personification of agricultural affluence.

Winter Barley

Winter barley continued to remain marooned in the doldrums. Pioneer was an improvement over the old variety, Bere, and was still the only winter barley on the NIAB List in 1960, having first been introduced in 1949. Apart from the lack of good varieties, winter barley was not a popular crop. In the first place, the growing of spring barley was still one pivot of the rotation 3yr. Ley – winter wheat, winter wheat, spring barley – which had become so widely adopted in South Warwickshire and elsewhere since the early 1940s. Undersowing spring barley was the usual way to establish the ley.

Secondly, we had a chicken and egg situation. Winter barley was the first cereal to ripen and, because so little was grown, any crop became the target for every bird in the neighbourhood. For many yards into the field, sparrows stripped every head of grain, treating themselves to a real feast and then, presumably, retiring into the hedge to sleep it off. Any laid patches out in the field, and Pioneer was not stiff in the straw, were soon attended to by rooks. Incidentally, even today, bird damage in winter barley is by no means unknown. Lastly, winter barley had no edge on spring varieties when it came to yield.

Frank Horne was the Director of the National Institute of Agricultural Botany from 1945 to 1970, and played a key role in the development of the Institute during these vital years. Those of us in NAAS who were herbage seed inspectors, made the annual pilgrimage to the NIAB at the end of April every year for a refresher course. During the morning coffee break, Frank Horne always joined us, moving from group to group discussing matters of common interest. It was typical of the man that he found time out of a busy day to spend half an hour with the then young rank-and-file of the Advisory Service.

One April morning in the early 1950s, he came up to Frank Bennison and myself, asked where we came from and then, 'How should our breeding programme be directed to meet the needs of clayland farming?' We both said that a pressing need was a stiff strawed, high yielding winter barley. 'That's interesting,' came the reply and then our talk turned to other matters.

Writing in the *Agriculture* in 1961, Dr.G.D.Bell, a well known plant breeder, noted that crosses between Proctor and Pioneer were in the pipeline. By 1969, the NIAB List contained two more winter barleys, Maris Otter and Senta. The former was a variety that could produce a malting sample, and did so regularly. It was much sought after by maltsters, so much so that it was grown for many years after it had been removed from the Recommended List as being *outclassed.*

Dea was another winter barley variety which was introduced at much the same time. It was high yielding by the standards of the day and stiff strawed, but it had one serious defect, grain quality. It was appalling: long and thin, and could easily be mistaken for rye!

By the early 1970s, new winter barleys came on the market in profusion. Today there are some twenty varieties on the NIAB Recommended List – A far cry from the early 1960s, when Pioneer was the sole variety listed. In common with other crops, yields have increased dramatically over the last fifty years. In the 1940s, the average for spring barley was recorded as 16 cwt./acre. Today Nix puts the average yield for feed winter barley at 51 cwt./acre and at 42 cwt./acre for spring varieties. Most cereal growers in South Warwickshire will look for yields much in excess of these figures.

Some indication of the relative importance of spring and winter barleys can be obtained by the number of entries in each class in the annual crop competition run by the Stratford-on-Avon Branch of the National Farmers' Union. These are as follows:

Year	Winter Barley	Spring Barley
1992	12	2
1993	10	6
1994	13	7
1995	11	3
1996	21	4
1997	15	4
1998	10	4
1999	9	6

Comparison between winter and spring barley

The picture is clear and underlines the strong trend towards winter barley in the 1990s. It goes without saying that the entries of spring barley came, almost exclusively, from the lighter land in South Warwickshire. Is it significant that the gap has narrowed in 1999, or is this a blip? Are the newer spring barley varieties narrowing the yield gap? Are lower variable costs and, possibly, a better chance of a malting sample, factors in persuading growers on the lighter soils to drill a bigger acreage of spring varieties. Only time will tell.

Be that as it may, there is no doubt that better varieties of winter barley, which became available in the late 1960s, were instrumental in producing such a spectacular increase in the acreage drilled with winter varieties, and which has been such a feature of barley growing in South Warwickshire during the last three decades.

18. OATS

A crop in decline

Oats are a crop in decline, at any rate in much of lowland England. At the beginning of the 20th century, no less than 50% of the total cereal acreage was accounted for by oats. Since about 1880, at the beginning of the great depression, the wheat acreage had been falling. But the oat acreage remained the same. The reason was the increase in the horse population since the coming of the railways, because more horse transport was needed to feed the stations along the ever-growing rail network. In short, the market for oats was domestic, supplying a large horse population both rural and urban, and was still the main feed grain for cattle of all kinds. The post-war decline in the oat crop is illustrated by the following figures:

Year	Total Acreage	Oats as a % of total corn acreage
1946	3.5m	
1965		13%
1966	907,000	
1988		5%

The decline of oats as a crop, 1946 – 1988

The decline in oat production has continued ever since. The entries in the annual crop competition run by the Stratford-upon-Avon Branch of the National Farmers' Union give some indication, however crude, The class each year was for oats, winter and spring. In practice, winter oats dominated to the almost total exclusion of spring varieties. The most popular winter oat in the 1990s was Image. In 1993 there were 3 entries; in 1994, 4; in 1995, 3; 1996, none; 1997, 2; 1998, 2; 1999, none.

Oats are a crop for wetter districts and are, thus, not ideally suited to South Warwickshire with a rainfall of between 25" and 28". To the best of my recollection, spring oats have always been a minority crop. Spring barley could be relied upon to give better yields and, in any case, barley from the 1960s onwards had started to replace oats as the main feed grain for cattle and sheep.

Nor, incidentally, had oats been popular with feed compounders, because it is lower in feed value than wheat or barley, and bulky to transport and store.

Frit Fly

Another reason why spring oats were never as popular as spring barley is the fact that they were very susceptible to late spring drilling, due to the ravages of Frit Fly. On clayland, sowing in the first half of March cannot be guaranteed, to put it mildly, and even on light land delayed sowing could be disastrous.

This can be illustrated by considering the spring oats harvested in 1944 after winter broccoli, which were grown by Len Sisam on a field at Moor Hall, near Biford-on-Avon. One third of the broccoli crop consisted of an early variety which was cut and cleared in early March; the oats were drilled immediately afterwards, and yielded an excellent crop. The next lot of broccoli was cleared in the first half of March and again drilled immediately cutting had been finished; a moderate crop was the result. But the last part of the broccoli crop was not cleared until later which meant that the drilling of the spring oats did not take place until April, and these failed due to Frit Fly. Later, of course, insecticides became available, applied twice, which gave protection against this pest But, by then, this was only of academic interest.

Winter Oats

In South Warwickshire, therefore, winter oats dominated until the acreage of these dwindled away to insignificance, but even in their heyday these could have drawbacks. They were not invariably winter hardy, and in a prolonged period of cold weather the crop could suffer from frost lift, especially if drilled late. The young plants could then still be dependent upon the seed rootlets, and these could become detached from the seedling because the thin underground stem could be broken due to frost lift. A sure indication of this was green, healthy, strips of plants across the field in the tractor wheelings where the soil had become compacted and frost lift prevented, the rest of the field looking sickly with plants dying off altogether here and there.

Another drawback to winter oats was a tendency to shed. When the crop was cut with a binder it was a different matter, Oats were always cut when the upper part of the straw was still green. The crop matured in the stook; the old saying being that oats 'had to hear the church bells three times when in stook.' This prevented shedding and increased the feed value of the straw.

When oats were combined it was a different matter. Severe weather, heavy rain and high winds, could wreak havoc during combining or just before. A crop of winter oats at Drayton, the NAAS Experimental Husbandry Farm near Stratford, comes to mind. Here each trailer load of grain went over the weighbridge, so one knew exactly what was happening as harvest progressed.

One season, while the one field of winter oats was being combined, there was a night of heavy rain and high winds, accompanied by thunder – not an unusual occurrence in August. After this the yield in the remainder of the crop was reduced by one ton/acre.

Those with long enough memories will recall that the 1960s, as a decade, were very wet, with above average rainfall culminating in extensive and damaging flooding in the Avon valley in July 1968. But the wet seasons suited oats, and one farmer in South Warwickshire reckoned that this crop gave a better gross margin per acre in some of those years than either wheat or barley. From time to time a come-back for oats has been heralded in the farming press, but these were false dawns. As far as South Warwickshire was concerned, the 1960s were the swan song for winter oats.

Varieties

To Moor Hall, Bidford-on-Avon, again where, in the autumn of 1944, Len Sisam co-operated in drilling a demonstration of winter oat varieties. Amongst these was the old variety, Grey Winter. This had straw about 6 feet in height and, not surprisingly, went flat at the whiff of an empty fertiliser bag. There were two other varieties which were a great improvement, the Picton and Unique, which were grown to some extent for a time until the other two varieties in the demonstration took over and established a near monopoly. These were S.147 and S.172, both from Aberystwyth, as indicated by the *S* prefix. (An interesting side note is that the establishment near Cambridge happens to be located in Maris Lane, and uses the *Maris* prefix for its strains.)

S.147 was the most widely grown in South Warwickshire and was a great advance on anything which had gone before. It yielded well by the standards of the day, and had a fairly long straw. But when it lodged, it had the convenient habit of doing so by knuckling over about one foot to eighteen inches above ground level. This meant that the cutter bar of the combine could run under the straw and little was lost. A crop laid in this way was, at least, preferable to one standing and at risk from shedding in a sudden storm.

Its sister variety S.172 was much shorter and stiffer in the straw and thus well suited to the strongest and most fertile soils. Its grain quality was inferior to S.147, inclined to be thin and with a higher proportion of husk, but it had its place and was a good variety.

As with other cereals, many new varieties appeared over the years. Powys and Peniarth were the first real challengers to S.147 and were first listed by the NIAB in 1965. This was followed by Maris Quest a year later, which was stiffer and shorter in the straw, a substitute for S.172. These varieties were widely grown in South Warwickshire for a number of years and were, of course, succeeded by others.

Today the following figures are significant, relating to the numbers of varieties appearing in the NIAB Recommended Lists. Winter wheat 22; winter barley 20; winter oats 6 and naked oats 3. Among the current varieties are Image, which has already been mentioned as being grown in South Warwickshire. It is a specialist variety producing a very high quality grain for milling. Aintree is another winter oat grown locally. These figures underline the fact that a crop in decline over much of the country has little attraction for plant breeders.

Yields

In common with other cereals, Nix reports a very great increase in average yield per acre over the years. This is, of course, due partly to better varieties, but also to a greater use of fertilisers, improved herbicides and the wider use of fungicides.

Nix does not differentiate between winter and spring oats until the edition of September 1976. That year, the average yield of winter oats is given as 34 cwt./acre. In 1998, twenty two years later, this had risen to 54 cwt./acre.

19. BEANS & PEAS

Winter beans are a traditional crop for heavy land. During times of agricultural depression – the last quarter of the 19th century and the 1920s and 1930s – the acreage of beans went into sharp decline, for the very good reason that so much heavy land was laid down, or just fell down, to grassland, usually of a most indifferent quality. The claylands of South Warwickshire were no exception.

However, during the ploughing-up campaign of the 1940s, the acreage of winter beans in South Warwickshire rose steadily, and was a welcome source of protein for feeding on the farm. But 1948 was a disastrous year for the bean crop in this district. Almost every field was decimated by an early attack of Chocolate Spot. I can well remember Mr. W. J. Barnett, of Mount Pleasant Farm, Walton, writing off his crop of winter beans, constructing a makeshift silo and using a big tractor-driven chopper blower to fill it with the remains of the bean crop. What the feeding value of this silage was at the end of the day, history does not relate.

After this set-back to bean growing in South Warwickshire, the acreage dwindled away, until, in 1959, it was only 1/10th of the peak acreage sown in the 1940s.

Winter Bean Varieties

Beans are largely, if not entirely, cross pollinated. Until 1968, when the NIAB published its first Recommended List, bean varieties, as we understand the term today, did not exist. The publication was the result of some twenty years work. For, in 1948, NAAS District Advisers were asked to collect any strains or types of winter beans recognised as such which were being grown in their districts.

The bean crop, thanks largely to cross pollination, carries out within itself a process of natural selection. The naturally occurring crosses which produce the highest yielding plants contributing most to the final yield.

Thus, the best practice in those days was either to keep a stock of one's own beans, or buy from a local grower who had a reputation for growing good yielding crops, and whose bean seed was much in demand as a consequence. In South Warwickshire, such a farmer was Homer Harris of Newnham, a hamlet near Aston Cantlow, and uncle to Wilf Harris of *The Newnham Long Teat* fame. It was a sample of his seed that I collected and sent on to the NIAB. Incidentally, his Red Clover seed was also much sought after.

Throws MS was the first real bean variety in the true sense of the word, and its introduction made a big contribution to the renewed interest in winter beans. It was introduced in 1954 by Ranks Hovis McDougall Ltd., and could be obtained locally from Three Counties Agricultural Services in Stratford-on-Avon.

A survey was carried out on 23 farms in Warwickshire in 1967. The total acreage in the survey was 600, and was split equally between winter and spring beans. Of the winter varieties, Throws MS was the most popular and was grown on seven farms, while Daffa was sown on only one. Of the spring varieties Blue Rock (5 farms), Minor (4 farms) and Maris Bead (3 farms) were the most popular.

However, by 1982, both Throws MS and Daffa were listed by the NIAB as being outclassed. The recommended varieties in that year were Banner, Maris Beaver, Bulldog and Maris Beagle; all had yield ratings well above the older sorts. This was confirmed by trials at Drayton in 1984, Throws MS coming lowest in the yield league table and Banner top. By 1997, all these recommended varieties had disappeared from the NIAB list, their places being taken by Punch, Bourdon, Striker and Target.

Spring Beans

Although winter beans have always been more widely grown in South Warwickshire than spring varieties, for obvious reasons, spring beans have always been sown to a limited extent. There has been a niche market provided by Midland pigeon fanciers.

Apart from lower yields compared with winter beans, to the tune of about 5 cwt./acre on average, spring beans are rather more demanding in some respects. They are very susceptible to dry conditions. The ideal soil, therefore, is one that is retentive of moisture but, at the same time, is light enough to allow early drilling, that is in February or early March. One East Anglian farmer, whom I got talking to at an NIAB Fellows Day, got over the problem by broadcasting and ploughing in spring beans during December or early January; by the time they were showing in the row any danger of winter kill was over.

Spring beans had one advantage of those sown in the autumn. They were much less susceptible to the fungal disease, Chocolate Spot, which could cause a complete failure on occasion and frequently led to much reduced yields of winter beans. Today, modern fungicides give a good control, but this can be an expensive business since a contractor with a high clearance sprayer often has to be employed. Spring beans are more prone to aphid attack, which can seriously reduce yield, although the pest can be controlled with insecticides.

Listed in the early NIAB Recommended Lists were varieties such as Tarvin and Maris Bead. The latter was still on the NIAB Recommended List in 1997, a long lived variety because, with its small seed, it was popular with pigeon fanciers. A real break-through came with the introduction of the varieties Troy and Alfred, first provisionally recommended in 1986. These did a great deal to close the yield gap between winter and spring varieties and, as always, have been succeeded by newer varieties as the years have gone by. For example, by 1997 Alfred was no longer listed and had been superseded by five varieties fully recommended and six on the provisional list.

Sowing and Hoeing

Broadcasting and then ploughing in is a common enough method of sowing a bean crop. This is often done by the simple method of taking the tubes out of the drill coulters and broadcasting in this manner before ploughing. The old way was to have a bean box fixed to a single furrow horse plough. This had a small wheel which ran in the furrow and turned a brush feed in the box. This could be put in and out of gear by the simple expedient of lifting the wheel off the ground by means of a cord. The bean seed was sown every third furrow, giving rows about 18" to 21" apart.

These bean boxes are now museum pieces, which makes me feel my age. For the first ploughing I ever did was sowing beans in this way. The idea was that, as the harrows followed towards the end of the day to break the furrow crests and level the seed bed, neighbours would not be able to see how crooked my ploughing might have been. In the end the result was not too bad. Blossom, the old mare, knew a lot more about the job than I did, which was just as well.

There were, and are, special bean drills. One which was popular in its day was based on a Bomford Superflow chisel plough. Seed boxes were mounted on the frame and plastic tubes were clamped behind the cultivator arms, feeding the beans down behind the tines. This ensured a good depth of sowing. One of these was used at Drayton for some years.

Beans, with their open habit of growth, were always regarded as a fouling crop, and with every justification, leaving the land dirtier and full of weeds of all kinds. Because of this, and before the advent of suitable herbicides, beans were always horse hoed and, hence, were grown in rows wide enough to allow of this.

The Come-Back

Two husbandry factors played a very important part in restoring bean growing to its rightful place in the farming of clayland in particular. The first was the introduction of the pre-emergence herbicide, Simazin. This removed the necessity of inter-row cultivations for as long as crop growth permitted. And secondly, the breeding of improved varieties, the first of which was Throws MS.

Other factors also played an important part and of these, economic developments were paramount. For example, in 1968 an acreage payment of £5 for registered crops was introduced. There was a move to grow beans on contract, Three Counties Agricultural Services, now moved to Abbey Mills at

Alcester, pioneered contract growing in Warwickshire. There was, however, one snag: new seed had to be bought each year from the contracting merchant. It could have been that the advantages of an assured market and price was diminished somewhat by the extra expense of new seed each year.

In the 1970s, good prices were being obtained, a market driven partly by a buoyant export trade. In 1971, it was reported that 58.4% of the 1969 crop had been exported, 7.7% was used by feed manufacturers, 9.5% used for seed and 24.2% used on the farm or sold directly for feed. Guaranteed prices for registered crops played a part, as did subsidies, for compounding and seed production. Latterly, of course, EEC Arable Area Payments have assisted in maintaining the acreage.

Beans, with their ability to increase soil nitrogen and improve soil texture, have always been a traditional entry for winter wheat. This crop can now provide a useful break on intensive cereal farms on the heavier soils, where combineable crops are the only practical option.

In all this work at the Drayton EHF has played an important part. From the outset, as an experimental husbandry farm, it was thought that work on beans should be undertaken, as this was a traditional clayland crop. One practice at Drayton, in particular, should be noted. Simazine was not applied until just before crop emergence and, at the same time, Paraquat was sprayed to clean up any weeds already emerged.

Finally, the hysteria (and it is nothing less) over the growing of genetically modified crops might possibly be taken to an extreme absurdity. Consumers, and particularly the all-powerful supermarkets, may well demand meat and animal products which have been fed on non-genetically modified grain only. This applies particularly to soya, the American crop containing a high proportion of genetically modified varieties. Home grown beans are obviously an acceptable alternative, especially as importers of soya cannot possibly guarantee that their product has been sourced from non-genetically modified crops. However, varieties of soyabean suitable for the English climate are now in the pipeline. There have been many false dawns for soya as a crop in this country, but there seems some prospect of success in the near future. Time will tell.

Peas in South Warwickshire

In South Warwickshire peas have always been a minority crop. This observation has to be qualified, however, in the case of those harvested green and, in days gone by, picked by hand. Such crops were a feature of the market gardening scene and, to an extent, still are but with a much reduced acreage. The arrival of the pea pickers, often gipsies and other itinerants, during the second half of the summer was not greeted with any enthusiasm by the locals, for they were a rough, thieving, rowdy lot. Market gardeners could not do without them, though.

Ever since the advent of the all-arable farm on the South Warwickshire claylands in the 1960s, the search for a combineable cash crop as a break from cereals has been unceasing. The original, and traditional, break crop was, of course, winter or spring beans. In the next chapter, the story of the establishment of oilseed rape in this role will be described.

Chequered History

Peas for combining have had a chequered history in South Warwickshire, to say the least. For the most part, they are spring sown and, as a crop, are demanding as far as a seedbed is concerned. This must be fine, reasonably firm, but uncompacted. For this reason, pea growing is confined to the lighter soils, due to the difficulty of providing a suitable tilth in the majority of seasons on the heavier land.

Another potent factor is the climate. In contrast to the Eastern counties, we in this district very often suffer a spell of wet weather during the second half of July and the first half of August, just when peas are ready for combining. On the large arable farm in East Suffolk, where I was retained as a consultant for a number of years, we never seemed to have this problem and a substantial acreage of peas was grown every year as a matter of course.

However, there has been a sporadic interest in the crop as the following figures for Warwickshire show:

Year	Acres of peas
1976	None grown
1978	215
1980	121
1982	245

Pea crops in Warwickshire

Dwarf Beans

The introduction of stiffer strawed, semi-leafless varieties altered the picture to some extent. John Lampett, of Thelsford, Charlecote, grew the crop for some twenty years with success from 1970 until 1990. In due course, dwarf beans for selling fresh to supermarkets, or for freezing or pulping for baby food, took the place of peas.

John started with 1 – 1.5 acres of dwarf beans in 1986, then 12 acres the next year, and now grows 40 – 45 acres each year. He is a member of a group with four other members in Worcestershire, who share machinery and arrange marketing.

Driving through South Warwickshire this year (1999), I see that there has been another revival of interest in peas for combining, noting a number of roadside crops.

Ted Kerby, with his sons later in due course, of Billesley Manor Farm, near Stratford-on-Avon, have been growing peas and beans for freezing and canning since the mid 1950s. When there was a dairy herd on the farm, the pea haulm was made into silage.

At first, the crop was harvested by static viners and sent to Smedleys of Evesham. These were replaced by mobile trailer models and then by self propelled machines. Then broad beans replaced some of the peas and these were both sent to for canning to Stratford.

The Kerbys have always taken extra land for growing these crops, the total acreage of which peaked at 500 at one time. In 1999 about 300 acres of peas were grown and 50 acres of broad beans. The former are chilled on the farm before sending to the processing plant, while the broad beans are transported there in water tanks.

In short, there have been able and enterprising individuals who have incorporated peas (and broad and dwarf beans) into their farming systems with considerable success, but they have been the exception. Thus, over the years, the pea acreage in the county has fluctuated widely from year to year, but peas have always remained a minority crop.

Mixed Corn

Finally, an historical footnote. In the 1940s, and indeed into the 1950s, peas, often with beans, were grown as mixed corn for grinding and feeding on the farm. The idea being that the pulses increased the protein content to go some of the way in balancing the starchy cereals, something that was attractive, in theory, when protein was in short supply. Professor H.I.Moore in *Crops and Cropping* (1943) gave the following mixtures:

Barley or oats	10 stone/acre
Grey peas	4 stone/acre

or

Barley	4	stone/acre
Oats	3	stone/acre
Tick beans	3	stone/acre

Vetches	2 stone/acre
Grey peas	2 stone/acre

The crops were, of course, spring sown. Such mixtures were common enough at one time in South Warwickshire. But there was the usual gap between theory and practice. The proportion of pulses to cereals when harvested was very different to that which was drilled. And, even given the greater latitude provided by harvesting with a self binder, the difference in ripening between the cereals and the pulses could pose problems. For these reasons, and with harvesting by combine becoming universal, mixed corn as a crop disappeared into the mists of time.

20. OILSEED RAPE

In spite of the opinion held by the less well-informed, who lose no opportunity to denigrate present day agricultural practices, oilseed rape is not a new crop, although the considerable increase in the acreage grown in Britain is the result of the agricultural policy of the EU. The fact is that oilseed rape, cole seed or colza as it was then called, first appeared in this country around 1560 and a hundred years later was well established as an important crop; a role that it was destined to play for about the next two hundred years.

The following quotes are from Low's *Practical Agriculture*, (1843 edition):

> The turnip and early cole will usually ripen their seeds in the same year.

In other words spring oilseed rape, as it is called today.

> The proper period, however, of sowing the seeds of rape in this country is in the summer or autumn, that they may ripen their seeds in the following summer.

This refers to winter oilseed rape. The crop was then kept clean by horse and hand hoeing, to ripen in July.

> The plants are best reaped by sickle, and the operation is to be performed with care, so as to prevent the loss of seed by shaking. The plants may be bound into bunches and placed in stacks until it is convenient to thrash them. But it is better to thrash them as soon as they are dried. This may be done in the field if the weather is good, by thrashing on boards with sheets of canvas spread underneath; or the crop may be carried to the barn and thrashed there.

Flails, of course, were used to thrash out the rape seed. A contemporary print shows the crop being harvested and carted by means of a large sledge, with poles at each corner between which was slung a canvas to catch the shed seeds. (It is interesting to note that in 1948, a similar sledge, this time constructed of steel tubing, but complete with canvas, was used to carry a crop of cocksfoot seed on Dodwell Farm, near Stratford-on-Avon, when this crop was still being cut by binder.)

> The seeds are spread for a time on the granary floor, not less than three weeks. They are then bruised in mills of different construction.

The mills in common use were identical to the cider mills with which we are familiar. Essentially a circular stone trough with a stone wheel running in it, the motive power being provided by a horse. The point is made that on the

Continent, where the acreage of colza grown was greater than in Britain, these mills were usually found on the farms. However,

> In England the seeds of the oil plants are always sent to the oil-manufacturer, the preparation of the oil forming a distinct profession.

It is this fact, and thanks to the research carried out by Dr. Bob Bearman, the chief archivist at the Shakespeare's Centre in Stratford, which makes it certain that colza was grown in South Warwickshire in the 17th century. Ely Street in Stratford was formerly known as Swine Street until about this time. Then an oil mill was set up in the street which became known as Ullye (oily) Street; Ely was, in fact, a corruption of the older name. Far from being a new crop in South Warwickshire, oilseed rape was grown in the district some three hundred years before the crop became, once again, a common enough sight in our neck of the woods. The oil was used in industrial processes, in the manufacture of cloth and, of course, in oil lamps.

It was known a Colza oil and sometimes the lamps in which it was burnt were referred to as Colza lamps. Low would not have given so much space to describing the cultivation, harvesting and processing of the crop in his book, if colza seed was not being grown extensively in the mid 1800s. However, from then on, paraffin supplanted colza oil in lamps, which, in turn, and in the fullness of time, were made redundant by gas lighting and then by the electric light bulb. And that, for the time being, was that. Oilseed rape disappeared from the farming scene in this country in the second half of the 19th century.

It was not until the early 1970s that the crop started to be grown again. I do recall seeing some very indifferent crops of spring sown oilseed rape somewhere in Worcestershire in the 1960s. One way to track the come back of oilseed rape into the farming scene is to refer to successive editions of the *Farm Management Pocketbook* by John Nix. The first edition, in 1966, makes no mention at all of the crop. In 1969, we have the first note and this year, in common with the early 1970s, spring sown oilseed rape is given pride of place over autumn drilled crops. In these years, the gross margin per acre is paltry compared to that forecast for feed wheat. For instance, £15/acre as against £38/acre for feed wheat. Going forward to 1985, when oilseed rape had really become established, we find that it was competing very favourably at a gross margin of £263/acre with feed wheat at £200. Ten years later in 1995, oilseed rape stood at a gross margin of £265/acre, with feed wheat at £275. The boom years were almost over. In the 1999 edition, the predictions for the 2000 harvest are oilseed rape at £192/acre and feed wheat at £219.

Incidentally, all the above figures relate to the Nix *Average*. Of course, by the year 2000, the recession in farm prices across the board had set in, with little prospect of improvement in the foreseeable future. It is the relative position of oilseed rape to winter wheat that is important, and it is clear that the return from the former crop can now be expected to be somewhat below that from the latter. The results of an ADAS survey into the husbandry and importance of oilseed rape in the West Midlands, published in 1975 and presumably relating to the 1974, or even the 1973 harvest, is illuminating.

Warwickshire heads the list as far as the area grown is concerned at 209.5 acres in 9 fields. The areas grown in the other counties in the survey were almost insignificant, acreages in two figures only. There was, I believe, a very good reason for this. By then, for reasons already stated, the all-arable farm on the Warwickshire clays had become an established fact. Thus the search was on for a combineable break crop to take the place of the ley, which had been such a feature of the mixed farming scene in South Warwickshire for the previous thirty years. Beans, of course, had provided the traditional entry for winter wheat. But, although varieties, weed control, and general husbandry had improved, many found yields to be unreliable and erratic. Oilseed rape fitted the bill admirably. Moreover, its adoption was aided by the swing to winter barley. This was harvested in late July or early August and thus gave ample opportunity for the preparation of a seedbed and the timely drilling of oilseed rape.

In the early days, farmers who pioneered the growing of winter oilseed rape were doing the wood pigeon population a great favour. Like ripening winter barley, before this crop became widely grown, bird damage was a problem. Oilseed rape crops, being then few and far between, became the target for flocks of wood pigeons, especially in a hard winter. Today, this does not seem to be so much of a problem. In the first place, wood pigeons have now a much bigger acreage to graze. Secondly, growers have got better at establishing crops; pigeons will do most damage when crops are thin and with bare patches that provide a suitable, and inviting, landing ground.

No story of the growing of oilseed rape in South Warwickshire would be complete without mention of Eric Wynter, who did so much to popularise the crop in this district and further afield. Eric, who lives at Stretton on Fosse, at one time worked for Quenby Price, a firm which had an interest in oilseed rape and, at the time, and along with United Oilseeds, accounted for by far the highest proportion of the crops grown on contract.

In 1975, Eric decided to strike out on his own, forming his company Fieldcare (Oilseeds) Ltd. He also had an interest in other break crops, notably peas and beans. He offered farmers contracts for the growing of these crops, mainly, of course, oilseed rape. He proved to be an agronomist of the first rank, this knowledge of the husbandry of the crops in which he had an interest was second to none, and he played a leading role in the development of the agronomy of oilseed rape in this country. To him must go much of the credit in establishing oilseed rape as the most valuable break crop on the all arable farms, especially those in South Warwickshire on the stronger soils.

As mentioned above, Low, in his book, stated that the proper time to plant oilseed rape was in the late summer or autumn. Just another example of farmers having to relearn what was the common knowledge of previous generations. The re-introduction of oilseed rape was based on spring varieties to be superseded by autumn drilling. Today this crop is the most commonly grown in Britain after wheat and barley.

21. Cash Roots

Let it be stated straightaway that cash roots-potatoes and sugar beet now play only a minor role in the farming economy of South Warwickshire. Today, to the best of my knowledge, there are only two farmers who grow sugar beet in this district, and potato growing is now confined to a comparatively few farms on the best land. This is not to say that potatoes are not an important crop as far as the county as a whole is concerned.

Many grow the crop on the better, easier working soils in the centre and the north of Warwickshire. But during the 1940s and early 1950s, the needs of the food production campaign dictated that these cash roots were grown on soils that were anything but suitable. Thus in those years substantial acreages had to be grown in South Warwickshire on land that was not ideal, to put it mildly

Sugar Beet

While the main purpose in growing sugar beet was, of course, the extraction of sugar, it had an added attraction to livestock farmers (the vast majority). It provided a succulent feed in the form of the crowns and leaves and, in addition, growers had first call on supplies of sugar beet pulp, a by-product of the extraction process.

In contrast to the present, for much of the time when it was grown on a significant acreage in South Warwickshire, it was labour intensive. It had to be singled by hand, probably hand-hoed again at least once and horse or tractor hoed until the leaves met in the rows.

In the autumn, the roots were loosened with a sugar beet plough and pulled and topped by hand. The tops were left on the ground to be fed off later, and the roots carted off into clamps adjacent to a hard road, before being loaded into lorries to be taken to the factory at Kidderminster. These lorries were a common enough sight on the main Stratford to Oxford road at one time.

Gangs of Irishmen used to come into South Warwickshire for the sugar beet harvest, and during the war years, and just after, POWs, especially Italians, were also available. In reasonable autumn weather, it was not too bad a job, even on soils which should never really have been growing sugar beet at all. But in a wet time it was another matter. The autumn of 1946 was especially wet. The Grassland Improvement Station had had to grow its quota of sugar beet as a matter of principle, and I can well recall seeing a gang of Italians digging sugar beet by hand with forks in a field on Drayton, because it was too wet and sticky on that heavy land for the sugar beet plough to work.

In this day and age, it is all a very different story. The original sugar beet seed was in fact a fruit, from which several seedlings could emerge, necessitating hand singling. Over the years, many devices were introduced in an effort to mechanise, to a greater or lesser extent, the singling of sugar beet. One method was cross blocking in order to leave small bunches of seedlings to be singled by hand. Now monogerm seed is used exclusively which, along with the use of precision drills, eliminates all hand work in the establishment of the crop. Again, there are now a wide range of both pre- and post-emergence herbicides to deal with weed problems, taking the place of hand and horse or tractor inter-row cultivations.

Harvesting is now completely mechanised; the first mechanical harvesters being introduced in the 1940s. Both precision drills and harvesters became more and more sophisticated, and expensive. This meant that acreages had to justify the machinery investment involved or reliance has to be placed on contractors, which is sometimes the case in areas where the sugar beet acreage is such that contractors find it worthwhile to offer a service. The consequence was that growers had either to increase their acreage of sugar beet, or cease growing the crop. In South Warwickshire the majority chose the latter course.

Potatoes

In many ways it is much the same story with potatoes. During the 1940s many farmers in South Warwickshire were forced to a grow a limited acreage, often on soils that were totally unsuitable. This, added to the fact that those thus coerced had neither any knowledge nor liking for growing potatoes, resulted in foul, weedy crops which yielded but poorly. This was compensated to some extent by a fairly generous acreage payment.

It was Government policy to grow a sufficient acreage to ensure adequate supplies even in a dry year, or when Potato Blight reduced yields. Any surplus over and above what was needed for the domestic market, and there was one in most years, was purchased by the Ministry of Food, dyed purple so that they could not be used for human consumption and then sold as stock feed. Over the years this worked well, but in the disastrous season of 1947, after a wet, late, spring followed by a severe drought, yields countrywide were abysmal and potatoes were rationed in the following winter.

It should be pointed out that those on good potato land, who set about making a job of growing the crop, and also, of course, established potato growers on such soils, found the crop profitable, continuing to do so long after all Government control over cropping had been abandoned.

As in the case of sugar beet, the war time expansion of the potato acreage was achieved with a minimum of mechanisation. The essentials were a row crop tractor, or one that could be adapted to row crop work, a tool bar with ridging bodies and a trailer spinner for harvesting. But on many farms, especially the smaller ones, all the field work continued to be done with horses. A ridging plough opened up the furrow, the seed potatoes were planted by hand and then the ridges were split back to cover them. Any inter-row cultivations were done with a horse hoe before a final ridging up. The crop was harvested with a lifting plough, but horse drawn spinners were made in the 1930s, later converted with a draw bar for tractor use. One firm, Hornsby, made a plough with a ridging body which could be replaced with one for ploughing out the crop. Whether a spinner was used or a lifting body, the crop still had to be hand picked.

Trailed spinners specifically made for tractor use were common enough in the 1940s. These were improved and direct mounted in the 1950s. Elevator diggers had been manufactured in the States before domestic versions, made by Johnson Engineering and Peter Standen, became available in the 1950s.

Efficient mechanical potato planters made an appearance in the early 1950s, notably one direct mounted on the *little grey Fergie* which was hand-fed. Fully mechanised planters of various makes followed.

Up to this point, and for some time to come, harvesters and planters were still within the financial reach of those growing moderate acreages of potatoes, but there was still a lot of hand work involved in harvesting.

However, as planters and harvesters were developed for greater efficiency and higher output they became more expensive. Growers then had to make the decision to increase their acreage, if they had suitable land available or if they could rent some on an annual basis, in order to justify the capital investment, or to get out of potato growing entirely. As with sugar beet, many chose the latter.

This is not to say that there were not, and still are, very successful potato growers in South Warwickshire. Special mention must be made of two, whose methods were enterprising and unconventional in their day.

Ernest Bomford, of Rushford, Salford Priors farmed some six hundred acres, all arable, growing a variety of crops which included early potatoes, sprouts, savoys and cabbage, cereals and herbage seeds. In those days, the late 1940s and early 1950s, it was still possible to compete with other growers of earlies in Pembrokeshire and, to a lesser extent, Cornwall. Salford Priors, just north of Evesham, was one of the earliest parishes in South Warwickshire and much of the land was light. Another factor was that Ernest was able to irrigate a proportion of his farm.

Now it is an established fact that once-grown seed from Scotland produces an earlier crop than new seed. Ernest decided to grow his own seed for planting on his main holding and, to this end, rented land off the Hall brothers on the top of Meon Hill, on the northern Cotswold fringe. At that time, such land, because of its altitude, was considered suitable for growing A seed, now designated AA. SS seed was then the top grade and Ernest purchased this, which would have produced A seed if it had been certified. Ernest did his own roguing and kept a rain gauge on the Hill to compare the rainfall there with that at Rushford. Meon Hill also had the added advantage of being virtually frost free. The crop from Meon Hill was burnt off in due course and stored and chitted in the old granary at Rushford. This exercise was successful and, as far as I know, continued until the farming system was simplified and potato growing ceased.

Another innovative potato grower in South Warwickshire was Charlie Warhurst of Chesterton. In addition to an acreage on his own farm, he used to take fields on quite strong land which were in ley, but eligible for the £7/acre ploughing grant, which was available at the time. The arrangement was that the owner pocketed this grant, Charlie ploughed the land and grew his crop, then planted the field to winter wheat for his landlord to harvest. He used to grow the variety King Edward, lifting the crop early in August and September. The combination of this variety, a strong soil and plenty of organic matter produced a superb sample with clear, clean skins which found a ready market locally.

Frank Bennison, when he was managing for Colonel Warriner at Weston Park, near Shipston-on-Stour, is typical of those who gave up growing potatoes in the 1970s. He was an enthusiastic grower, producing good crops, because he was able to irrigate. But the crunch came when he was forced to consider considerable capital investment for further mechanisation or give up growing the crop. He was already utilising all the suitable land for potatoes and thus was unable to increase the acreage to make the investment a viable proposition. Incidentally, an old stone building was converted to a ventilated potato store, one of the advantages of which was to give the workers an inside job during the winter months. This conversion won a Country Landowners Association award in their annual competition for the best farm building or conversion.

The potato crop, at one time, played an important part in the economy of many South Warwickshire farms. The standard of husbandry was high, and there were innovative growers both in the methods of production and in marketing. Sadly, today, their numbers are much reduced.

22. SEED PRODUCTION

Seed production is not a farming activity that many would associate with Warwickshire. Although crops grown for this purpose are in a small minority, on some holdings they played, and play, an important part in the farm economy. As I have been, at one time or another, intimately concerned with seed production in the county, it is appropriate that I put on record this aspect of Warwickshire farming with which many may not be familiar.

Vegetable and Root Seeds

East Anglia, and Essex in particular, with its dry summers, was the traditional area for growing these types of seed. In the 1940s, owing the restriction of imports, farmers in Warwickshire were encouraged to try their hand at producing flower, vegetable and root seeds.

I have in front of me an old, battered notebook in which I recorded the names of such seed growers with the crops that they grew in 1947.

> Mr. Griffiths of Knightcote: Siberian Wallflower.
>
> Mr. Thornley of Radford: Mangold and Broccoli.
>
> Mr. Hewitt of Meriden: Mangold.
>
> Mr. Passmore, Wormleighton: Carrot, onion and cabbage.
>
> Mr. Goode, Broadwell: Broad beans and swedes.

I also have a note in another book of Mr. Goode's swede seed growing, as follows.

> Swedes for Seed Production. Notes on a crop grown by A. Goode Esq. , Broadwell.
>
> Crop sown August 26th. 1946. Seed rate 2lb./acre. Rows 2 feet apart and plants singled to 1 foot apart in the rows. Harvested July 20th. 1947. Cut with a binder with a sheet under the sheaf carrier.
>
> A man walked beside the binder and lifted the sheaves off the carrier with a fork and laid them on the ground. Estimated yield 10 cwt./acre @ 112 shillings/cwt. (£1.60 /cwt). Plants should have formed small bulbs by the time growth ceases in the back-end.

Mr. Goode also grew some flower seeds, if I recall correctly. The flower heads were cut by hand, dried in bunches and threshed by rubbing over a fine sieve. A labour-intensive process, which was carried out by his daughters.

At this point, it should be noted that root crops are biennials. That is, as with swedes, they are sown in one season, forming a small bulb and then produce seed heads from it the following year.

Sugar beet seed crops were grown by Messrs. Hughes and Cotterill, both of Fenny Compton, George Robinson and David Darbishire, both of Wormleighton.

The sugar beet plants were called stecklings but, unlike swedes, were lifted and re-planted, usually by hand with a dibber. I have a record of a trial laid down on George Robinson's farm, Stoneton Manor, to compare autumn stecklings to those planted out in the spring. This showed clearly that stecklings lifted from the seedbed and pegged out in the autumn, yielded very much better than those left, then lifted and transplanted in the spring. The plots were cut by hand on September 15th. and 16th. 1947, left in the stook for two weeks, when the combine was driven into the field and threshed the plots out, straight from the stook.

Vegetable and root seed production was a demanding, labour-intensive business, as will be gathered by the notes above. The shedding of the seed was a constant problem. Maurice Passmore had metal trays fitted under his binder to catch the seeds of carrot, onion and cabbage. I remember that the carrot seed shed badly and frequent stops had to be made to empty the trays, which quickly became full. It may well have been that the binder threshed out more seed than the drum or combine!

For the above reasons, although undoubtedly profitable at the time and providing a challenge to the bolder spirits, by the end of the 1940s, vegetable and root seed growing virtually ceased in Warwickshire.

Potato Seed Production

I was engaged in the inspection and certification of potato crops for seed from 1948 until 1967, but, regrettably, never really dealt with enough acres each year to get as proficient as I would like to have been.

In the early years, we went for training and refresher courses to the agricultural college at Sutton Bonnington, now part of Nottingham University. The national collection of potato varieties was kept there, under the supervision of the redoubtable Mrs. Mac. Her knowledge of potato varieties and husbandry was encyclopaedic, and she had the great gift of inspiring and imparting her knowledge to others.

Later, on her retirement, the potato variety collection was moved to the National Institute of Agricultural Botany at Cambridge and Tom Webster, who had been an assistant at Sutton Bonnington, took over and proved a worthy successor to Mrs. Mac.

In 1966, the Plant Health Branch of the Ministry of Agriculture took over the field inspection work for seed certification and also the inspections under the Plant Disease Regulations. The latter was not one of my favourite jobs, involving, as often as not, scrambling about in railway trucks or vans in mid-winter. A stated number of sacks had to be inspected and tuber counts taken, frost damage, dry rot and skin spot being the main causes of trouble and complaint. The latter had to be made within a certain number of days of taking delivery, which in many cases gave us a let out.

Another job under the plant disease regulations I did enjoy concerned wart disease. The maincrop variety King Edward is susceptible to wart disease, and crops thus infected had to be dug up and the haulm and tubers burnt. Many gardens and allotments in Birmingham, and particularly on the northern side of the city where new development had taken place on farmland, were infected with this disease, which made its appearance from mid-summer onwards in a wet season. The City Corporation's horticultural adviser was usually the first point of contact, after which I had to accompany him to the affected garden or allotment, usually confirming the disease and instructing as to the action which should be taken.

Two incidents spring to mind. On one occasion, we had to assure a distraught young mother, who had fed her young child on potatoes from her garden where we had found Wart Disease, that her little boy would not come out in king-sized warts and be disfigured for life.

The second occasion was a visit to some old-established allotments not really very far from the city centre. These were occupied by the older generation, in contrast to the age of the allotment holders and gardeners further out on the newer estates. On this particular allotment, my horticultural friend had arranged for a reporter and photographer from the Birmingham Post to attend, to write a story and take pictures, which duly appeared in print. The tenant was one of the old school, retired, with a black suit and white muffler across the chest, secured with a tie pin, and, of course, a cap.

The hut on his allotment was his second home complete with Tortoise stove, carpeting and an armchair, along with the necessary for making tea or cocoa. He made much play of the fact that his address was No. 10 Downing Street, and election nights were the occasion for a party. He was turned out of the house by his wife in the morning and not allowed to return until his former knocking off time. The attentions of the Press made his day and that particular edition of the Post must have been shown off on every possible occasion.

In 1966, I went potato inspecting for the last time, in Norfolk in fact, allegedly supervising two inspectors who had just finished their training. They knew more about it than I did! But the weather was good and Norfolk is one of my favourite counties. I stayed with Jack and Marie Gibbs in Cromer. Jack was the postmaster in Cromer and Marie the sister of Ethel Edkins, wife of Spence who kept the Kings Head at Aston Cantlow. Marie was an excellent cook and her packed lunches the envy of my colleagues. Altogether, a very pleasant fortnight and a fitting end to a job which I had enjoyed for nearly twenty years.

But that is over-running my story. In Warwickshire and in the neighbouring county of Worcestershire, where I went to help out on many occasions, the crops were put up for inspection for what was then known as an H Certificate (now CC) in most cases. Some applied for an A Certificate (now AA) with a view to growing on again. Today, as I understand it, seed crops have to be burnt off by a certain date decreed by the inspector. In the 1950s and 1960s, growers more or less pleased themselves, burning off when blight threatened. Otherwise, they were quite happy to use the smaller tubers for seed when the main crop went to the ware stage. There was an ever present danger of the late spread of virus diseases after the crop had been inspected and passed.

For two years I went inspecting in the Black Mountains where a few acres of an SS (stock seed) for producing A or H seed provided a welcome cash crop on these upland farms. The crops, never more than a few acres, were all well grown, well cherished and subject to much TLC. It was a red letter day when the inspectors arrived and we were made very welcome. The standards for inspection were very high, much more so than for A or H certificates. It was almost a hands and knees job. In theory we put a cane against each plant that we wanted rogued. In practice, the grower followed us with a fork and sack, taking out the offending plants as we went along. An excellent practice, as there were always some early spuds to take home with us.

The main early varieties inspected in Warwickshire and Worcestershire were Arran Pilot, Eclipse and Home Guard. One had to be very much on the ball with the latter in a dry season, because Home Guard had the habit of dying off very early under drought conditions on the lightest soils. One year, I very nearly missed the boat, but not quite, with a crop grown on the NAAS Luddington Horticultural Station, as it was then.

Of the maincrop varieties, Majestic and King Edward dominated the scene. In the case of the latter, and its variant Red King Edward, I enjoyed one of life's minor triumphs. The two varieties were being grown in the same field by Sam Moreton or Charlie Warhurst, I cannot remember which. There was, of course, the statutory strip of bare cultivated land between the two varieties which, to the casual observer, were identical, but the red version had a distinct red tinge to the leaf stems.

Where two varieties were being grown in the same field, a sketch map showing their locations had to be provided. On this occasion, I was able to spot that the varieties had been transposed, the red version being grown on the side of the bare strip described as being planted to the ordinary variety. With tongue in cheek I threatened to turn down both varieties, and then amended the sketch.

My stock rose instantly, having created the impression that I knew what I was doing.

There was one grower whose crop proved to be a headache every year. In the first place he planted Irish seed. This was an excellent practice as such seed was graded better than that from Scotland, and the bags sealed by the inspector after grading. The snag was that the Northern Ireland growers planted only a few acres each. The consequence was that, instead of having one or two certificate numbers relating to the parcels of seed planted in, say, a twenty-acre field, there could well be four or even more. This needed extra care in case there was trouble with one lot of seed.

Secondly, the farmer in question was not in the first flight, to put it as kindly as possible. The land was very light and ran to squitch at the slightest opportunity. So much so, that in some parts of the field being inspected it was difficult to find the potato plants under a dense cover of the weed. Under these circumstances, and according to the book, one was entitled to turn the crop down. But I never did, threshing my way through the densest patches of squitch with my ash stick to find the potato plants lurking under a canopy of leaves.

As already mentioned above, potato seed inspections and the plant disease regulations were taken over by the Plant Health Branch of MAFF. In the twenty, or so, years that I was doing these jobs, I learnt a lot about potato husbandry and met many forward-looking and interesting farmers.

Herbage Seed Production

This was a branch of seed production with which I was much concerned from 1950 until 1982, when I retired from the Agricultural Development and Advisory Service as NAAS had, by then, become. During the early years, we were dealing almost exclusively with the Aberystwyth, or 'S,' varieties.

Prior to the introduction of these, by far the greatest proportion of grass sown in the UK consisted of commercial seed. Some of this was grown in the UK, for instance Irish and Ayrshire perennial ryegrass. But much was imported, such as Danish Cocksfoot and American Timothy. Commercial seed produced plants which, although generally early to start growth in the spring, had a low proportion of leaf to stem – all stem and little leaf, in other words. As the leaf is the most nutritious portion of any grass, commercial seed gave rise to swards which were inferior and, in any case, were not persistent.

However, there were some strains, prior to the introduction of the *S* varieties which were leafier and longer living. Two perennial ryegrasses spring to mind, Kentish Indigenous and Hawke's Bay Certified from New Zealand.

There were also native varieties of the clovers which were superior to imported seed. These included Kentish wild white, and Montgomery, Cornish marl, Dorset marl, all red clovers and Kersey large white.

The fact remains that the above superior varieties were more expensive and supplies not unlimited. Thus the vast majority of seeds mixtures contained commercial seed, which gave rise to swards which were inferior in feeding value and persistency.

In the 1920s and 1930s, all this was to change thanks to the work of Sir George Stapledon and his colleagues at the Welsh Plant Breeding Station. Under-funding, as it is now called, was an acute problem at one juncture. However, money was made available from the Empire Marketing Board without which the breeding, multiplication and distribution of seed of improved strains of grasses and clovers would, at best, have been much delayed and almost certainly not available for the food production campaign which started in 1939.

Imitation is the sincerest form of flattery, and once mainland Europe had recovered from the ravages of the Second World War, grass breeding programmes were instigated which, in the fullness of time, produced new, improved, varieties in profusion. Today the old *S* strains are all but things of the past.

Much of Wales was unsuited for the multiplication of grass and clover seeds, and this started on a farm scale in the counties of Hereford and Montgomery. In 1939, there were under 1,000 acres of certified seed crops of *S* strains. By 1941, this had risen to 1,597 and, due to wartime pressures, to no less than 21,099 acres in 1949. This was no flash in the pan, for, by 1960, the acreage had risen to 40,000.

The certification scheme was administered from Aberystwyth from 1940 to 1954, and during this period no less than 300,000 acres were inspected and certified by NAAS staff.

Thus, in the earlier years, we had to travel to Aberystwyth for training and the annual refresher course. In those days the town was not at its best, to put it as kindly as possible. The pier had been partly demolished in 1940, as a wartime measure, and had not been repaired. The hotels on the front, which had been built in the heyday of the town as a seaside resort in Victorian times were either boarded up or occupied by offices. There was still one open and this is where we had to stay.

This was a dump, to put it bluntly. The decor, the furniture and the plumbing was all original 19th century, and certainly not in mint condition. When we descended from all quarters of England, it must have been the only occasion in the year when the hotel was full. Meal times were exciting, to say the least. Clearly a team of Blodwens had been recruited from the surrounding hills to supplement the regular waiting staff. Their enthusiasm was not matched by their skill. Some of your soup was just as likely to end up in your lap and the same could be said of the other courses.

I spent one night in this ghastly place which I shall never forget. A Force 10 westerly gale was blowing, and the whole building shook all night. Lying awake and trying to read, I could see the roof timbers moving under the wallpaper, for my grotty little room was on the top floor. In the morning we found that, such was the force of the gale, the road behind the hotel was strewn with shingle. Nor were conditions for field work on the plots, located on fields above the town, any better. It was either raining, or blowing, or both.

Happily the grass and clover collections were eventually laid down on the National Institute of Agricultural Botany's trial grounds, Huntingdon Road, Cambridge. It could be cold, but at least it was dry. The hotels that we were booked into were palaces in comparison, and Cambridge, in late April, could be beautiful. For me, for just over twenty five years, the annual pilgrimage to NIAB was something to look forward to; a gathering of old friends, a pub lunch, dinner in the evening in one of the many excellent eating places, and a leisurely stroll through Colleges to the Backs, with the trees in blossom and daffodils in bloom.

Although the vast majority of grass and clover seed crops I inspected were the *S* strains, the very first crop was not. White clover seed production was very much an opportunist job. If, by chance, the grazing and subsequent weather had been right, there could be a mass of white flowers in high summer and good money to be made if the crop could be harvested in good order.

If a sward had been sown to Kentish Wild White and the clover, possibly several seasons later, could be identified as of this type on inspection, the NIAB would issue a certificate to this effect.

Bert Warren and his father were tenants of Park Farm, Shelfield, and asked for such a crop to be inspected. This I duly did one fine summer's evening in 1944 and then, everything being in order, repaired to the Kings Head, Aston Cantlow, with Bert for a pint or two.

Herbage seed growing in South Warwickshire tended to be concentrated in the West of the district. The growers in these parishes included Sam and Walter Pritchard, Grenville Stevens, Bill Palmer, Ragley Home Farms and Ernest Bomford, of Rushford, in the parish of Salford Priors.

Grenville Stevens farmed at Upper Spernal as his grandson, another Grenville, still does. Every year, in January, I used to visit Upper Spernal to fill in the necessary forms for the crops to be sown in the following season.

On one occasion, on New Year's Day1953 to be precise, we were sat at the kitchen table happily engaged in this task, when there was an almighty rushing noise, shaking the old house. Grenville rushed to the kitchen window, wiped it to reveal an aeroplane crossing and then landing in a field well below us. 'He's low,' said Grenville – an understatement as we were looking down on the plane. As we watched it pitched over to one side and a wing and an engine came off before the rest of the craft disappeared into the morning mist.

I grabbed the phone – it was dead. So we jumped in my car and drove down Spernal Lane to where we thought the plane had landed; eventually we came across gaps in the hedges where it had skidded across the lane, into one of Sam Pritchard's fields. The remaining wing had hit an oak tree, bringing the plane to a halt, facing the way it had come and straddling a deep ditch.

Although the cabin top had been crushed by a branch, miraculously nobody was hurt, with the exception of the second pilot, who was bleeding profusely from a cut in his head. My abiding memory is of Walter Pritchard and Grenville Stevens supporting the unfortunate man in the middle of the lane and discussing whether or not they should take his muddy boots off before putting him my car to take him to Stratford Hospital.

When I took Grenville back to Upper Spernal we found that the plane, an Aer Lingus Dakota, had taken the telephone wires with it between the first and second pole from the house – too close for comfort.

Away from the parishes mentioned above, there were others who grew herbage seeds, some for many years, others for only a few seasons. These included, amongst others, G. R. Davies of The Crofts Farm, just outside Stratford; Ian Hughes of Crimscote; J. George of Wixford; A. H. Hiller at Dunnington; E. Kerby of Billesley; A. Minors, Oversley; Hedley Longford, Alveston; what was then the National Vegetable Research Station, Wellesbourne, and Aubrey Seymour of Weston Mill, near Shipston-on-Stour.

To the best of my knowledge, Grenville Stevens, grandson of my old friend, who is still at Upper Spernal and manages the Spernal Estate, is the only herbage seed grower left in South Warwickshire. At its peak his acreage, at 600, made him the largest grower in the country. This has now been reduced to 500 and in the foreseeable future will fall to 350. He grows mainly perennial ryegrass varieties but also Tall Fescue, Red Fescue, Meadow Fescue and, for good measure, some sainfoin.

We used to start inspecting the early varieties in the second week in May, as soon as we had returned from the NIAB. It was an enjoyable job, especially if the weather was good. The walking was easy, compared with potatoes or cereals, and the countryside was looking at its best, Spernal Woods, in particular, being an unforgettable sight at this time of the year, with the leaves of many species of tree, fresh from the bud, and every conceivable shade of green.

There was, and still is, a Warwickshire Seed Growers Branch of the National Farmers' Union. Branch Meetings were always well attended, the Annual General Meeting being followed by a dinner. I was a member, my personal association with those farmers growing herbage seeds being a close one.

Cereal Seed

Cereal crops for seed production account for a significant acreage in South Warwickshire. In terms of acres, they have always been the major seed crop.

In this day and age, when it is illegal to sell uncertified seed, it may be difficult to appreciate that, not all that long ago, those merchants purveying seed of any kind had more or less a free hand. The Seeds Act, passed in the early 1920s and the National Institute of Agricultural Botany, established at much the same time, were the first measures to try to ensure that growers were protected against being offered seed, which was quite unsuited in every way.

The regulations stipulated a minimum germination and minimum standards of purity, that is in relation to weed seeds and other impurities. For example both winter and spring barleys were required to be 99% pure with 90% germination, and wheat 100% pure with the same germination. Seed of wild oats, cleavers, charlock, corn buttercup and wild onion were considered to be particularly obnoxious in corn seed. Seed testing stations were set up at the NIAB and Aberystwyth, used, of course, mainly by the trade.

The national seed houses, such as Gartons, would presumably have their own inspection schemes for seed crops. But, to the best of my knowledge, country seed merchants bought seed locally very much on the appearance of the sample and took trueness to variety very much on trust. Great emphasis was placed on change of seed from one soil type to another. For instance, it was thought that seed from the poorer Cotswold land would produce good crops when grown on the richer, South Warwickshire soils. It might be added that there was never any scientific evidence that this was so. Nevertheless, local merchants would often seek their corn seed supplies largely from Cotswold farms.

The great increase in the acreage of cereals from 1940 onwards obviously gave rise to a greater demand for seed. Leslie E. Cook, the Executive Officer of the Seed Production Committee at NIAB, Cambridge, writing in 1946 said:

> It was soon apparent that many farmers were obliged to use corn for seed which was not of good quality due to the presence of weed seeds, or seed borne diseases, or admixture with other cereals. . . . . The problem of finding adequate supplies of good quality seed was more acute in those counties where there had been a very big increase in the cereal acreage than in the principal corn growing districts.

He also noted there that, in several counties, corn growers had inaugurated schemes for the inspection of crops and the approval for those suitable for seed.

Warwickshire was one such county. By 1943, it had become obvious to members of the Technical sub-committee of the Warwickshire *War Ag* that stocks of seed of cereal varieties, wheat in particular, as a result in the rapid increase in acreage had become impure.

Accordingly, they decided that the Technical Officers, as we were then called, should receive a crash course in variety identification and that an inspection scheme would start for the 1944 harvest. Thus, in January 1944, we were sent to the NIAB at Cambridge to be given such a course in varietal identification and inspection procedures. I shall never forget that drive in my 1937 Morris 8, with two colleagues as passengers. No heaters in those days and the wind whistling up through the gaps where the pedals went through the floorboards. Car rugs were standard equipment, but even these did not stop frozen feet, resulting in chilblains. It took the best part of half a day to get there at a steady 35 mph on the level, and it was bitterly cold.

The piece of paper that the grower received after we had inspected his crop, and providing it passed, was not a seed certificate as such but a 'Threshing Priority Certificate.' This simply said that the crop was considered suitable for use as seed and that threshing contractors should give such crops priority in the immediate post-harvest period, to ensure supplies for autumn drilling. However, in the eyes of farmers and local seed merchants, such certificates were regarded as giving some sort of guarantee that the seed was of the variety stated and reasonably free from weed seeds, especially wild oats.

Farmers were invited to enter their crops, often at the instigation of those merchants who habitually bought seed from them. In the first year, 1944, we inspected 2,292 acres of winter wheat; in 1945, 2,340; in 1946, 1,636 acres of winter wheat and 176 acres of winter oats. In the last year, by which time national schemes were up and running, the acreage fell away to 465. Thereafter, the trade became responsible for this inspection work, latterly to have spot checks carried out by NAAS or ADAS, but that was to be many years in the future.

It was a foul job, wading through crops that were much longer in the straw than today. There was no herbicide to deal with cleavers and a crop badly infested with this weed was a nightmare to walk through. And, of course, there were no tram-lines.

The inspections had to be carried out between colour change in July and harvest. It always seemed to be hot and humid, with the thunder bugs rampant. You always wore out a pair of drill trousers every season, just above the knee. It was a job which I, for one, was heartily glad to see the back of.

But it was worthwhile. The worst fears were confirmed by the first year's inspections. We were by no means expert at the job with only a short training course and no experience. But, at least, we could tell red from white chaff, red grain from white grain and long straw from short (but not much else!) and we knew wild oats when we saw them, which was frequently. Even on this crude basis we turned down at least one third of the crops inspected on the grounds of contamination with other cereals, varietal impurities and weed infestations. It was all very interesting, and after the first year there was a satisfying rise in standards. So we had accomplished something.

Today it is all a very different story. Crop inspectors are skilled and experienced; standards are much higher; weed control, thanks to modern herbicides, has improved beyond recognition, as has the efficiency of seed processing plants.

Nowadays, a considerable acreage of cereals is grown on contract in South Warwickshire. I am told that Countrywide Ltd., formerly Midland Shire Farmers, have some 2,000 acres of cereal seed crops on contract in the district.

But special mention must be made of the seed enterprise of John Stanley and his sons David and James of Milcote Manor, Clifford Chambers, near Stratford-on-Avon. They established their seed business in 1987 with storage and a seed processing plant. In their first season, they traded some 300 tonnes of seed, today this has risen to 2,500 tonnes. Following the modern trend, some 70% of cereal seed is sent out in half-tonne bags.

On their own farm, they grow some 230 acres of wheat and barley for seed, also an acreage of stubble turnips. In addition, they have 20 farmers growing seed on contract for them. At the moment, they are taking advantage of the strong pound and importing seed from the Continent, notably linseed.

From small beginnings in the *hungry forties*, and as a result of the food production campaign, seed production in South Warwickshire is still very much a part of the farming scene.

23. Minority Crops

Many are called but few chosen

Fibre Crops

During the Second World War, a limited acreage of flax was grown in Warwickshire. The resulting fibre was used for a number of wartime necessities, such as parachute harnesses. Much of the acreage had to be hand pulled in those days, although the process was mechanised and flax pulling machines became available.

Lately there has been a revival of interest in growing fibre crops, notably hemp and flax. Various rules and regulations regarding the former require that hemp growers are licensed, on the grounds that the crop might be used in the manufacture of illegal drugs. But there seems to be a market for the fibre for making door linings, etc., in car manufacture. Whether this will develop into a crop grown on a significant scale remains to be seen. So far, to the best of my knowledge, none has been grown in South Warwickshire to date.

Linseed

This is the same species as flax, but grown for its seed, rather than its fibre. In our district, it has had something of a chequered career.

In the immediate post-War years, in the second half of the 1940s, it became Government policy to grow a substantial acreage of linseed because of a world-wide shortage and a near monopoly of supplies by Argentina. Not a great acreage was ever grown, yields were poor and, at the prices ruling at the time, linseed was hardly an attractive proposition.

My own experience of the crop was not a happy one. At the time I was an assistant to Dr. D.H.Robinson, who was the NAAS crop husbandry adviser in the West Midlands. In view of what was thought to be the importance of the crop at that time, 1948, the powers that be directed that field trials should be conducted by NAAS to gain information on the husbandry of linseed, which was sadly lacking at the time.

The Grassland Improvement Station had recently relinquished its original headquarters and the farm at Dodwell (along with its farms in Staffordshire, Mixon Hay, and Colesbourne in the Cotswolds) to concentrate its efforts at Drayton, before its eventual move to Hurley. But Dodwell was leased from Mr.

Walter Higgs, of Hockley Heath. The lease still had few years to run and, thus, the farm became the responsibility of the *War Ag* We used it for field trials of various kinds for several years, and a multi-factorial one on linseed growing was duly drilled in 1948.

Varieties, levels of fertilising, seed rates and dates of drilling were the matters being investigated. One set of 24 plots was drilled in mid-March and repeated four weeks later. We were assisted by a tractor driver, whose nationality I will not mention for fear of giving offence. He drove the combine on the farm, the deck of which was operated manually. The previous season, wishing to prop it in an intermediate position, he gently lowered it onto the activating knob on the top of the fire extinguisher carried on the machine, which fortunately was defective. The extinguisher thus failed in its original purpose but proved ideally suited to its secondary one.

Fertiliser had to be spread on the plots by hand. When this character was handed a bucketful and told where to spread it he said 'he did not do that sort of work.' He had his pride. His peak of achievement, after the whole trial had been completed – all 48 plots involving an enormous amount of work, measuring, laying out and so on – was to drive the tractor and drill diagonally across the lot, from corner to corner of all of 2 acres. Fortunately the drill was out of gear, but I can still see, in my mind's eye, D.H., in shirt sleeves with red braces displayed, jumping up and down, waving his arms and shouting, purple in the face with rage.

Harvesting was just as traumatic. Linseed straw is like wire and the knife of the binder was not up to the job; constant blockages were the order of the day. The sheaves in each plot had to be kept separate and labelled and then came the problem of how to thrash such small quantities. We tried several methods, but ended up with an onion seed thresher. This was driven by belts with a stationary engine. The sheaves were fed into the miniature drum, the seed and chaff falling into a box below it, while shakers sent the straw up a wooden chute and into a heap on the ground. This did not work very well! The straw kept wrapping round the drum until I noticed the shakers were going the wrong way; I twisted the belt driving them and all was well thereafter.

And the end result, after all the time, effort and trauma? Precisely nil; nothing made much difference to the very poor yield.

With world supplies, and thus imports, returning to normal, linseed disappeared from the UK farming scene almost entirely. That is, until the EU introduced a very generous acreage payment which gave an enormous boost to the crop. The UK acreage in 1984 was 2,879, but by 1993 it had risen to 370,650 acres; this was 94% of the EU total. Potential yields have not improved over the years. Nix gives the average as 0.55 tonnes/acre. At £100/tonne, the market value is just £56/acre; the arable area payment is £148/acre, which makes the crop just viable. It also has the advantage of attracting AAP even when grown on land which is not eligible for AAP for other crops.

Winter varieties are now available and, of course, there are spring varieties which were not on the scene fifty years ago. At the time of writing, it does not seem that sowing the crop in the autumn has any clear advantage. As long as the EU AAP continues, linseed will have a place. But its economic viability is entirely dependent upon EU policy.

Sunflowers

This is yet another crop which, from time to time, is predicted to have a bright future, but one that has not materialised to date. However, at the end of the 1990s there was an acreage sown in South Warwickshire. Possibly this was the result of an enterprising seed merchant promoting the crop.

A number of crops could be seen from the roadside and very spectacular they looked when in full flower, with their plate-like seed heads fringed with yellow petals. So much so that passing motorists had stopped and they, and their families, helped themselves leaving an area just within the gateways, denuded of flowers with an additional area of the crop well trampled and rendered useless.

It was all a nine-day wonder and the crop has now disappeared from the South Warwickshire farming scene.

Lupins

Looking through my files of press cuttings, various enthusiasts have sung the praises of this crop at fairly regular intervals over the last fifty years as a source of protein rich grain or as a forage crop. As far as I know, lupins have not been grown as a commercial farm crop in South Warwickshire. In the second half of the 1940s, however, the edict went forth that NAAS was to take a look at the husbandry of the crop.

Lupins are essentially a crop for light acid soils and we duly drilled some observation plots on a roadside field near Packington. Lupins are, of course, a leguminous crop and their nitrogen fixing capacity is dependent upon the appropriate bacteria being present in the soil. This is usually the case with the commoner legumes such as the red and white clovers, but as in the case of lucerne, it is prudent to inoculate the seed with the necessary bacteria, the inoculum being supplied with the seed where the legume has not been grown before.

In the case of lupins, no such inoculum was available, so some bags of soil from fields on which lupins had been grown was sent with the seed, which was duly sprinkled into the drill before sowing. Incidentally, these fields were situated in the sandland district of East Suffolk with which I was to become very familiar many, many years later.

There were two varieties of these sweet lupins. One had blue flowers and an erect habit of growth, the other was yellow flowered and more prostrate.

As in the case of the sunflowers, the sight of blue and yellow lupins in full flower and in a roadside field was too much for the motorised morons with no respect for the property of others. One weekend a whole area of the crop adjacent to the road was stripped. Fortunately this was a buffer area around the main trial, which was duly harvested, the yellow variety out-yielding the blue by a significant margin.

24. FODDER CROPS

Mangolds

The modern spelling is *Mangels* and is one I refuse to adopt. The original version with its *-golds*, rather than *-gels*, is more evocative of a large, well rounded root, or so it seems to me. But that is by the way.

At the beginning of our period, in 1940, there would be few farms in South Warwickshire on which a crop of mangolds would not be found. Indeed, even on the heaviest land the only arable would likely to be a few acres of mangolds, some kale if there was a milking herd, and oats for the horses. Mangolds were fed to cattle of all kinds after Christmas, for they had to mature in the clamp after lifting, and were much prized for feeding to ewes at lambing time.

Mangolds are, of course, grown in wide rows. This, before the days of herbicides, allowed inter-row horse or tractor hoeing. Mangolds, along with other roots, were cleaning crops and played a part in the old rotations in keeping land free, or comparatively free, from weeds.

The seed of the mangold is, in fact, a fruit that gives rise to two or three seedlings, which have to be singled, leaving just one. In passing, it must be pointed out that monogerm seed can now be obtained for the higher dry matter mangolds and fodder beet. But this is not the case with the traditional, or low dry matter, mangold, and hand singling is still necessary.

When a mangold crop was singled, the remaining plant could suffer from a condition known as strangles. The stem went black, withered and collapsed, separating the leaves and crown from the root. This was most common in hot weather accompanied by a drying wind. Many a farm visit did I have to make when a grower had his crop thus affected for the first time. There was no cure. The risk of the condition occurring could be minimised by not growing the crop on the ridge, not a common practice in South Warwickshire in any case, and making every effort to cover the singled plant with earth after singling, something that was easier said than done.

Even in the days when the fertilising of corn crops was meagre by modern standards, root crops were usually treated generously. If possible, farmyard manure was applied and ploughed in during the winter, so that the furrow slice could be weathered by frost to produce a good tilth in the spring. Then fertiliser would be applied into the seedbed. Nitrate of soda and fish manure were favourites and, in later years, a compound fertiliser with a high potash content.

On the Warwickshire clays, the better farmers realised the need for a generous application of phosphatic fertiliser, in addition.

Harvesting was all hand work. The mangold root sits on the surface of the soil and can be pulled up by hand. Because my left arm was badly broken and badly set when at school, I always found it easier to pull the root with my left hand and hold the knife in my right. A quick pull, a swing and at the same time cutting the leaves from the root, sent it sailing onto a small heap, the leaves being dropped in a circle to be forked over the mangolds to protect from frost until they were carted.

The roots were then loaded into cart or tractor trailer by hand. The unforgivable sin was to pierce the skin with a fork. Then they were clamped and covered with straw and earthed up, leaving a ridge of straw for ventilation. With the advent of the pick-up baler, clamps were often made with bales. I recall one such monster clamp at New End Farm, Great Alne. Sam Pritchard, being Sam, never did anything by halves. Not only did he build bale clamps bigger than anyone else's, but horrified his neighbours by not topping the mangolds, clamping them whole. They survived the winter in perfect condition, the leaves simply withering on the roots.

Today the growing of mangolds is a thing of the past. With the introduction of modern herbicides, the need for a cleaning crop in an arable rotation has long since disappeared. Silage has largely taken the place of roots in the feeding of cattle.

Fodder Beet

Fodder beet as a feed for cattle is still very much with us. As already mentioned, monogerm seed is now available, eliminating the need for handwork in singling. The harvesting of fodder beet can also be mechanised, so little hand work is involved in growing the crop. As with mangolds, high yields of highly digestible dry matter can be obtained, and this is the great virtue of the crop.

Little, if any, is grown in South Warwickshire today. What is fed is usually purchased and I am told that there is one grower just over the county boundary in Gloucestershire. Mike Dowler of Manor Farm, Ilmington, tells me they used to purchase fodder beet for feeding to the dairy herd from this source. In the end, and especially when they started complete diet feeding, they found that contamination with soil was a problem, even when the beet had been washed, and so they stopped feeding it. However, judging by advertisements in the Farmers Weekly and Farmers Guardian, there is a lively trade in fodder beet from growers to dairy farmers.

One historical curiosity is worth a mention. When animal feedstuffs were still rationed and when pig production still had a place on the general farm, the high dry matter fodder beets were thought to have a place in feeding pigs. By 1950 high dry matter varieties of fodder beet became available from breeders in Europe, notably Denmark and Holland. NAAS undertook trials to compare varieties, particularly as regards dry matter.

One such observation trial was laid down on the old aerodrome at Atherstone-on-Stour, at the time being farmed by the *War Ag.* My notes record that the plots received 20 to 25 tons of farmyard manure per acre and one ton of Hadfields root fertiliser overall. The plots were drilled on May 5th. 1951, in 24" rows and singled to 15" in the row. The plots were harvested on November 6th. 'after heavy rain.' A random sample from each plot was taken for dry matter determination.

There were seventeen varieties in the trial. Pajberg headed the dry matter league table at 22. 2% with Stryno at the bottom at 11.2%. Although an English mangold was included in the plots, no determination of the dry matter was recorded. But it would be somewhat less than Stryno.

Over the years fodder beet has had a role in cattle feeding and will, no doubt, continue to have its devotees.

Kale

As recorded in the chapter on feeding the dairy cow, kale was, at one time, grown in a similar manner to mangolds, in wide rows and then chopped out to space the seedling in the row. This is worthy of a footnote.

Bill and Margaret Craig were farming Cutlers Farm, Wootton Wawen, in the 1950s. As those familiar with this part of South Warwickshire will know, this is an isolated holding lying in a valley with woods on each side behind Edstone Hall, with the land running right up to Eric Newcombe's former gravel pits at Langley.

Bill was a clever engineer, and farmed well. When they left Cutlers, he played a significant part in developing the Massey combine. But while there, he invented, and had made, a machine for cutting and carting the kale crop grown in the old way, thus avoiding the unpleasant chore of cutting and carting by hand.

The frame of the Cutrake, as it was called, was a buckrake cut down to the same width of the tractor and with the tines shortened a little and a cutter bar with reciprocating knives from a grass mower fitted across the length and driven from the power take-off. The job was completed by fitting a steel mesh back and sides, forming a three sided cage.

The method of working was to drive at speed in reverse into the standing kale, which was cut, and which fell into the steel mesh frame, as neatly as daffodils packed in a box ready for market. Strange as it may seem, it worked perfectly, gathering some 5 cwt. of kale at a time.

There were then two options. If the crop was being grown near to where it was to be fed, often on some old turf in the autumn and early winter, the cutrake was driven with its load, which was then spread out in a line in the normal way. On the other hand, if the kale was to be carted any distance, it could be loaded by fork onto a flat trailer. This hand work was certainly preferable to taking a slashing hook to the standing crop.

The cutrake could also be used for cutting maize to be fed green. This was practised to a limited extent as an insurance against a late summer drought.

In the 1950s the, the little grey Fergie tractor was almost standard equipment on most of the smaller farms. The cutrake was mounted on one and Ferguson did, I believe, manufacture a small number. Bill Craig also developed a device for carting silage from the clamp or pit, in the days before silo barns and self-feeding.

The grazing of kale became standard practice on dairy farms in the 1950s, when most herds fell in the range of thirty to sixty cows or thereabouts. As noted above, poaching posed problems in a wet autumn and one that could be overcome, to some extent, by direct drilling into a grass stubble burnt off with Gramoxone. It was usual to graze kale into December and then open the silage clamps for feeding for the rest of the winter. Pit or clamp silage, hand fed, therefore took the place of mangolds, after the kale had been finished.

The grazing of kale was, of course, controlled by means of an electric fence being moved every twenty four hours to present the herd with a day's ration. To avoid having to cut a swathe through the crop by hand to erect the fence, two or three rows of swedes were sometimes drilled at suitable intervals amongst the kale and grazed off *in situ* with the main crop.

But as herd size increased year by year, the grazing of kale became no longer a practical proposition, and was replaced by the silo barn and the self-feeding or bunkering of silage throughout all the winter months.

Swedes

These, in contrast to mangolds which thrive under low rainfall conditions, are essentially a crop for the wetter districts. Thus they have been grown as a fodder crop only to a limited extent in South Warwickshire with its rainfall of only some 25"/year. The acreages never approached those of mangolds and kale.

Rape and Turnips

Rape and turnips, the quick growing stubble turnips in particular, have been grown alone, or in a mixture, to provide sheep keep on which to finish lambs in late summer and autumn. These would normally be sown after winter barley to gain some extra three to four weeks growth. This is still practised to some extent but not, I imagine, as extensively as in the past. This is symptomatic of the tendency to simplify farming systems with labour on most farms cut to the bone.

Fodder Radish

This could be described as one of British agriculture's nine-day wonders. In the 1960s, it was hailed as the fodder crop to help fill in the trough in grass production in July and August. It was quick growing, too much so in one respect. Managing the grazing of it was not easy, for it had the habit of suddenly shooting up into head when, of course, it became unpalatable and the cows would not touch it. As far as South Warwickshire was concerned, it was a short-lived craze. A few years ago, and for reasons which need not concern us here, I did try to purchase some seed and the suppliers had some difficulty in finding any.

Cow Cabbage

Not grown commonly, but it had its devotees amongst those on the smaller dairy farms up until the end of the 1960s, or thereabouts. The plants had first to be drilled into a seedbed, lifted when large enough to handle, and then pegged out, usually by hand at a yard square. For done well, cow cabbage could grow to a considerable size. They were easier to cut and load by hand than kale, and could produce good, heavy yields per acre.

George Elliot farmed a County Council smallholding in Cher(r)ington; *gardened* would be a more accurate description for his little farm, which was always a prime example of good, tidy husbandry. He always grew cow cabbage for his small dairy herd. He was, by birth, a Devonshire man, a county in which the crop was popular. George always bought his plants from a grower there. His patch of roots, which included mangolds, was his pride and joy, and had every reason to be.

Fodder Rye

There was a vogue for growing this at one time, mainly in the 1960s, to provide an early bite for dairy cows in early March, or even late February in a kind season. It was, however, essential to have an acreage of Italian Ryegrass to follow on. Early sowing was necessary but, as most of the best varieties came from Hungary, in particular, drilling was sometimes delayed by late delivery.

Rye, unlike other cereals, is largely cross pollinated and so the seed has to be renewed each year, and is expensive. The need for this practice was demonstrated very clearly one season. Guy Spencer of Mansell Farm, Newbold-on-Stour, grew fodder rye for a number of years. On one occasion, a small acreage got away from the cows and was left to be combined to provide some seed for the following year. He drilled this alongside fresh seed, which he normally bought. When the crop was established the lack of vigour of the home-produced seed was only too obvious.

As fas as I know, the growing of rye in South Warwickshire for an early bite is a thing of the past.

Indeed, this is so for most fodder crops. For they belonged to an age when there was more labour on farms, on the smaller ones family labour in particular, and when herd size was very much smaller, allowing for grazing in situ without an unacceptable level of poaching in a wet time. Their place has, to a great extent, been taken by silage. Greater quantities are now being made per cow, commonly as much as ten tonnes, now mainly bunker fed. The one exception to this trend is fodder maize grown for silage, as described in Chapter 5, Milk Production.

Lucerne

Lucerne must be one of the older of all forage crops. It was known to, and valued by, the Greeks and Romans, which is not surprising as lucerne thrives in a hot, dry, Mediterranean climate.

In England, it has had a somewhat chequered history, and this is certainly true of South Warwickshire. Interest in it has been intermittent but, in my experience, sharpened after a particularly dry summer. Certainly in the 1940s and 1950s, I spent a significant amount of time advising in its establishment and management. So much so that, in the days of strict petrol rationing when one might be stopped at any time anywhere to explain on what business you were bent, I always carried in my bag and an undated letter from Spence Edkins, landlord of the Kings Head, Aston Cantlow, requesting advice on growing lucerne to justify my presence in the pub!

Lucerne's great virtue is that it is very deep rooted and, thus, extremely resistant to drought. It will continue to grow in a dry summer, and is capable of giving three, or even four, cuts in a season. Conversely, it will not tolerate a high water table.

In practice it was not easy to use effectively. When being made into hay, the leaf would shatter easily and much of this most valuable part of the plant would be lost. When conserved as silage, a satisfactory fermentation was often difficult to achieve, something which could be overcome to some extent if it was being grown with a companion grass. Whether modern additives would make any difference, I know not. As will be mentioned later, it really came into to its own when dried artificially. Indeed, an acreage in the cutting programme was essential if a drying plant was to achieve an economic throughput. This was certainly the case in South Warwickshire, and its acreage in the district was at its peak when the grass drier at Bearley was functioning.

Lucerne is not really a grazing plant, certainly not by sheep; they graze so closely that they damage the crown. Since it is a legume, it causes blowing in cattle as Bertie Watts, of Willicote, found out to his cost. Bill Craig, of Cutlers Farm, Wootton Wawen, solved the problem by wilting first. The lucerne was cut one day behind an electric fence and allowed to wilt twenty four hours. The fence was then moved to allow the herd of Jersey cows to graze the day's ration while that for the next day was being mown, and so on.

Lucerne, with its erect, open, growth cannot compete well with weeds. Indeed, at one time, it was common practice to grow it in rows to allow inter-row horse hoeing. Later, it was grown with a companion grass, but cocksfoot, which could match its drought resistance, only too often became aggressive, smothering the lucerne. In an effort to overcome this problem, the Grassland Improvement Station at Drayton grew cocksfoot and lucerne in alternate rows. As was the best practice with lucerne, the last autumn growth was allowed to die down. The lucerne-cocksfoot sward was then grazed heavily with cattle during the winter. This seemed to work, the crop producing heavy cuts for silage the following season. Today, of course, those growing lucerne have a wide range of herbicides to keep the sward clean.

Another, and less known, attribute of lucerne was its effectiveness as a soil conditioner. The late Ken Smith took the tenancy of Walcote Manor Farm in the mid 1940s. On the east side, the land rises to meet Withycombe Wood and the top one third of these boundary fields, notably Middle Hill and North Hill, are heavy and difficult to work down to a seedbed. Incidentally, some of the most intractable soils in South Warwickshire are found where the Keuper marl meets the Lias Clay. The Walcote fields have a marl subsoil, while Billesley Manor Farm above Withycombe Wood is on the clay.

When Ken took to Manor Farm, the top ends of these fields were not cultivated, the sward consisting of tor grass and other inferior grasses, and the fields also grew brambles in profusion. Ken, who made full use of the Bearley drier, sowed these fields out to lucerne for drying and successfully grew good crops for a number of years.

When the time came to plough and return to arable cultivation for a few years, the effect on soil structure and workability was outstanding. Ken always put this down to the ameliorating effect of the deep rooting system of the lucerne, and was wont to refer to this for the rest of his farming life.

Today, to the best of my knowledge, very little or no lucerne is grown in South Warwickshire. If global warming actually becomes a reality, and England eventually comes to enjoy a Mediterranean climate, the virtues of lucerne may be re-discovered. Especially if modern herbicides and silage additives can overcome the problems of keeping the lucerne sward free of weeds and of achieving a satisfactory fermentation when making the crop into silage.

25. GRASS

All flesh is grass, and all the goodliness thereof is as the flower of the field

The Grassland Survey 1938-1940

In 1939, at the outbreak of the Second World War, the grassland of Britain was in a parlous state. Mention has already been made of Sir George Stapledon and the profound and far-reaching influence he had in promoting the value of the ley, in the breeding of new varieties of the most productive and valuable grasses and in their establishment and subsequent management.

During the years 1938 to 1940, Sir George, together with Dr. William Davies, assisted by T. E. Williams, G. P. Hughes and 'Canada' Davies, carried out a survey of the grassland in England and Wales. The results were as follows.

Grade	Description	Proportion
1	Ryegrass pastures	1.6%
2	Ryegrass pastures	5.8%
3	Agrostis with ryegrass	27.4%
4	Agrostis or Agrostis with Fescue	60.6%
5	Agrostis-Fescue with rushes and sedges	4.6%

Use of grassland in England and Wales, 1938-40

For the benefit of non-farming readers, it should be explained that perennial ryegrass can be regarded as the most productive and persistent of those grasses which are regarded as being of value in agricultural terms. Thus the swards were graded by the proportion of ryegrasses which they contained.

From the above table it will be seen that only 7.4% of the grassland surveyed contained a goodly amount of ryegrass. The 3rd and 4th grade pastures accounted for no less than 88% of the total, while 5th grade pastures were common enough on the worst drained grassland in South Warwickshire. Of course, all the pastures in all grades would contain many other species besides those recorded. There would be an abundance of Poa species, Crested Dogstail, Sweet Vernal Grass and Yorkshire Fog to name but a few. These, of course, would all be more common in the lower grades of swards.

There has been no comparable wide-ranging survey carried out in recent times. But if such a survey was to be undertaken today, it would paint a very different picture. A much higher proportion of grassland would be in Grades 1 and 2 and in the lowlands, as opposed to upland farms, the vast majority of swards would fall into the first three grades. This, quite frankly, is a guesstimate, but what is not in doubt is that there has been a dramatic increase in the productivity of the nation's grassland since 1940.

Traditional Hay Meadows

There are those amongst us so utterly ignorant of the fundamentals of animal welfare as applied to cattle and sheep, and of the realities of making a living from the land that they seem to regard this increase in grassland productivity as an act of vandalism. The accusation is made that modern farming methods have destroyed all but a small proportion of what they are pleased to call traditional hay meadows, in other words the lower grades of grassland, as described above. In addition to the grasses of the lowest productivity, there would be buttercups in profusion, daisies, a variety of herbs such as burnet and plantains, amongst many other broad leaved species of no use whatsoever.

In passing, the narrow leafed plantain was called *fireleaf* in some parts of the country. This was due to the fact that when all the herbage at haymaking time appeared to be dry and the crop fit to carry, the narrow leafed plantain was, in fact, still sappy. If there was a sufficiently high proportion in the hay, it would heat and could result in the hayrick catching fire.

The function, in fact the only function, of any field put up for mowing for hay, or silage, is to produce the highest possible yield of herbage of good nutritional value. It is not to provide a colourful spectacle for townies to drool over and titwilly through, botanising as they go!

In the 1940s and into the 1950s, there was a great deal of grassland – too much – which fell into the traditional hay meadow category. Perhaps some of the worst examples were to be found on some of those small dairy farms which, at one time, ringed the outskirts of Birmingham. The grassland on some of these holdings did little more than provide an exercise ground for the small dairy herds of anything from half a dozen to twenty cows! At best, these swards would produce only a very light crop of hay of grasses of inferior quality, and broad leaved weeds of many kinds. In South Warwickshire, such dairy farms were to be found commonly enough in the parishes of Studley, Tanworth-in-Arden, Oldberrow, Beaudesert, Henley-in-Arden, Preston Bagot and others further to the north. But traditional hay meadows were, by no means confined to these parishes; they could be found almost anywhere in South Warwickshire.

The cattle on such farms were, of course, entirely dependent on these traditional hay meadows for their winter fodder, which was of the lowest feeding value and usually insufficient in quantity. The state of these cattle by the end of March was pitiable, in extreme cases just skin and bones, and the remainder in poor condition. I know, I saw enough of them. The almost complete disappearance of the traditional hay meadow, in terms of animal welfare, is a matter for congratulation and certainly not one for concern.

South Warwickshire Grassland

In South Warwickshire as a whole, the best grassland (almost exclusively permanent pasture) was, needless to say, on the better managed farms. Usually, the best swards were those closest to the farmstead. But special mention must be made of the riverside fattening pastures at Whitchurch, on the Stour, and farmed by the James family. These were superb and turned out finished beef of the highest quality.

Across the district as a whole, the state of the grassland reflected, only too accurately, the results of Sir George's survey. Without very much doubt, the majority of the better swards would fall into Grade 3, that is Ryegrass/Agrostis; those in the first two categories, predominantly Ryegrass, would be none too numerous. Grade 4 grassland, Agrostis/Fescue, would be only too common.

In addition, much of the permanent pasture in South Warwickshire was badly drained as a result of the general agricultural depression and the consequent lack of maintenance of ditches and drain outfalls. So a proportion of South Warwickshire grassland would fall into the lowest category with rushes growing in the furrows of this ridge and furrow country. Tussock grass was typical of the wetter fields.

In the most neglected pastures, anthills and young thorn would abound. This was the final degradation before the land reverted to thorn scrub and there were many, many acres of this in our district in 1939: Crimscote Downs, much of Knavenhill and the Grove Farm in the parish of Ettington, Nardey Bush, and Loxley Bushes are just a few examples. The process of reclaiming these has already be described, as has the condition of one South Warwickshire farm, which was taken over by the *War Ag* in 1940, which, regrettably, was so typical of so much grassland in South Warwickshire at that time: under grazed and under stocked; badly in need of drainage; no field stockproof because of poor hedges and fences; tussock grass and small thorns in evidence and, of course, no trough water supply. This state of affairs was echoed by Sir George Stapledon, when describing Dodwell and Drayton, when the Grassland Improvement Station was established on those farms in 1940.

But in case the impression is given of too gloomy a picture, let it be said that many farms in South Warwickshire were well run by the standards of the day, reflecting great credit on the occupiers, who had coped so well through the years of depression. In any case, the state of those farms, which left much to be desired, was certainly not the fault of the farmers concerned, but the result of a political decision which resulted in the acute depression of the 1920s and 1930s. 'We were putting out £1 to get back 15 shillings (75p),' as one farmer of the old school once put it to me.

Money was very short. Labour had had to be cut to the bone and the maintenance of hedges, ditches and so on inevitably suffered. Stocking rates of grassland proved to be a sure indication of the varying fortunes of farming through the years from the last quarter of the 19th century, during the second great depression after the First World War, and recovery in the early 1900s and from 1940 onwards.

In the early 1960s, a student who lived in Shipston, Pam Harman by name, came to me for some help with a project concerning Warwickshire farming which she had been set at College. After some discussion, it was decided to concentrate on the fortunes of farming through the years in three South Warwickshire parishes, Brailes, Tredington and Stretton-on-Fosse. The usual measures of farming prosperity, or otherwise, were the levels of rents and the price of wheat. I suggested to Pam that she did something different and more specific; that was to work out the stocking rates in those parishes from the agricultural returns, however imperfect they might be, especially in the early years following their introduction in 1866 and bearing in mind that working horses had to be included in the calculation.

Stocking rates were then expressed in terms of forage acres per livestock unit The higher the stocking rate, the fewer acres of grass and other fodder crops needed to sustain a livestock unit. Today, dairy farms tend to be more heavily stocked than those running beef cattle or a sheep flock. The former, in South Warwickshire, would probably average around 1.2 acres per livestock unit, sometimes less; in the 'grassy' counties with a higher rainfall, stocking rates will be higher still, down to 1 acre per livestock unit. There will, of course, be considerable differences from farm to farm.

In the case of beef or sheep farms, the stocking rate will tend to be lower, of the order of 1.4 forage acres per livestock unit. Both these sets of figures are quoted simply to set standards by which Pam's investigations can be judged.

In summary, she found that stocking rates fell drastically in times of depression and then rose with the onset of better times. For example, in the depth of the 19th century depression in 1890, the stocking rate fell to 6 forage acres per livestock unit. In other words, there was the equivalent of one cow wandering about on six acres of poor grassland, which in consequence deteriorated from under utilisation, as well as from the other factors mentioned above. It was equally a measure of the depletion of farmers' capital on the mixed and all grass farms of those parishes.

The early 1900s were a period of painful re-adjustment to the new situation. Stocking rates rose gradually from then onwards, only to plummet again in the

1920s, reaching their nadir in 1929. Recovery from 1939 onwards was gradual, and increased in pace from about 1955 onwards.

Apart from the onset of better times from 1940 onwards, there were number of husbandry and technical developments that all contributed to the great increase in the productivity of grassland in South Warwickshire and throughout the country as a whole. These are described below.

Ley Farming

The widespread adoption of ley farming was undoubtedly of the greatest importance. In South Warwickshire, before 1939, there was a distinct separation of arable and grassland. Of course, on many clayland farms there was little or no ploughland. Where there was, and on also the lighter land, the arable received most of the farmyard manure, with land destined for roots receiving the greatest proportion. Any leys would be one or two years in duration, based on ryegrass and red clover and cut each year for hay.

The normal practice was to undersow spring corn after two or three crops of winter cereals, say two crops of wheat and one of winter oats. When one or two year ley mixtures containing Italian and early-heading ryegrasses, and red clover, were the order of the day, these seeds were always sown broadcast when the spring corn was well up. This was because in a wet spring the grasses and clovers would grown up into the corn if sown at the same time, making harvest difficult. In the case of the longer ley consisting of the later heading, with more prostrate grasses and white clover, the risk of this happening was much diminished. It became good practice to sow the seeds mixture immediately after the spring corn had been drilled. Sir George also advocated drilling the seeds mixture rather than the older practice of broadcasting, for this ensured that the seeds were placed directly into moister soil and thus had a better chance of germinating rapidly. A refinement of this was to drill the larger seeds, such as the ryegrasses and cocksfoot, and broadcast the smaller seeds, like timothy and white clover which might suffer if drilled too deep.

Direct Re-seeding

Direct re-seeding was also advocated as a means of quickly improving the productivity of grassland in fields that were not suited to arable cultivation. This involved ploughing and re-seeding immediately without the intervention of an arable crop. These fields would include river meadows liable to flood, well wooded parkland, and the like. In 1944, the Warwickshire *War Ag* initiated a contract service for direct re-seeding, the cultivations being carried out by one of the machinery depots and the operation being supervised by the District Technical Officer.

Perhaps my colleagues had better luck, or more ability, but my fields were not successful, or only partially so. I had three of them under my supervision, two traditional hay meadows, one on the River Alne on Manor Farm, Haselor, tenanted by Mr. David Goulbourne and the other on the Ragley Estate on the River Arrow. The first problem was getting rid of the old turf; this was in the days before Gramoxone or Roundup. The best practice was to disc the sward heavily before ploughing. This left a great deal of dead, or not so dead, trash. The second difficulty was the silty soil itself. This worked down to a shot tilth, which could not be reduced to a finer seedbed, do what you may. This, along with the dead sward, produced a puffy seedbed, liable to dry out. Nevertheless, more by luck than good judgement and some timely rain, good takes were achieved in both cases.

But success was short lived. In the first two seasons all was well. The new sward was clearly a great deal more productive than the old. The stock carrying capacity was much improved and cattle did well. But by the third season, the old rogue grasses started to come back in some form and order. There were probably two reasons for this. First, the old turf was not killed completely and grew back through the ploughing. Secondly, as these old meadows were invariably cut late for hay, many grasses might well have seeded before the crop was carried and thus the soil carried a heavy seed burden, which eventually partly re-established the original sward.

The third field was in Charlecote Park, then tenanted by Pete Edgar. This was a nice medium to light loam and a good *take* of the new seeds was obtained. But the pre-discing and ploughing activated the thistles, which came up in a mass; there were no herbicides to deal with them in the 1940s and cutting was the only answer. This parkland, too, reverted to the old sward before very long.

Needless to say, these problems did not exist when a ley was established as part of an arable rotation and this practice was undoubtedly a major factor in improving the productivity of grassland from 1940 onwards.

One might add that much could be done to improve an old pasture without recourse to re-seeding. The old Wilder Pitchpole harrow was the tool, with its tines fixed rigidly on axles carried in a steel frame. When these tines went in to the sward they stayed in, dragging out old fag and letting light and air into what auctioneers like to refer to as sound old pasture.

At my suggestion, one small field on a bank on Grey Mill Farm, Wootton Wawen, was treated in this way. It was a slow business. After harrowing, the trash had to be raked up, loaded into trailers and carted to the muck heap. Eventually it was done, 4 cwt./acre of superphosphate and 2 cwt./acre of Nitro-Chalk applied and the gate shut at the end of February. Six weeks later the field looked as if it had been re-seeded, and at a fraction of the cost. A highly successful operation, which improved the production beyond recognition.

Leys v. Permanent Pasture

Not all farmers were convinced of the advantages of the ley over permanent pasture. The latter was held to provide a more even growth through the year, possibly because the spring flush of grass was not so great as with a ley; this was an objection of some substance. These new swards poached badly in a wet season and especially in the winter, in the days when by no means all the stock on the farm were yarded and the practice of in-wintering ewes from the New Year onwards had not been re-established.

It was also pointed out that the leys invariably received more fertiliser than the older swards, which was true. It was held that well managed permanent pasture, well fertilised, could nearly equal the ley. Wallace Steele of Mayswood Farm, Wootton Wawen, always took this view and demonstrated, by the good husbandry of his old pastures, that he was correct.

Fertilisers

The greater use of fertilisers on all grassland, both new and old, has been a potent factor in improving productivity. Until 1940, and indeed, for some years after, basic slag was almost the only fertiliser to be used on grassland. Its effect on the phosphate-starved soils of South Warwickshire, combined with heavier grazing, was almost miraculous, improving the clover content of swards and thus their productivity.

The use of slag on fields known to grow mushrooms was taboo. When rain followed a dry, hot spell of weather, these could be a most valuable crop in a cash-strapped farming world. Soot, however, was held to be beneficial and was applied to such fields. John Warren, of Glebe Farm, Aston Cantlow, was a firm believer in such treatment and certainly grew heavy crops of mushrooms.

The value of a soluble phosphatic fertiliser soon became realised, especially on the phosphate-deficient soils of South Warwickshire. The ordinary 18% superphosphate and the 48% triple superphosphate were the usual sources, but di-ammonium phosphate had the advantage of applying nitrates in addition. The usual practice was to use superphosphate in establishing the ley and slag thereafter.

There had always been a strongly held belief that nitrogenous fertilisers, then Sulphate of Ammonia and Nitro-Chalk, *drew* the land; the second state, after their application, being worse than the first. However, nitrogen in an organic form was quite acceptable, fish manure being much favoured for use on arable and root crops in particular.

The use of nitrogen on grassland slowly became accepted practice. Nitro-Chalk, with 15.5% N, was the preferred source of nitrogen for grassland; being held, with justification, as being less harmful to clovers. 2 cwt./acre (31 units of N) being a normal dressing for both hay and grazing.

Things have moved on from those days. Intensively grazed dairy pasture will commonly receive some 170 units N during the season, and often more. Grass for silage will get some 180 to 200 units N, supported by phosphates and potash, usually in the form of a compound fertiliser. Grazing for dairy followers, beef cattle and sheep would be dressed with about 140 N, again supported by phosphates. However, the fertiliser practice varies greatly from farm to farm.

Grazing Management – Dairy Cows

The dairy herd is usually grazed intensively, relative to dairy followers, beef cattle and sheep.

Without any doubt, the invention of the electric fence in the late 1940s was the most important development in utilising grazed grass to best effect. It is light, portable, and easy to erect and dismantle. It is difficult to imagine good grassland management without it.

There are a number of methods of controlling the grazing of dairy cows to best effect. One of the most common is strip grazing, when the fence is moved forward across the field on a daily basis, offering the cows fresh grass every day. Except when fields are small and cow numbers are large, it is good practice to use a back fence where possible to allow the grass to recover and grow afresh, ready for the next time round. While the mechanics are clear enough, in practice there is much skill in rationing the grass by these means.

When such a skill is lacking, other means of pasture management should be looked at, as I found out the hard way. For some years, I was much involved in a farm in South Warwickshire as a consultant. From the first, it was clear that the cowman had not much idea and, as a consequence, by the time the electric fence was nearing the boundary of the field being grazed, the grass was very much past its best, indeed almost ready to thresh!

My client and I then considered paddock grazing, but rejected it on the grounds of expense and the difficulty of ensuring a good water supply. Fortunately, the fields grazed by the herd were fairly small in relation to cow numbers, only one having to be split in two by means of an electric fence. It was then possible to graze them in rotation on a twenty one day cycle, each field being dressed with a nitrogenous fertiliser immediately the cows were turned out into the next one. This worked well and had the advantage of eliminating the need for the fence to be moved daily, the lesson being that any system of grazing management must fit the man.

True paddock grazing involves splitting the grazing area into some 21-28 equal sized paddocks. Each paddock is grazed in a day and, again, usually top-dressed when the cows move on. Paddock size must be related to cow numbers to provide a day's grazing without waste. For example, for a herd of 100 cows with 25 paddocks, each paddock should be about 2 acres. Every paddock must have a water point and access is given to them by means of a trackway. Frank Bennison grazed the dairy herd at Pepperwell Farm, on the Weston Park Estate, successfully in this way for many years, as did many others.

With strip, paddock or whole field rotational grazing, excess grass should be made into silage, the introduction of baled silage making this that much easier.

Finally set-stocking, or continuous grazing, is occasionally practised. This involves the herd staying on one pasture throughout the grazing season, stock numbers being adjusted to grass growth. Here, top-dressing with nitrogenous fertiliser plays an essential part.

All these systems have been practised on dairy farms in South Warwickshire, or variations of them. There are as many ways of organising the grazing of a dairy herd as there are ways of killing a cat, but in every case the aim is the same: to present the cows with an ample supply of fresh grass every day, to be consumed without waste as far as is possible.

Grazing Management – Sheep

In the 1960s and 1970s, the search was on for ways and means of increasing gross margin income from grass stocked with sheep, dairy followers and beef cattle, to a figure that compared more favourably with that obtained from combineable crops. This almost became the Holy Grail of UK agriculture. In the end, little, if any success was achieved. But to some degree, such pastures were stocked more heavily than in the past, due to the general factors described below.

In the case of sheep, paddock grazing with forward creeps for the lambs was all the rage at one time. Leys were divided into paddocks with sheep netting and at great expense. Lamb creeps were provided so that the lambs could have access to the fresh herbage in the paddock into which the ewes would be turned next.

There was no doubt that very heavy stocking rates could be achieved – twelve ewes and lambs per acre was considered a minimum – during the grazing season. This system was adopted in Gloucestershire, as the answer to the shepherd's prayer. What was not mentioned were the facts that this system of intensive sheep grazing needed a considerable acreage of permanent pasture as a back-up for winter grazing, and that the system tended to produce large numbers of store lambs per acre, which had to be finished by more conventional means. Apart from turning parts of the farm into a bird cage, little, in practice, was achieved and the whole exercise proved a dead end.

Cattle

There has been a general improvement in stocking rates and, since the 1940s, cattle are now being slaughtered at a younger age than was the previous practice. Both these factors have tended to increase income from pasture land grazed by beef cattle and dairy followers.

A great deal of valuable work was done at the Drayton Experimental Husbandry Farm in developing the production of eighteen month beef from reared calves, making the best use of grass, both grazed and conserved as silage. Much of this was adopted and adapted by farmers into their own beef systems.

Drayton also demonstrated how stocking rates could be raised to increase gross margin per acre. There were, however, some snags when attempting to translate this into farming practice. On many holdings, winter yarding, not the summer stocking rate, limited the numbers of cattle that could be kept. In addition, and even if yarding was not a limiting factor, there was the problem of the increased working capital needed to finance a more intensive beef system. In the end, beef production from grass has tended to remain an extensive system, with inevitably gross margins per acre lagging behind those obtained from combineable crops.

A very considerable area of permanent pasture on some farms in South Warwickshire posed a problem. River meadows, steep banks and parkland are unsuitable for the plough, but have to be grazed by something, sometimes for mowing for conservation. Ragley Home Farms had this problem with river meadows, parkland and steep banks around Weethley, with permanent pasture numbered in hundreds of acres. One solution, which cuts the capital cost, was the contract rearing of dairy heifers.

Seed Mixtures

Mention has already been made in the section on herbage seed production about the new bred varieties of grasses and clovers, initially originating almost exclusively from Aberystwyth. Also of the limitations of the so-called *commercial* varieties, which until the 1940s or thereabouts, were almost the only constituents of the seeds mixtures then being sold.

In the early days, it was common practice to include a blend of commercial and bred strains in seeds mixtures. Another feature of the older mixtures was the inclusion of *bottom grasses*, such as rough stalked meadow grass and crested dogstail. These contributed little to yield, but were valued as helping to establish a sound *sole* to a pasture as quickly as possible.

One very popular mixture was the Cockle Park. This provided good cuts of hay in the first two years and good grazing thereafter. It did, however, by definition, have one drawback. Taking a hay crop for the first two seasons tended to inhibit the establishment of the more prostrate, leafier and more persistent grasses

Seed	lb./acre
Perennial Ryegrass	16
Cocksfoot	10
Timothy	4
Late Flowering Red Clover	4
Trefoil	1
Wild White Clover	1

Composition of a typical Cockle Park mixture of seeds

upon which the final establishment of a good grazing sward depended. Nevertheless, there was one advantage. As has already been pointed out, the amount of root growth a grass makes is in direct proportion to the aerial growth. In other words, taking two hay crops in succession, early in the life of a sward, will encourage root growth and, thus, the ability of the sward to stand grazing in a wet time with the minimum of poaching. A typical Cockle Park mixture would be as follows:Originally, the majority of grasses and clovers would be commercial seed, with possibly a small proportion of the superior indigenous strains. In the 1940s, it became the practice to substitute, in all types of mixtures, a proportion of the commercial seeds by bred strains. The latter were, of course, more expensive, and cost-conscious farmers were reluctant to discard them completely on these grounds alone.

This is well illustrated in Sir George Stapledon's *Plough Up Policy and Ley Farming*, written in haste and published in June 1939, just after the announcement of the £2/acre ploughing-up grant. Sir George lists a number of mixtures suitable for hay, and for all grazing, specialist mixtures based on timothy or cocksfoot alone, or in combination with meadow fescue.

The table below is an all-grazing mixture and illustrates the inclusion of both commercial and bred varieties. It will be noted that grasses are classified in the mixture above as hay, pasture or intermediate. Today, modern varieties are described as early, intermediate and late heading.

As time went by, seeds mixtures consisted entirely of what we would now call bred varieties. The original bred strains from Aberystwyth eventually became outclassed and were replaced largely by varieties, some of them tetraploid. These were produced in continental Europe, notably by firms in the Netherlands and Denmark, but also in Belgium and Germany. In addition, there were strains bred in Northern Ireland and elsewhere in the UK.

Seed	lb/acre
Italian ryegrass	10
commercial perennial ryegrass	2
New Zealand certified perennial ryegrass	2
Aberystwyth hay perennial ryegrass S24	2
Aberystwyth pasture perennial ryegrass S23	6
Aberystwyth intermediate perennial ryegrass S101	6
Wild white clover	2

Composition of All-Grazing seed mixture advocated by Sir George Stapledon

None of the above should detract, in any way, from the value of the pioneering work carried out by Sir George Stapledon and his colleagues in breeding much improved grasses and clovers. But it must not be forgotten that this would all have been in vain without farmers being willing to master the husbandry of growing grasses and clovers for seed, and South Warwickshire had its fair share of these. Thus the *S* strains became widely available to play their part in improving the productivity of grassland.

26. FODDER CONSERVATION

Good hay, sweet hay, hath no fellow

For many centuries, in fact ever since the days when human beings ceased to be nomads and food gatherers and became farmers, cultivating their fields and raising livestock in and around settlements of one kind or another, the making of hay was the only method of providing winter fodder for their stock. This was, and still is, very much at the mercy of the weather, as it involves using the power of the sun to dry the fresh herbage to a point at which it can be stored in stacks for the winter. .

There was, it is true, a flurry of interest in silage making in the late 19th century, and in the 1930s grass drying by artificial means had created some interest. Nevertheless, the fact remains that, as late as 1970, 85% of the grass crop in the country was still conserved as hay.

Research and Development

All research and development in the conservation of grass for winter fodder has three aims. First, to reduce the dependence of the process on a fairly prolonged spell of dry weather. Secondly, to reduce the loss in feeding value to a minimum during the process and, thirdly, to improve, if possible, the nutritional value of the final product. The work at Drayton Experimental Husbandry Farm, and on commercial farms, has played an important part in the partial achievement of these aims during the last fifty years or so.

Quick Hay Making and Barn Drying

Development work at Drayton concentrated on improving the field drying rate and on the barn drying of hay. The former became known as *quick* haymaking, the object of the exercise being to increase the rate of drying and thus lessen the risk of spoiling by rain.

Traditionally, it had been the practice to mow and then leave the swathe undisturbed for a number of days, indeed until the top layer was well bleached. The theory was that the unbroken swathe was less likely to suffer damage from rain.

At Drayton, the swathe was broken immediately after mowing, either by tedding or crimping, which had the effect of bruising the grass as it was mown thus increasing the drying rate. This method used weather forecasts, so that advantage could be taken of a spell of three or four days without rain.

Barn hay drying allowed the crop to be carried before leaf shatter occurred. A combination of the two techniques, swathe conditioning and barn drying, allowed hay to be carted from the field on the third day after mowing. This substantially reduced the weather risk, in comparison with traditional methods which needed at least five days in the field, and often more, if wet conditions intervened.

It should be noted that rapid drying in the swathe is as important in the making of wilted silage as in making hay. The whole concept was accepted readily by farmers and by machinery manufacturers, who produced a range of machinery for swathe treatment.

Until 1970, all haymaking had been done using the old, small bale. In 1970 a prototype Howard big baler was acquired by Drayton EHF and Basil, the farm mechanic, suggested a number of modifications which were adopted. The big baler produced bales of half a ton in weight, the equivalent of some twenty five small bales. These, of course, could hardly be stacked in a barn and blown in the same way as the smaller bales. A method of building a tunnel of big bales was devised at Drayton so that these could be blown as well. Whilst the development of barn hay drying was being investigated, comparisons between the cost, feeding value, etc., of fodder made by this method and silage were being carried out.

In 1962, a variation of barn drying was tried. The box, formerly used for a silage trial, was used to set up a fully mechanised chopped hay system. Grass was mown, crimped, turned and rowed up to be picked up by a forage harvester. The grass was then blown into this box, which was fitted with a barn drying floor and blown in the usual way. This worked quite well on a small scale. The disadvantage was that chopped hay was a very much less dense material than baled hay. Thus the provision of sufficient boxes to store a commercial quantity was not a viable proposition.

Barn Hay Drying at Ilmington.

For a description of barn hay drying on a commercial farm, I can do no better than quote from the notes I made at the time on the experiences of Mike Dowler of Manor Farm, Ilmington.

In the early 1960s, the farmstead where the dairy herd was in-wintered was in the centre of the village, some distance from the main holding. On this there was a three-bay Dutch barn in which silage had been made for a number of years; the disadvantage was that this had to be carted daily to the cows in the winter months. By converting to hay feeding, one load a week sufficed, the bales being stored in a shed next the yard.

There was already on the farm a Lister diesel driven fan, used for drying corn and this had sufficient puff for barn hay drying. The barn was converted very cheaply. The sides were made of straw bales, supported by timber and wire and lined with sisalkraft paper to make the whole thing airtight. A trench four feet wide and four feet deep was dug in the clay along the centre line of the barn and along its whole length, the fan being fitted up at one end. Farm timber was laid over this to carry the weldmesh floor onto which the bales were loaded and through which the air was blown.

In 1961, some eighteen acres were cut for barn drying. The first cut was on May 11th, before many had started silage making, and was tedded twice before baling on May 13th. As soon as the first layer of bales was in place, the fan was started and subsequent layers added. Blowing was continuous and, early on a cool May morning, water vapour could be seen rising from the barn and the remark was heard to be made 'Mike is breathing well this morning.' There was no need for double handling, each cut being stacked on top of the previous one, the barn in effect acting as a store as well, as the bales remained there until needed for feeding during the winter.

Naturally enough, the first cut was light, some 15 cwt./acre, but of superb feeding value. The dry matter was 84.7%, the protein 16.7% and fibre 25.1%; 15 lb. of this hay with 8 lb. of cereals was sufficient for maintenance ration and two gallons of milk.

The second cut, also a three year ley, was mown on May 15th and baled on May 19th, giving 23.9 cwt./acre of dried hay, having been tedded each day from mowing to baling. Needless to say, the protein was lower than the first cut and the fibre higher. The third cut was on May 27th, tedded each day and baled on May 30th. The analyses and yields of the second and third fields were broadly similar.

In practice, a mixture of bales from the three fields was fed the following winter, 20 lb. providing for maintenance and 1 gallon of milk from Mike's Red Poll herd. Incidentally, one useful lesson was learnt from the first season. It was necessary to block up the end of the tunnel once blowing had finished to prevent the entry of moist air, otherwise the bottom bales went mouldy on their undersides.

Barn hay drying continued for a number of years at Ilmington until a new set of buildings was built on a green field site adjacent to the original barn. These were designed for self-fed silage and the Red Polls were gradually replaced by Friesians.

The barn hay drying at Ilmington aroused a great deal of interest and some followed where Mike had led, for improvements in the methods of making hay were always seized upon eagerly. Anything to avoid making silage, which was looked upon in those days without enthusiasm by the majority of livestock farmers.

Silage Making

Thus during the 1940s and the following two decades, the gap between the theoretical advantages of making silage and its adoption in practice was a wide one. During the food production campaign of those decades, it was official policy to plug the making of silage, and its praises were sung on every possible occasion by NAAS advisors and ICI staff in particular.

In passing, the contribution that ICI field staff made to grassland improvement and productivity in general must be acknowledged. Graduates and college students regarded a career with ICI as a field advisor as one of the plum jobs and the firm certainly had the pick of the brightest and most personable from the universities and colleges. Ken Deighton was the ICI man for South Warwickshire and became a personal friend. He left to go dairy farming on his own in Cheshire, his herd being one of the many victims of the Foot and Mouth Disease epidemic of 1967-68, which caused such devastation in that county. He was followed, if my memory serves me correctly, by Paul Scudamore, who later became a pioneer in the use of computers on farms. The firm he founded, Farmplan, became a leader in this field.

But to return to silage making. The practice has many advantages over hay making; grass can be cut at its most nutritious stage. In the early days the crop is mown at a very much younger stage of growth than is the practice today, as described in Chapter 5, Milk Production.

Another advantage of silage making over hay was the fact that the former was less dependent upon a spell of uninterrupted fine weather for its making. Silage making uses grassland to better effect, for earlier cutting made for a quicker recovery of the lattermath for grazing or for a second cut of silage.

The Drawbacks

In spite of these advantages, it was very many years before silage making became accepted as normal practice on livestock farms and on dairy holdings in particular.

There were a number of reasons for this. First, the innate and very understandable conservatism of the older generation of farmers. During the years of depression, the more capable and successful on the better land farmed according to the best practices of the day. The taking of risks in the form of innovation, venturing into the unfamiliar and unknown, was for those in a big way of business or with other financial resources. For the majority, it was just a matter of getting by in hard times.

Secondly, there were problems with logistics. Silage making involved handling large quantities of fresh, wet, heavy herbage from the field to the silo, pit or clamp. The forage harvester, as we know it today, was something very much in the future back in the 1940s. Green crop loaders, real mankillers, were the only mechanical means of loading grass into trailers, with the exception of the Wilder Cut-Lift, a machine beyond the resources of many and designed to handle short grass only.

Then the crop had to be manhandled into the silo, stack or pit. There were cutter-blowers, but again these were few and far between and found only on the largest farms. Sometimes the ordinary wooden elevators, normally used for hay or corn sheaves, were pressed into service to make a stack or fill a round silo. these were made of wood, or concrete slabs or simply weldmesh lined with Sisalkraft.

In the third place, the processes and techniques of making silage successfully were not fully understood. There were many disappointments due to poor fermentation and a high percentage of waste. It was hardly surprising that the verdict on the making of silage was 'an expensive way of producing stinking rubbish.'

Fourthly, once the silage was made there was a great deal of hand work in feeding it. It had to be cut out of the stack, pit or clamp with a hay knife, forked on to a trailer and then off into a manger, behind a feed barrier or fed in the field. It was certainly harder work than foddering with hay.

In short, in the 1940s and then for some time after, there were neither the field machinery, nor the fixed equipment, nor the knowledge available to make good quality silage in the quantities with which we are familiar today, without unacceptable waste.

The Buckrake

The Patterson buckrake gave a great boost to silage making in the 1950s. Designed by Rex Patterson, it was first manufactured by Taskers of Andover and subsequently by others – Ferguson, New Idea, Bentalls, and so on. In combination with the, now almost universal, hydraulic lift, it was ideal for carting fresh grass short distances and for loading herbage dumped by trailers into a clamp. Moreover, it was inexpensive.

Latterly, its main function was loading grass into the silo and the newer models were fitted with a device for pushing the herbage off the tines, thus speeding up the process.

Incidentally, the original design was, in practice, put to may other uses as well as silage making. The tines were used for carrying bales, pallets loaded with sacks, transporting churns, crates and so on.

In combination with pits or clamps in the field, the buckrake revolutionised silage making.

Pits and Clamps

Before self-feeding became standard practice on dairy farms, winter fodder rations were often based on grazed kale until about Christmas and then feeding silage in the New Year until turn-out. Thus the quantities of silage needed were very much less than the 10 tonnes/cow which is a common enough target figure today.

Naturally enough, feeding regimes varied from farm to farm. 40 lb. of silage/cow/day was probably the maximum, giving a silage requirement of the order of 1.5 to 2.0 tonnes/cow at the most.

In passing, it must be noted that the design and efficiency of green crop loaders had improved by the early 1950s. Nevertheless, the buckrake was the main tool for shifting fresh grass over short distance.

This being so, clamps and pits were often sited in the field to reduce the travelling distance. Wedge-shaped clamps were the most common in South Warwickshire, and it was highly desirable to make these as wide as practicable. Nasty accidents could happen when tractors were driven too near the edge, toppling over in consequence with occasionally fatal results. Some clamps were made in the shape of an inverted saucer and these were certainly safer.

Needless to say, side waste in the wedge shaped clamps was horrific by modern standards and the top waste very considerable, perhaps slightly less so with the inverted saucer type. It must be remembered that in the 1950s, when field clamps and pits were in use, polythene sheeting was something for the future.

Pits were the alternatives to clamps, the waste at the sides and back being considerably less than with clamps. The depth of pits depended upon the terrain and water table. In good conditions they could be five or six feet deep and being able to take advantage of a slope in the ground was ideal. Often the bottom of the pit would be stoned and tile drains laid to deal with the effluent. It was soon found that these could not be led into field drains, as they would soon be blocked by a jelly like substance formed by the silage juices.

The 1950s were a more robust age. The *Environment*, and its burgeoning bureaucracy, had yet to be invented. Thus it was common practice to lead the silo drains into the nearest ditch. In the case of clamps, the effluent just oozed out of the sides, forming puddles along the bottom, the contents of which just soaked into the soil, to be broken down in Nature's way. Out of sight, out of mind.

As a footnote, after a long interval of many years, more sophisticated versions of the silage pit made their appearance for the very simple reason that the construction of silo walls became very expensive, something that was aided and abetted by bureaucracy insisting on unrealistic building standards. These new pits had a very much greater capacity than the old types, were usually built into a slope, had sides lined with concrete slabs and concrete floors with drains. Polythene sheeting weighted down with tyres were used to seal the top, as was the case with all outside clamps. Pits such as these were built for the new dairy unit at Ragley Home Farms, at Weethley.

Silo Barns

In the days before plastic sheeting the tops of pits or clamps were, of course, open to the elements, often being sealed, after a fashion, with ground limestone. Obviously a clamp under cover had great advantages.

During the 1950s, many Dutch barns were converted to grass silos, or new ones built. The latter incorporated concrete sides into the structure, one example being marketed by Crendon. At this time, MAFF grants became available for new silo barns, or the conversion of existing Dutch barns. Only the taller of the latter were suitable, as the height had to accommodate a tractor working on top of a full silo. One also had to be certain that there was no rotting of the upright stanchions at ground, as considerable pressure was exerted on them via the walls, when the silo was full and the silage settling. It might be added that, when erecting a new silo barn, the whole structure was grant-aided, thus it was a method of getting a new Dutch barn on the cheap; some of them, regrettably, never seeing any silage.

Although Dr. Beeching's closure wholesale closure of branch railway lines has proved, half a century later, to be an appalling mistake, it did lead to large quantities of wooden railway sleepers becoming available at very reasonable costs as the tracks were taken up. These became the standard method of constructing the sides and backs of silos in existing barns, and in new ones as well. RSJs were bolted in between the barn stanchions and the sleepers laid against these, the bottoms resting in a concrete gutter.

Floors were of concrete and drains were usually made of bricks laid on end in concrete gutters running down each side of the silo floor. A concrete apron was provided outside the barn on which grass could be dumped before being buckraked into the silo.

Forage Harvesters

At the same time as silo barns were becoming commonplace there were considerable developments in the design of forage harvesters. So much so that the Royal Agricultural Society of England organised a national demonstration of forage machinery at Shillingford in 1950.

Among the manufacturers of forage harvesters was Wild-Thwaites. Mr Basil Thwaites was an engineer of great ability and an innovator in his day; he lived near Leamington and farmed at Chesterton. Hayter rotary grass cutters formed the basis for the Silorator grass forage harvester, which made its appearance in the 1950s. Incidentally, all forage harvesters blew the grass into attendant trailers, thus making the man-killing green crop loader a thing of the past.

Fig. 11 Silage making 1960s. Blakes of Loxley.

Flail type forage harvesters had become popular by 1960 and there were a number of machines available from Bomfords, International, Kidd, Lundell, Massey Ferguson and Holland, to name but a few.

Eventually, self-propelled forage harvesters were developed. These were high capacity machines much favoured by contractors and were also adapted for handling forage maize.

Self-Feeding

It could be said that in the 1950s and 1960s the practice of silage making was being established as commonplace, particularly on dairy farms. The former difficulties that had inhibited the widespread adoption of silage making as a method of grass conservation had been overcome.

The buckrake and forage harvester had largely solved the logistical problem of cutting, loading, carting and then ensiling large amounts of fresh, wet, heavy grass. The silo barn provided weatherproof, and nearly airtight, storage. The importance of excluding air at the sides by lining the sleepers with old fertiliser bags and sealing the top with plastic sheeting was, by this time, fully appreciated. By these means, waste was reduced to a fraction of what it had been in clamps and pits.

The practice of self-feeding, or vertical grazing, allowed the cows to help themselves and did away with the daily chore of cutting out, loading and carting silage to where it was to be fed.

In short, in the 1950s it was all coming together. Mechanisation, improved silos, and self-feeding had eliminated the former drawbacks and, also, the technique of ensiling grass was now generally better understood.

Providing cows had twenty four hours access to the feeding face, it was necessary to allow only six inches of feeding face/cow. Herds were, of course, much smaller in those days, and a Dutch barn converted to a grass silo with sleeper walls which was thirty feet wide could accommodate a milking herd of sixty cows; even slightly more, if the dry cows were housed elsewhere.

It was a common arrangement to have lean-tos built onto each side of a silo barn to house the herd, always providing the stanchions were sufficiently high to allow straw bales to be stacked above. This was an ideal arrangement; for littering was just a matter of throwing the bales down into each yard, cutting the twine and spreading the straw.

A wide concrete apron along the front of the silo and yards served as a dumping site for loads prior to buckraking into the silo, and might even be used as a collecting yard. There were, of course, many variations on this theme.

Mention must be made of the pioneering work of Sam Moreton, at his Burnt Heath Farm, Offchurch. In March 1957, he decided to self-feed his herd of sixty Friesian cows. He visited Northern Ireland and then developed his own set-up at Burnt Heath, on a *bed and breakfast* principle.

He already had extensive Dutch barns which he converted to a grass silo and yards. Once the silage had been made, the clamp was covered with a thick layer of ground limestone. The cows had access to this as a lying area by means of a ramp, thus extending considerably the yarding area.

With Sam's co-operation, the NAAS county staff conducted an investigation into cows' behaviour when self-feeding, which produced a great deal of interesting data. Sam's initiative and the NAAS work was of great benefit to dairy farmers in the county at that time.

Vacuum Silage

Although, finally, vacuum silage proved to be a dead end, it had a profound influence on the practice of making silage. Vacuum silage is always linked with Peter Van Zellar, a former member of the Warwickshire NAAS staff. Peter had been seconded for a time to the agricultural advisory service in New Zealand, where vacuum silage was a popular technique. He did a great deal to promote the practice, and was much in demand as a speaker at meetings and demonstrations.

Vacuum silage consists of making silage on a large polythene sheet, which is then folded over to form a plastic envelope containing the grass. The polythene sheets are joined with plastic pipes clipped into half pipes to make an airtight seal. The air is then evacuated by means of a pump driven from the tractor power take-off; waste is almost non-existent.

Vacuum silage was a nine days wonder; it was never adopted widely, or for any length of time, but it did underline the need for silos to be as airtight as possible. This led to the lining with plastic sheets of silo walls, which were also used to seal the top of the silo.

Making Silage

In the early days it was thought that the bottom layers of grass must be allowed to heat up to about 90 to 100 °F before continuing to fill the pit or the clamp. It was common practice to start cutting and filling on Friday, so that the grass could heat up over the weekend ready for a fresh start on Monday. Much of my time in late May and early June was spent testing the temperature in many a pit or clamp first thing in the morning. Once the desired heat was reached it would work its way up through the grass, being controlled by rolling with a tractor, the final layers being especially well consolidated before sealing.

Diluted molasses was then the only additive used, which was always applied as a matter of routine. The method was invariably an old watering can with a kitchen spoon lashed onto the bottom of the spout with binder twine. This gave a very satisfactory fan of molasses, put on to each layer of grass!

By the early 1970s, a whole range of acid based additives appeared on the market to be followed in due course by inoculants and enzymes. The choice today is very wide and the watering can and spoon have been replaced by dispensers on the forage harvesters.

Personally, I have never been convinced that the significant additional cost of these additives was ever worth while, except under very wet conditions when one just had to press on. It always seemed to me that there were other factors, other than the use of additives, which had a greater influence on the final result under most conditions. By now, of course, waiting for the heat to come up was a thing of the past; silos were now filled as rapidly as possible and the quicker the better.

My views on additives were confirmed by the experience on the farm where I was heavily involved in my last years as a consultant. Silage of very good quality was made, year after year, without the use of an additive, and thus without additional expense, when making some 1,500 tonnes annually. With maize, of course, it is a different story. An additive is essential to prevent secondary fermentation at the face when the clamp is opened.

The wilting of grass destined for the silo is now common practice and has been for a number of years. Although some crops are still direct cut in the original manner, when this is the practice, the use of an additive is essential.

In South Warwickshire, the practice of wilting is now almost universal. The crop is mown, allowed to wilt for about twenty four hours according to the weather, two rows are put into one and then picked up with a forage harvester. Wilting ensures better fermentation, and a greater weight of dry matter is transported in each trailer load; the dry matter of the resulting silage is higher, and thus cow intake is greater. Effluent is reduced or eliminated.

Above all, the quality of silage is dictated by the stage of growth at which the grass is cut. The ideal time is just when the grasses are coming into head, the date of heading being a function of day length. The majority of grasses in a mixed sward will be heading about the middle of May. Thus this is the time to start making silage, as feed quality falls off rapidly once all the grasses are in head.

South Warwickshire is a dry district, although sometimes one would not think so. Cold, dry, springs are by no means unknown. While spring weather does not affect heading date, it certainly affects yield. When growth is backward, the decision has to be faced whether to wait for the crop to bulk up and accept a lower feeding value, or cut one's losses, as it were, go ahead and then hope for a good lattermath. Never an easy one.

Bunker Feeding, Block Cutters, Forage Boxes.

When Sam Moreton set up his *bed and breakfast* system in 1957, he was milking some sixty cows, which was a big herd at that time. As the years rolled by, herd sizes in South Warwickshire doubled, taking Sam's cow numbers as the benchmark. Dairy herds in this district simply outgrew their self-feeding arrangements which, when they were installed, were considered the very latest thing. From the 1970s onwards, dairy units were designed along entirely different lines.

A feeding passage between the yards became normal, silage being fed in bunkers, or more usually behind a feed barrier. Silos were now built outside – something plastic sheeting had made possible – of a size to provide ten tonnes/cow, instead of six, which had been considered adequate for self-feeding.

In precisely the same way that mechanisation had made silage making itself a practical proposition some twenty years previously, mechanisation took the form of block silage cutters, fore-end loaders, forage boxes and mixer/feeder wagons. This allowed the daily cutting, carting and feeding of large quantities of silage to fodder herds at least double in size of those in the self-feeding era.

Moreover, such a system allowed greater flexibility in the composition of cow rations. Complete diet feeding became popular with no concentrates fed in the parlour, as previously described. There were variations in this method of feeding, using forage boxes, rather than the more expensive mixer/feeder wagons. With the former, it is perfectly possible to feed mixtures of grass and maize silage, brewers grains, sugar beet pulp, rolled barley or whatever.

The making and feeding of silage today demands the investment of considerable sums in silos and machinery. It is all a far cry from the mower, buckrake, and a hole in the ground, and then a hay knife, a muck fork and a tractor and trailer to move the silage from pit to where it was needed. Silage is no longer a cheap and cheerful alternative to making hay. In consequence, the more intellectually agile may well be looking at novel and alternative feeding regimes in the years that lie ahead.

Silage Effluent

In the early days, silage effluent was not considered a problem, although unwilted grass produced greater quantities in proportion to the tonnage made. Today it is a very different matter.

In the first place, the tonnages made are very much greater than in the 1950s and 1960s. It is now realised that silage effluent is very vicious stuff, capable of de-oxygenating river water with a devastating effect on fish and aquatic life. Dairy farmers are, therefore, required to take measures to prevent any effluent from entering ditches and thus, eventually, water courses and rivers.

It is now realised that silage effluent has feeding value and is relished by cows; collecting it in a tank and then spreading on the land is, quite frankly, a wicked waste. In addition, underground tanks for the collection and eventual disposal of effluent have to be built to exacting standards and are thus expensive.

One solution is the installation of an *Eff bag*. One such was incorporated into the silos built at Manor Farm, Walcote, when the dairy unit was modernised in 1996 and cost no more than a storage tank. The bag itself is made of very heavy gauge plastic sheeting, like a gigantic hot water bottle, holding several thousand litres of effluent. A large shallow pit is dug and the bottom lined with heavy plastic sheeting to protect the bag, the installation being completed with a protective net over the whole.

The effluent is collected in channels with grids, running the whole width of both silos and then into the bag. A header tank was built high in the roof of the cattle yard, feeding troughs in each yard by gravity. The effluent is pumped from the bag into this, the electric pump being controlled by a float switch. The cows find the effluent very palatable and milk yield increases.

Baled Silage

An abortive attempt was made in the mid-1950s to use the pick-up baler for silage making. This was adjusted to produce half-size bales. Bertie Watts tried this method on Nobbs Farm, Weston-on-Avon, in 1955. A pit was dug and the grass cut and baled. The bales were duly carted to the pit and stacked in it, with the strings at right angles to the sides, working from the outside inwards with the last bale being jammed in to make a tight fit. Each layer was rolled with a tractor and the top sealed with ground limestone, as was the practice at that time.

This made perfectly good silage, the snag was in the feeding. It was a messy business. The half bales had shrunk, leaving the silage dangling on the two strings. A waterproof apron had to be used and handling the bales was not a pleasant task. This was why the method never caught on. In any case, forage harvesters were coming on the scene and small bale silage was a nine-day wonder.

Not so, when the big baler came along in the second half of the 1970s, and was used for silage making. But until bale wrapping machines were developed, the process was rather labour demanding. The foreloader was fitted with a spike to carry the bales to the stack. There, two men were needed to put the plastic bag over the bale, tying the neck tightly with wire. When mechanical wrapping was introduced, it removed the one obstacle to further development and adoption.

Baled silage eliminates the need for expensive silos. It is ideal for the smaller herd, and it is very useful for ensiling further grass when the main silos are full. It introduces a degree of flexibility into grass conservation, and, moreover the big bales can be handled mechanically and are often fed in round feeders.

Tower Silos

Tower silos were another non-starter. They were popular in America, where they are used for ensiling very high dry material. In this country, silage dry matter is in the range 25-30%, the latter being considered very high. The unloaders, whether of the top or bottom variety, proved in practice to be unsuitable to handling this comparatively wet material. This, along with their high cost, made their popularity short lived. In South Warwickshire, a number were installed by Clyde Higgs Farms, but were later sold. One was built on Sweet Knowle Farm, Preston-on-Stour, and another at Dorsington, the latter never being used.

Conclusion

The establishment of silage making as an important method of grass conservation has been one of the success stories of the last fifty years, a development that was only made possible by the mechanisation of harvesting, ensiling and, latterly, feeding.

Fig. 12 Big bale silage. Early days.

27. GRASS DRYING

The Holy Grail of grass conservation has always been the ability to preserve grass at its most nutritious stage of growth, more or less independent of prevailing weather conditions. An impossible dream in reality, but in the 1930s it seemed that the artificial drying of grass by means of a flow of heated air might come very near to the ideal.

It is significant that the first edition of *Agriculture, The Science and Practice of British Farming* by Watson and Moore, published in March 1924, makes no mention of grass drying. The fourth edition (April 1937) devotes no less than six pages to the artificial drying of grass. Both a continuous flow drier and a tray batch drier are described, as is the Wilder Cutlift for cutting and carting the fresh herbage.

Grass drying, necessitating heavy investment in plant and field machinery, was essentially a operation for large farms. Mr. Clyde Higgs, of Hatton Rock, Stratford-on-Avon, farming some 2,500 acres, installed a grass drier to feed his bail-milked Ayrshire herds in the 1930s. But by the 1960s winter fodder was based on silage making.

In 1947, the food situation in the UK was desperate. The wet autumn of the previous year and the prolonged drought produced a meagre harvest. So much so, that the following winter saw the rationing of both bread and potatoes, something which had not been necessary even at the height of the U-boat campaign.

Bearley

It was against this background that it was decided that grass drying could make a useful contribution to the protein supplies for farm stock, and dairy cows in particular. Milk production was still given priority, and the Milk Marketing Board (MMB) was the chosen agency for the establishment of a number of co-operative grass drying plants, located in various parts of the country. Thus it came about that one of these was built at Bearley near Stratford-on-Avon. It must be remembered that, at this time, silage making, mainly due to the fact that the mechanisation of field work and self-feeding were things for the future, had yet to become a widespread practice. It was thought that baled dried grass, with a good protein content, was a more acceptable fodder and easier to feed than silage.

One of the reasons for the choice of Bearley as a site was its proximity to Bearley Station, which was a short haul for the supply of coke. This was the fuel for the two tray driers that were installed.

Construction of the plant was started in the summer of 1947 and operations began on April 25th of the following year. This was a good season to start, as the spring was warm and sunny to be followed by a cool, wet summer, ideal for grass growth. To put this in its context, 1948 saw what was almost the complete failure of the winter bean crop, due to Chocolate Spot. The acreage in South Warwickshire failed to recover from this for some years, that is until the work at the Drayton Experimental Husbandry Farm gave a new lease of life to this crop several years later. Although rain made the corn harvest difficult, the average yield of wheat reached an all-time high of 20.7 cwt./acre, barley 19.4 cwt. and oats 17.7 cwt. The then so-called selective hormone weedkillers, MCPA and 24-D, were first introduced in 1948.

Principles and Practice

The affairs of the grass drier at Bearley were run by a committee of prominent local farmers. These were assisted by staff at Drayton, then the Grassland Improvement Station, also initially by Sam Turner, who was the NAAS District Adviser at Stratford in 1948, to be succeeded by myself a year later. A representative from the MMB attended committee meetings from time to time.

A great deal of thought and organisation had to be put into the cutting programme. The basic problem was to ensure an uninterrupted flow of grass, at its most nutritious growth stage, into the drier throughout the season because the economics of the operation depended very largely upon achieving the maximum throughput. If my memory serves me correctly, the break-even tonnage of the plant was to operate at a profit was 800 tons.

This was, of course, a contracting operation. Farmer customers paid a rate per ton according to the time of year. A low rate very early in the season was set to encourage farmers to offer grass as soon as possible in March. The highest rate coincided with the spring flush, starting about the third week in April. The rate per ton fell again during the trough of grass growth in the difficult months of July and August and rose again slightly in the autumn.

Those who availed themselves of the grass drying service provided by the plant at Bearley were referred to as *co-operating farmers*. This was a fair description in most cases, but a misnomer in the case of others; there was always much complaint if a farmer missed the end of a low rate period by a day or so.

South Warwickshire is, of course, in a low rainfall area, only some 24"/annum. It soon became clear that, to be able to offer herbage to the plant in mid-summer, it was essential to have approximately a third of the contract acreage in lucerne. The area of this fodder crop in the district did increase in consequence.

At first the dried grass was baled, leaf shatter being a particular problem with lucerne. The problem was solved, in part, by sacking up the broken leaf and dust from below the baler and returning to the farmer concerned, along with his bales. This gave rise, in the case of one plant manager, to a dodgy practice.

Fig. 13 Grass Drying at Bearley c. 1949. Note green crop loader and Milk Marketing Board lorry before the Silorator was acquired. Also one of the tray driers with a trailer being unloaded and a stack of bales of dried grass in the foreground. (P.Hicken)

The performance of every MMB plant was monitored, not only by the weekly throughput, but also by the protein content of the product, samples being taken from each batch and analysed. There was considerable rivalry between plants, with Bearley well up amongst the leaders on the quantity and quality of the dried grass. But it came to light that one manager, whose term of office came to an abrupt end in consequence, boosted the protein content of the samples by the simple expedient of adding a few handfuls of the broken leaf and dust to the sample for analysis, which, as already described, accumulated underneath the baler. After this episode we had to take check samples, either myself or an assistant doing this at regular intervals.

The problem of leaf shatter at baling was eventually solved by milling the dried grass and the installation of a cuber. This was a great advance, the cubed product being delivered back to the farmer in bags.

Labour

At first, grass drying at Bearley was a labour intensive operation. Grass was cut with an ordinary mower and picked up with a greencrop loader. This was eventually replaced by the first forage harvester to come onto the market – the Silorator. Mowing and loading became one operation but was not without its drawbacks. Grass harvested by these means was much shorter, and tended to make a denser mass when at first loaded into the drying tray, which made for slower, and more expensive, drying.

Secondly, the fresh herbage had to be loaded by hand into the first tray, then unloaded and forked into the second tray. The labour force consisted of men from the European Volunteer Workers camp, housed in the old RAF buildings on the former aerodrome at Snitterfield, nearby. These were mainly Poles, Latvians and Estonians with other nationalities, all being unable to return to the lands of their birth. There were, if my memory serves me correctly, eight men to each shift working the plant. When the grass driers were working to full capacity, three eight hour shifts had to be worked.

When the camp closed and the men went their various ways, some homewards but the majority to start a new life in this country, there had to be a re-think if grass drying was to continue at Bearley. Obviously the demand for labour was highly seasonal and ways and means had to be found of running the plant with a permanent staff employed all the year round.

The problem was solved by the installation, in 1951, of a Ransome automatic, three-stage drier. This, along with the Silorator and a cuber became the ultimate, and last stage of drying grass at Bearley. A few years after the Ransome drier was installed, feedingstuffs came off the ration and dairy farmers, in particular, thankfully returned to the cake bag.

Thus, in June 1956, the grass drier at Bearley closed down and the plant and site were purchased by the local farmers' co-operative, Warwickshire Farmers. The drier was converted to drying grain, a comparatively simple matter and did service in this capacity for many years.

The buildings were extended and Warwickshire Farmers produced their own brands of animal feeds. This firm later amalgamated with other co-operatives to form Midland Shires Farmers and compound feedingstuffs continued to be manufactured at Bearley until the 1990s.

Finally, mention must be made of the long record of service achieved by Mr. P. A. Hicken at Bearley, which spanned some forty years. He was foreman at the grass drying plant with the MMB. He continued working for Warwickshire Farmers and then with Midland Shires Farmers, retiring eventually in 1987.

Looking back, the grass drier at Bearley did make a useful contribution to fodder conservation over a period of eight years. There is no doubt that dairy farmers in South Warwickshire, who availed themselves of the service it provided, did benefit. In the meantime, silage making was slowly becoming established as a viable and more widely used alternative, a story which has already been told.

Portable Grass Drier

The grass drier at Bearley was not the only one operating in South Warwickshire. There was, for a short period, a portable drier manufactured, if I recall correctly, by Opperman. The central portion, to which a drawbar was fitted for towing with a tractor, housed the oil-fired furnace and the fan. The two drying trays folded up against the central part for transport, being let down into their working position when the drying operation commenced.

The drier was let out to local farmers on a contract basis by Western Farm Implements Ltd. Its fatal flaw was that output was far too low. Set up in a field of any size, the grass grew away past the stage at which a product of a worthwhile protein content could be dried. The alternatives, then, were to continue drying to produce a low protein product, which was not an economic proposition, or to pack up and move, literally, to pastures new!

The idea of taking the drier to the grass was a good one, but clearly it was impossible to make a machine of sufficiently high capacity which, at the same time, was portable.

Long Compton

A privately owned grass drier, also Government assisted, was built at Long Compton at about the same time as the one at Bearley. It continued functioning for a rather longer period, as the result of a consortium of farmers in South Warwickshire and Oxfordshire forming a co-operative to build and run the plant. My former colleague, Frank Bennison, was much involved in the early stages and the day-to-day running of the drier was entrusted to B.A.Hull Ltd.

From what I have been told, there was amongst the local farming community some lack of understanding of the true function of grass drying, that is the production of a high quality feed, comparable in feeding value to dairy cake. There was a considerable resistance, as a consequence, to the charges which had to be made. Indeed, some even regarded grass drying as a substitute for the making of hay in a difficult season.

I had no direct contact with the drier at Long Compton and was not privy to its affairs. But from enquiries that I have made, it would seem that the quality of product did not match that from the MMB plant at Bearley, taking the drying season as a whole.

I understand that the plant and buildings were eventually purchased by B.A.Hull Ltd. and the drier converted to grain. Incidentally, a continuous flow drier was installed right from the start; unlike Bearley, Long Compton did not have the advantage of a plentiful supply of labour in the early days.

Harbury

Some years later, about the mid 1960s, when grass drying had long ceased to be carried out at Bearley or Long Compton, a new plant was built on the Fosse, near Harbury, by a farmer partnership to dry grass commercially.

This venture was short lived. It may well be that the underlying cause was that the lessons learnt, somewhat painfully, by those running the plants at Bearley and Long Compton were not regarded.

In any case, the sudden and very considerable rise in the cost of fuel oil in the early 1970s sounded the death knell of grass drying in the UK.

28. Horticulture

The story of farming in South Warwickshire over the last fifty years, or so, would not be complete without reference to the growing of horticultural crops of all kinds. The following makes no claim to be a complete or exhaustive record of this sector, with which I was not directly concerned, over the last half century. Rather, it is a series of recollections.

Horticultural production was more or less confined to the lighter soils in the valleys of the Avon and Arrow, and was concentrated in those parishes situated in the south west of the county. These included Salford Priors, Bidford-on-Avon, Wixford, Exhall, Arrow, Alcester, Coughton, Weethley, Temple Grafton, Welford-on-Avon, Milcote and Weston-on-Avon, to name some of the main areas. In addition, Mickleton was noted at one time for early cauliflower production. The plants were raised under glass and planted out in March, mainly on land lying below the southern and western slopes of Meon Hill. The glasshouses were then devoted to tomato production for the remainder of the season.

On a much smaller scale, Ernie Carter had a fully justified reputation for producing tomatoes of the highest quality. His smallholding lay between Wimpstone and Ilmington. In 1939, he built a house and erected a number of greenhouses on land formerly part of the family farm at Admington, the land being heavy clay. Such was the quality of his produce that customers used to come from far and wide.

It is true to say that the development of the structure of horticulture followed, over the years, very closely that of agriculture. In short, it was characterised by the disappearance of the smaller producers and others who were unable to move with the times. and by increasing specialisation.

Smallholders and Market Gardeners

Fifty years ago there were, at the one end of the scale, market gardeners and smallholders, and at the other, the bigger growers whose holdings were measured in hundreds of acres, rather than in single, or double, figures. And there was, of course, every permutation and combination in between.

Welford-on-Avon

With regard to those on the smallest holdings, I can do no better than describe my neighbours in the village of Welford-on-Avon, where I have lived for the last fifty three years.

The village lies in a great loop of the River Avon. Standing on the top of Cress Hill and looking back over the Avon valley, the village appeared to be one vast orchard in the spring – a sea of blossom. Fifty years ago, the parish consisted of a considerable number of smallholdings and market gardens. Those cultivated on a part-time basis, like my own, might be as little as one acre in extent, or even less. Others could extend to ten or fifteen acres, or sometimes even more. The larger marker gardens might well consist of several parcels of land, possibly some distance from one another.

A few, like my good neighbour, Bert Hawkins, might boast one or two greenhouses, not necessarily heated. A great number would have one or more pigsties and a poultry house and run. There would be some grass orchards but in many cases the ground between the plum, damson, apple and cherry trees would be cultivated and cropped.

There was a great deal of pedalling about from one plot of land to another. As like as not, there would be a bucket on each handlebar, a hoe tied to the cross bar, a hand drill slung over one shoulder and the jacket pockets full of seeds.

By the 1940s, some would own a petrol driven rotovator, others might have some tractor ploughing done by contract when needed. But for the most part, the fork, the spade, the hoe, the push hoe, trowel and dibber were the main tools of the trade. A small harrow on the end of a rope might be dragged behind by hand. Wooden rollers, fitted with iron bands at each end, with an iron handle were commonplace. A hand drill, with wheels adjustable to varying row widths was an essential piece of equipment, and a wheelbarrow with a flat body would complete the necessities. W.L.Jones, one time *War Ag* District Officer at Stratford-on-Avon, later became secretary of the Stratford NFU Branch and also for the Bidford and Welford Branch. It was always his complaint that members of the latter had little to insure and thus provided him with a lot of work and little gain from commission on insurance premiums.

I always remember my neighbours with affection. There was, for instance, 'Ticker' Davies, so called because he walked with his feet at a quarter to three. One day he called round in some distress, saying that the Weights and Measures Inspector had called and condemned his scales, and would I take them to Leamington, where Avery's had premises, to get them repaired? Of course I would, so he duly barrowed them round and loaded them into the boot of my Morris 8. They were in a sorry state, all the iron frame and balance rusted, with the wooden frame and the tables worm eaten. When I opened the boot, the man at Avery's fell about laughing and said, 'what about the museum?' So Ticker had to obtain another set of scales!

Alfie Matthews tethered his goats to graze the wide grass verges along the Barton road (known in country parlance as the Long Acre), while another neighbour led his horse up and down grazing a free evening meal. It was a big horse, but its owner was a short, bandy legged little man. When ploughing, he managed very well, but when harrowing or flat rolling, when the draught was light, he almost had to run to keep up, the horse being a keen worker.

At cherry ripening time, there was no sleep for anyone from first light onwards. For those with cherry orchards would be intent on keeping the birds at bay. One favoured method was to tie tins, with pebbles in, onto the upper branches. These were connected one with another by lengths of binder twine, or the like; finally a thin rope led down to ground level. When this was pulled a loud rattle resulted and a host of birds took flight. The banging of frying pans and saucepans or steel sheets and the occasional blast from a shotgun all added to the general din.

Today there are few surviving market gardeners. Bernard Wilkes is one and runs a small shop selling his produce. The Italians, as they are known, have given growing a new lease of life in the parish. They have an extensive holding comprised of a number of pieces of land, some greenhouses, packing sheds etc. They are well mechanised and do the job supremely well. The Blucks, at Weston, farm a sizeable acreage growing corn, potatoes, sprouts (the quality of which is second to none) and other horticultural crops. Their produce is also sold in their farm shop and also marketed elsewhere. They have, as well, converted some of the old farm buildings into holiday cottages, and have a touring caravan site in addition.

But much of the market garden land has been built on and Welford is now almost exclusively inhabited by townies, the breadwinners, for the most part, commuting, and the retired completing the community. Of all this, more later.

Marketing

Much, if not all, market garden produce went to the produce markets in Evesham or Stratford, with the bigger men sending to Birmingham. Grass verges were dotted with crates or boxes of cabbage, savoys, lettuce, beetroot, peas, beans or whatever, awaiting collection by the carrier, in the case of Welford, Dave Careless or Jim Wise, the village coalman. Fruit often used to be taken to Binton Station by horse-drawn dray, its destination Birmingham.

Many transactions were in cash in the 1940s, far more so than is the case today. Food of many kinds was often sold on the free market with little regard for rationing or price controls. This was known as the Black Market.

To illustrate the extent of cash dealing and the amounts of money that must have been kept in house or cottage under the bed, one can do no better than tell the tale of a deal involving a small, Ransome crawler tractor, the MG2, a model much prized at the time for market garden work. Unobtainable new without a permit, and price controlled if auctioned, the deal was clinched in a pub in one of the market garden villages in South Warwickshire without regard to such niceties.

The amount involved was some £600, a very considerable sum in those days. 'I'll go and fetch the money,' said the purchaser, cycling off into the blackout. He returned with a bucket covered by a securely tied tea towel. The contents were duly tipped onto the table, mostly £1 notes and fivers, short by £20. 'Bugger. I must have brought the wrong bucket,' was the comment.

Broader Acres

Between the smallest market gardens, of which those in Welford were typical, and the biggest farms growing fruit, vegetables, potatoes and probably cereals as well, were a multitude of holdings of every size, quite a number of them owned by the Warwickshire County Council and let to tenants. Some of these were in Salford Priors parish and there were others elsewhere. They would be worked by the tenant and his family, with extra help at the busiest times.

At the top end of the scale were those whose acres were numbered in hundreds. They would be fully mechanised by the standards of the day, but still labour intensive to a very large degree. Sprouts, spring cabbage, savoys were staple crops. An acreage of potatoes would be obligatory in the hungry '40s and some cereals as well. Other crops could include stick and 'pinched' runner beans, spring onions and a variety of other crops, including top and soft fruit depending upon soil type and the skills and inclinations of the man concerned.

Michael Bomford, of Dunnington, and John George, of Wixford, would be typical of those on the bigger holdings. A. H. Hiller & Son, also a tenant of the Ragley Estate at Dunnington, were outstanding growers. Arnold Hiller was a gentleman of the old school, extremely capable, innovative and invariably courteous, at any rate to a young adviser in his first job. His son, Robert, followed very much in his father's footsteps. Top and soft fruit were major enterprises, which seasonal casual labour from the Black Country relied upon for picking.

In the same mould, but in a different way, was Ernest Bomford of Rushford, Salford Priors. Readers will already have gathered that I was much involved on his farm, indeed we were good friends until his untimely death at far too early an age. He was an acute observer of soil condition and crop growth, and one could not spend a day with him without learning something fresh.

As well as early potatoes, cereals, herbage seeds, sprouts, savoys, spring cabbage were the main crops, along with smaller acreages of other horticultural crops.

Those were the days of steam trains, and Ernest used to draw locomotive ash from Evesham station and laid down roads with this material right round the farm; there were only a few fields without a road around, or to, them. The farm lorry was loaded direct from the field with sprouts, or whatever, and went straight to market without any double handling.

Like others, this farm was labour intensive, employing, originally, some twenty two men. There were about half a dozen who could not drive a tractor and Ernest reckoned these spent three out of every five working days in the sprout crop, either pegging out, hand hoeing or picking. Each net of sprouts contained a label with the pickers name as well as the name and address of the farm. This was an incentive to pick well and cleanly and to produce a high quality sample.

As a final example of these larger farms growing horticultural crops, mention must be made of the Smith family, long established in the parish of Milcote.

Needless to say, these larger holdings growing market garden crops on a field scale have changed, almost without exception, out of all recognition. In the case of some, the land has been split up and the original holding no longer exists as an entity. On others, the cropping has changed, sometimes now confined to combineable crops only.

Michael Bomford's Dunnington farm has been incorporated into Bomford Ltd., produce growers and packers, the creation of John Roberts, the managing director. A.H.Hiller & Son Ltd. still exists and goes from strength to strength; although, sadly, Robert Hiller died in the 1990s, having suffered ill health for a number of years. Hillers farm shop is one of the largest of its kind. In addition, there is now a garden centre, gift shop and restaurant.

To conclude this section, two practices very common at one time must be noted. First, standing crops of, say, sprouts, spring cabbage or spring onions were often sold for the purchaser to pick, cut or pull and market. Secondly, taking land for one season to grow a single crop, often sprouts, from a farmer was commonplace. There were a number of variations on this arrangement. But the farmer would often plough the field in question, then work it down to a tilth, leaving the 'tenant' to mark out and peg the sprouts in, then keep the crop clean before picking and marketing.

After picking, the stems might be grazed off by sheep. They were then cut off by hand and carted away. If the field was by the river, it has been known for a stack of stems being made on the river bank, ready to be taken off downstream by the next flood. A method of disposal which, no doubt, would be frowned upon in this less tolerant age.

The New Look

As in farming, a high degree of specialisation is now the order of the day. For example, there is a grower near Snitterfield majoring on strawberry growing. Herbs are grown at Lighthorne and a large organisation specialises in raising cuttings under glass for others to grown on into marketable plants, mainly geraniums.

Two enterprises can be described as typical, in very different ways, of the new horticulture in South Warwickshire.

W. J. Findon and Son, of Bordon Hill, Stratford-on-Avon, have expanded steadily over the years and today have many acres of glass. The firm is now run by David Findon, the third generation. His grandfather must have seen the potential of the sheltered site, south facing under the slope of Bordon Hill, probably bought for very little money in the 1930s. During the post-war years, the area of glass and protected cropping has been added to almost annually, and has included the acquisition of another site at Weston-on-Avon, where more greenhouses have been erected.

This enterprise specialises in raising house plants, Poinsettas in particular. These are the most popular plant at Christmas, accounting for 85% of house plant sales at this time of the year in garden centres, supermarkets and so on.

Findons aim to produce plants of the highest quality, uniform, pest and disease free. The whole operation is 'high tech.' The environment within the glasshouses is computer controlled. The seed sowing production line is completely automated, the trays being filled with compost, labelled, the seed sown then covered with vermiculite and watered. They are then conveyed to a tray loading machine which places them on a mobile bench. A variety of tray sizes and seed can be sown using this machine with work rates ranging from 100 to 600 trays per hour.

Even more amazing to the layman is the tray inspection system and the automatic replugger. The first machine identifies those cells in the tray where the seed has failed to germinate, or in which the seedlings are under-sized, these latter being rejected. The second machine automatically re-plants those cells which are empty with fresh seedlings. All in sharp contrast to sowing seeds in trays by hand and then pricking them out.

Bomford Ltd. is one of the UK'S largest privately owned growers and packers of fresh vegetables, and is a major force in the UK market. It is the last remaining enterprise of its type in the Vale of Evesham. The company comprises several farms in South and Mid-Warwickshire with a total acreage of 2,500. The crop rotation currently includes brassicas, legumes and salad onions with cereals and linseed as break crops.

Although the majority of vegetables are home produced, the growing sophistication of the retail market demands year-round supplies of salad onions and legumes. Thus Bomfords is actively and directly involved in growing overseas specifically in Mexico, Egypt and Morocco.

Stringent quality control at the centre of operations and packing complex, currently at Salford Priors, with its state-of-the-art cooling and storage systems, eliminates sub-standard produce and ensures the highest quality to meet the demands of the supermarkets and major retail outlets.

The total acreages grown in 2000 was: broad beans, 150; baby broad beans, 120; peas, 900; dwarf beans, 650; sprouts, 400; salad onions, 1, 450; stick beans, 380; romano beans, 150; trials, 10; fruit, 30. This comprises 4,240 acres in total here and abroad. During the 1990s, Bomfords turnover rose from under £5m/year at the beginning of the decade, to 325m, a truly remarkable achievement.

All a very far cry from my good neighbours in Welford fifty years ago pedalling away from one plot of their land to another, carrying the tools of their trade with them. Selling a few eggs, the odd pig, leaving their boxes of produce on the grass verge to be to await the carrier and then to take their chance in the local produce market.

29. The Agricultural Advisory Services

Prior to 1939, agricultural advice was the responsibility of the Local Education Authorities, and in the Shires this invariably meant the County Councils. These operated under the umbrella of the Provincial Agricultural Advisory Services, situated either at a College or a University; in the case of South Warwickshire, at Harper Adams Agricultural College. Some counties boasted a Farm Institute, the first rung of the ladder of agricultural further education, offering one-year courses only.

The staff of these institutes concerned themselves with such extra-mural activities as *ad hoc* lectures, demonstrations, organising discussion groups and supporting Young Farmers' and Calf Rearing Clubs, as well as teaching the Institute students. Practice varied from county to county, but, as far as I can gather, one-to-one on-farm advice could, in some counties at any rate, play a secondary role only. Specialist advice and support was provided by either a college or the agricultural department of a university.

In counties in which there was no Farm Institute the County Organiser for Agricultural Education performed those duties mentioned above.

In 1939, some institute and college staff were seconded to the War Agricultural Executive Committees, either in an administrative or technical capacity, sometimes both. Specialist advice continued to be provided by college or university, the soil chemists, entomologists and plant pathologists being much involved in supporting the WAEC staffs.

The National Agricultural Advisory Service

In 1946, all this was to change. It had been decided during the War years that, now that the importance of farming in the UK had been given its proper weight under the stress of food shortages, agricultural advice should be provided on a national basis. Under the old arrangements, provision across the country had been uneven. The predominantly agricultural counties often had the lowest rate income which, in spite of Government assistance, sometimes meant that those areas in greatest need of a good agricultural advisory and education service had the least resources to provide them.

The structure of the new service, the National Agricultural Advisory Service (NAAS) was to be as follows. Provincial Centres, as they were then called, now removed from the Universities and Colleges, provided overall control with a Director and Deputy Director. Specialist advice was to be provided by plant pathologists, entomologists, soil chemists, livestock advisers, the milk service, machinery advisers and so on. The Lands Arm, staffed by surveyors and the Veterinary Service had their own organisations.

At county level there was a county adviser and his deputy. Specialist staff consisted of a member of the Lands Arm, and machinery, livestock and milk advisers. Each county was divided into districts, usually the same as the *War Ag* ones, with a NAAS district adviser in each. Laboratory facilities were provided at the Provincial Centres and sometimes at sub-centres as well; there was one at Evesham, which served South Warwickshire as well as parts of other counties.

Possibly, what had not been envisaged when the NAAS had been planned was that the old *War Ag* organisation would persist well into the post-war era. In practice, at county level, NAAS personnel had to take over many of the administrative duties of the peace time County Agricultural Executive Committees. This did less than nothing to enhance the reputation of the new advisory service amongst many members of the farming community, as one of the inherited functions was to service the county executive and district committees, the most important duty of these being the administration of the so-called *efficiency clauses* of the 1947 Act. Briefly, the bare bones of the Act were the provision of guaranteed prices but also an insistence on reasonable standards of livestock and crop husbandry, which was the job of the peace-time county committees to enforce.

Farms were still inspected by district committee members and graded according to the standard of farming. NAAS staff at county and district level were, in consequence, regarded with suspicion mainly on two grounds. First, individual advice on the farm was bound to be tempered by Ministry policy and thus not truly independent and not necessarily in the best interests of the individual farmer concerned. Secondly, it was considered, I believe unjustifiably, that there was always the risk that an adviser's visit might be followed by one from a district committee member to investigate alleged shortcomings. In short, the mantle of the *War Ag*, not a popular organisation in many quarters, fell squarely on the members of the new NAAS. And, it has to be admitted, very understandably so.

It took, arguably, nearly twenty years for NAAS to gain the reputation it deserved. By the mid-1960s, the administration duties in respect of the 1947 Act had long since disappeared. In any case, a whole new generation of farmers was taking over whose attitude to professional advice on husbandry, technical and business management matters was very different from that of their father's and grandfather's generations.

The West Midland Province

This consisted of the counties of Hereford, Worcester, Warwick, Stafford, Shropshire and Cheshire. The Provincial Headquarters were at Tettenhall, near Wolverhampton in premises which had been built as an emergency wartime hospital.

Members of the former county agricultural education organisations, college and university staffs had to make the decision either to remain in the academic life or to join NAAS. Some chose the former, not being attracted to the idea of becoming members of the Civil Service, which, of course, NAAS personnel were. Others opted to join the new advisory service.

Harper Adams Agricultural College, at Newport, Shropshire, had been the centre for specialist advice in pre-NAAS days. Morley Davies, the soil chemist there, transferred to a senior NAAS post at headquarters in London. The entomologist 'Killer' Newton and the plant pathologist 'Pongo' Preston elected to join NAAS (their nicknames followed them, as many of their former students were in NAAS in the West Midlands) and occupied provincial posts in the same disciplines at Tettenhall.

In addition to the provincial headquarters in Woodthorne, Tettenhall there was a sub-centre in Evesham. The Long Ashton Research Station near Bristol had, for a number of years, maintained this small laboratory, staffed by a plant pathologist and an entomologist, for the benefit of growers in the Vale of Evesham. When NAAS took this over, it was staffed in the same manner and housed in a pre-fab on a housing estate in the town. Later, it moved to what had been the old isolation hospital. The former two main wards made ideal laboratories and the smaller rooms were used as offices. It was a pleasant spot, out of the town and on high ground overlooking the Avon.

This, then, was the original set-up, which changed and evolved from time to time. In the 1950s the district offices were closed and staff either worked from home or from the county office. Much of the administrative work became concentrated at the new divisional offices, serving several counties; in the case of the one at Worcester, that county and Warwickshire and Herefordshire.

Mention must be made of the attack (this is not too strong a word) made on NAAS when Prior was Minister of Agriculture. Presumably, the disastrous Conservative Heath administration regarded a free advisory service for the farming community as running contrary to the Party's philosophy. The NAAS county newsletters were to cease publication. Farm visits were to be curtailed; in fact in one county advisers had to ask permission before paying a farm visit. Derisory redundancy terms were offered to those disposed to leave the Service and eventually the name was changed to the Agricultural Development and Advisory Service or ADAS, to reflect the change of emphasis.

The District Advisor – A Personal View

To go back in time when the National Agricultural Advisory Service came into being on October 1st 1946, I was appointed as an assistant crop husbandry adviser in the West Midland Province, Dr. D. H. Robinson being my chief. This was, I believe, due a chance remark to Morley Davies the previous year to the effect that my interests lay more on the arable side rather than in the livestock sector.

Sam Turner, who had been a senior adviser with the Warwickshire *War Ag* took over the Stratford District. Happily he received promotion three years later and I applied for his job and, on March 1st 1949, took over the Stratford office. At that time, it occupied the former Auxiliary Fire Service premises, which were in the garden of Mason Croft, with the entrance off Chestnut Walk. I was twenty-seven years of age and found myself in charge of a small empire with considerable responsibilities for which a BSc. (Agric.), and only just, seemed a hopelessly inadequate qualification.

Fortunately I had the backing of an excellent office staff, Sylvia Hawkins, Pat Wells and Barbara Court, the latter to spend her whole working life with NAAS/ADAS, much of it at the Drayton Experimental Husbandry Farm.

There were three machinery depots at Stratford, Henley-in-Arden and Alcester respectively, each in the charge of a machinery officer with foremen and tractor drivers. There were numerous Land Army hostels and a hostel at Bearley for foreign workers, all of whom were wartime refugees from Europe. There was, in the Stratford office, a labour officer in charge of allocating this gang labour. Also the drainage officer, Eric Fairbrother and assistants whose job it was to design drainage schemes, arrange the grants and, in many cases, carry out the work with drainage gangs.

Pay Day

Thursdays was pay day, when the wages for the Land Army girls and all the other workers had to be put up in the Stratford office. The schedule was a tight one. All the pay packets had to be ready shortly after lunch so that the forewomen could to take the land girls' money out to them, and the machinery and drainage officers to pay all the other workers in the machinery depots and elsewhere.

The wages were calculated in the Leamington office. The cheque, the list of what was due to each worker, and another list for the Bank of the necessary notes and coin required were all entrusted to a Mr. Briggs, a clerk at Leamington, who travelled on a bus which arrived at Bridgefoot, Stratford shortly after 9 a.m., which meant he should be in our office by 9:30 a.m. at the latest. To say he had no sense of urgency – he liked to do a bit of shopping on the way – was an understatement. The girls in the office and the Land Army forewomen were waiting to get on with the job, and if Mr. B. was unusually late he was met with a chorus of disapproval at best and strong language on more than one occasion.

Even then, I had to fetch the money from Lloyds Bank. Sam used to put all the notes in the official Gladstone bag and the coin in a canvas bag. I changed this and put everything in the Gladstone, which made it so heavy that nobody could run far with it.

In those days, the National Provincial Bank was on the opposite corner of Union Street to Lloyds. As I arrived at the latter in a Morris Eight with the two biggest land girls I could find as an escort, an armoured car drove up to the former with an armed guard to collect the wages for the workers in the Long Marston camp. Although we were forced to get to the Bank sharply at opening time every Thursday, no attempt at robbery was ever made; perhaps the presence of the military acted as a deterrent.

It was all something of a performance. I was glad when the whole operation was run down and no more wages were paid from the district office.

The District Committee

When I took over Stratford in 1949, many items of food were still rationed, and were to continue to be so for another four years or so. In addition, the UK was chronically short of foreign exchange, especially dollars at that time, and the exchange rate and balance of payments problems were to dog the economy for several decades to come. Domestic food production was still of prime importance. Thus there was continuing pressure on district committees to press on with the Farm Survey, which is the regular inspecting and grading of farms.

In 1949, there were some twelve farms or holdings under Statutory Supervision. On these the husbandry had been persistently unsatisfactory for several years. Such farms were regularly inspecting and subject to orders of varying kinds. If improvements were not made, the ultimate sanction was dispossession, something that was not resorted to in peace time in Warwickshire to the best of my knowledge. But the fact that a farm was under Statutory Supervision had to be recorded in the Land Register, and thus had an effect on its value.

In my time District Committee, meetings took place once a month instead of fortnightly as previously. The general format remained the same, but soon without reports from the machinery officers since the machinery depots were closed about 1950.

But now I had to write the minutes, from notes taken in shorthand by Pat Wells and later by Barbara Court. When the meeting was over, we went back to the office and I dictated the minutes, finishing about 7 p.m., at the earliest, on Friday evening. The typing was done on Saturday and Monday morning, ready for me to take for signature to the chairman, Freddie Walters of Castle Farm, Studley and then I had to take them on to the Leamington office.

Freddie Walters was a great character with a colossal sense of humour. He was inclined to bark, especially if he disagreed with anything you said. But it was worse than his bite, for I found him the kindest of men. He was, moreover, scrupulously fair. On one occasion, I was at Castle Farm a few hours after his little Russell terrier bitch, Trixie, of which he was very fond, had had one single pup. She was obviously miserable, in pain, with her back hunched up. 'What's wrong with the bitch, Mr. Woods? She has a dead pup inside her still,' I said. 'Nonsense,' barked Walters.

At the next committee meeting some days later, he said 'Before I start the meeting, Mr. Woods, I owe you an apology.' I wondered what was coming next. 'You were quite right about Trixie, we had the vet. and she had a dead pup, as you said.' Not many, I guess, would have bothered to have said that and in front of his fellow committee members.

The only NAAS assistant I had was Harry Isaac; before he came I was helped by ex *War Ag* officers. Harry and I shared the work of accompanying district members when visiting farms in the course of the Farm Survey. We had quite a heavy programme of trial work, mainly with cereals, every season, which was a legacy of my days as a crop husbandry adviser. Harry also did a great deal of soil sampling.

If a district member was concerned about the state of one of the farms for which he was responsible, he asked for a district inspection. This entailed a second visit to the farm accompanied by the district chairman, Freddie Walters, and myself. I had to make a record of the farm, field by field, the crops growing on each one, their state and potential (if any), the cleanliness of the farm, any drainage defects and the quality of the grassland. The report was rounded off by a description of the buildings, the labour, whether the man concerned was a tenant or owner/occupier and any other relevant information.

It was all quite a business putting together such a report, but very good experience which was to serve me in good stead in later years in the realm of farm business management. The report was then considered by the district committee, along with the comments that were made to the farmer by the chairman. It was usually decided to inspect again in, possibly, three months time. I then had to draft a letter for the chairman to sign, outlining those matters which required attention, saying that there would be a further visit in so many months time when it was expected that improvements would have been made, etc. A copy of the report and letter would be attached to the minutes of the meeting. If, on the next district inspection, no progress had been made, it was usual for the farm to be referred to the County Committee for them to decide what further action should be taken.

Fortunately there were not very many of these district inspections in my district in the course of twelve months. But I mention the matter to give some idea of the amount of time involved.

The Agricultural Returns and Crop Reports

We were not in the old fire station premises, off Chestnut Walk, for very long before we moved to a wartime wooden hut beyond the Ministry of Food meat store off the Alcester Road on the opposite side of the track to Stratford station. The meat store has long since been demolished and its remnants are now part of the foundations of the Evesham to Alcester by-pass. A Safeway supermarket now occupies the site, including that of the wooden hut, which was to be my office until all the district offices were closed down in the mid-1950s.

Frank Bennison, when he was District Advisory Officer for Shipston and Southam, inhabited a similar structure in the Darlingscott Road, Shipston. This came to an untimely end. One autumn, the Ministry of Works re-furbished the Tortoise stove and in the process clamped the metal stove pipe to one of the roof trusses.

When the job was finished, they omitted to send a supply of coke for many weeks, and it was a cold autumn. When eventually it did arrive, Frank made up for lost time and stoked up well. So much so that the stove pipe got red hot and set fire to the beam to which it was attached.

The whole place caught fire and burned merrily in spite of the efforts of the fire brigade. Now Frank was never enamoured of the paper work. The story goes that as soon as firemen rescued some files from the burning hut, Frank threw them back again into the flames, thus solving many problems. This tale may, or may not, be apocryphal. Be that as it may, Frank joined me in the Stratford office, bringing his clerk, Ed Warmington with him.

In 1950, or thereabouts, the Ministry suddenly woke up to the fact that it possessed a first class field organisation in the districts. Why should they pay for monthly crop reports to be prepared by a motley collection of local land agents, or who ever, when the district officers could do the job? So NAAS district advisers were landed with this task.

Similarly with the annual and quarterly returns. The statistics branch had been moved to Lytham St. Annes during the war, and the returns were sent out from there. It was now the job of the district officers to be responsible for their collection and checking. And what a chore that was, at any rate to start with. The whole process was riddled with errors and inaccuracies when we took on the task and needed a great deal of work. Fortunately, we had an extra clerk to cope.

In short, while we were under the impression that we had joined an agricultural advisory service, we had become agri-administrators. In contrast to some of my colleagues, this did not really worry me a great deal. I was only too glad to have what appeared to be a secure job, which I enjoyed doing and with a pension at the end of the day. Promotion was never for me; I had no great desire to sit at a desk, drunk with power, signing other colleagues expense sheets. As far as income was concerned I held the view that if the Queen could manage the bread and butter, I would look after the jam represented by a second income from journalism, lecturing and, later, private practice.

Soil Sampling and Analysis

In the 1940s and 1950s, this was one of the main advisory tasks. Some advisers thought that soil sampling, collecting dirt and putting in it in little bags, was beneath their dignity. I did not take this view, having found that it was an ideal way of getting to know the farms, the farmers and the soils in the district.

Originally it was one way of encouraging the use of fertilisers. It may seem strange today, but in the 1940s certainly, the purchase of 'bagmuck' was not part of the farming scene on many holdings.

Discussion Groups

These were originally a wartime measure. Many of that generation of farmers were not great readers, to put it as kindly as possible. It was thought that the spoken word was a more effective means of communication.

In the *War Ag* days, during the winter months, invitations were sent out from the Leamington to every farmer in the relevant parishes. One inducement to attend was the fact that the meetings were usually held in a pub. These were official occasions and it was legitimate, in the days of strict petrol rationing, to use the car, or van, to go to the meeting and have a drink.

There were groups in Henley-in-Arden, Alcester, Snitterfield (not successful), Ullenhall, and so on. By far the best attended was at Aston Cantlow. The back room at the Kings Head was crowded every meeting night. Eventually the groups had to become self supporting, both financially and in terms of arranging their own meetings.

Captain W. B. Dronsfield of Wilmcote Manor was, for many years, until he was tragically killed in a hunting accident, the chairman at Aston Cantlow. After his death, the chair for the evening rotated amongst members. The Aston Cantlow Farmers' Discussion Club is still going after all these years, but in a different form. The scope has been widened to include many non-farming subjects. Members gather for supper first, then the speaker takes the floor, followed by questions and discussion. The venue became the Navigation Inn at Wootton Wawen after the back room in the Kings Head was converted into an up-market restaurant by the new tenants. Subsequently, the Club moved back to Aston

Cantlow, meeting in the Committee Room in the Village Hall, with a caterer using the kitchen facilities to provide supper.

In the 1940s and 1950s, members had a wide range of interests. In South Warwickshire, the farming was truly mixed. Dairying, cattle rearing of dairy heifers and beef, sheep, pigs and poultry, cereals and root crops could all be found, with variations, on many farms in the district. Thus a talk on any one of these sections would have a wide appeal.

But by the middle of the 1960s, the writing was on the wall. Holdings became increasingly specialised, the truly mixed farm, in the old sense, almost became a thing of the past. Discussion groups with their evening meetings and farm walks had to follow suit.

Fig. 14 Meeting of Aston Cantlow Farmer's Discussion Club. (Mary Cherry, 1950s)

Cereal growing, for example, was becoming increasingly sophisticated. Herbicides became a study on their own, with the introduction of fungicides for cereals in the early 1970s, growth regulators, new varieties appearing with great rapidity, direct drilling and minimal cultivations. It all needed a great deal of keeping up with.

Accordingly, I decided, in 1966, to start a group dealing solely with cereals and other combineable crops based on the southern part of the district and thus called The Shipston Corn Growers. This proved good timing for the reasons mentioned above.

We used to meet at about 6:30 p.m., have a talk lasting about 45 minutes, then questions and discussion followed by supper and further talk and argument afterwards. Needless to say, we always met in a pub. We had several venues spending some winters at the Red Lion, Long Compton, a long run at The Bell, Halford, and settling finally at the Houndshill, Goldicote.

I arranged the programme and speakers, and took the chair at each meeting. The Shipston group was very successful and continued for a time after my retirement from ADAS. The local dairy farmers wanted a similar series of meetings, and this I arranged as well. With the run-down, and disintegration, at district level, of ADAS, these discussion groups became a thing of the past.

Agronomy

In the earlier years of NAAS, we were much involved with crop pests and diseases.

In the case of the former, wireworms, wheat bulb fly and leatherjackets were all pests of the ploughing-up campaign and, to a lesser extent, of ley farming. Many farm visits were concerned with the diagnosis and control of these insect pests. Later, aphids in wheat became troublesome and, with the advent of suitable insecticides, the decision had to be made as to whether or not it was worth spraying. This involved either going through the standing crop a few weeks before harvest, and not something to be undertaken lightly in the days before tramlines and high clearance sprayers.

It was always difficult to know what advice to give, especially as the wretched creatures could disappear on their own accord as quickly as they had come.

In the early days of the so-called hormone herbicides, that is, in the late 1940s and early 1950s, 'weed walking' was a frequent occupation of NAAS district advisers. This was really the first section of agronomy to be taken over by the trade. With the advent of cereal fungicides and the run-down of ADAS, agronomists, either employed by agricultural merchants and suppliers, or operating independently on a fee paying basis, took over most of the arable advisory work.

In South Warwickshire, we were fortunate in having such agronomists working in the area of the highest calibre and integrity. Amongst these were Eric Carter, Clive Fidler, Mike Davies and Martin Shaw, to mention just a few of those who were held in esteem and respect amongst the farming community.

Farm Business Management

Today, it must be difficult for those under, say, fifty years of age, to imagine a farming world in which the discipline, practice and techniques of what we now call farm business management simply did not exist.

In the early days of NAAS, raising farm production across the board and, thus, hopefully, profit was the name of the game. At that time rising farm productivity was highly desirable in terms of the national interest.

But the more forward looking had already seen the writing on the wall by the early 1950s. The day was coming when productivity could no longer be equated with profit. Moreover, capital was largely replacing labour, finding the money for mechanisation and improvements to fixed equipment became a pressing problem. NAAS should, therefore, be in a position to offer business and financial advice in addition to what had previously been considered its functions.

According to the Donaldsons and Barber (now Lord Barber) in their *Farming in Britain Today*, published in 1969, this view was not, at first, universal in the higher echelons of the Ministry of Agriculture. The Civil Service mind, it was alleged, shied away from officials giving financial advice with all the inherent dangers involved. Nor were these misgivings confined to the higher ranks. Some of us considered that, in view of all the other duties that had been, contrary to original expectations thrust upon us, being required to master a new and unfamiliar discipline was just about the last straw. However, as our in-service training progressed, our interest increased and before long all our first doubts disappeared.

Unlike other specialists, economists had been left in the universities at the formation of NAAS in order to demonstrate their independence and objectivity, essential in their role of financial data collectors. Until NAAS had appointed its own management specialists in the late 1960s, university staff, in the form of Farm Management Liaison Officers, acted as consultants to NAAS in this field.

Therefore, our initial training took place in the Department of Agricultural Economics, at the University of Reading. The courses were presided over by Professor Edgar Thomas CBE, who had been my lecturer in Agricultural Economics in the early 1940s. He was a great teacher and a kindly man of great charm. His other great interest was agricultural history and he was instrumental in founding the Museum of English Rural Life at the University.

Paddy Blagburn, of the Department, was appointed Farm Management Liaison Officer for NAAS in those counties serviced by Reading, of which Warwickshire was one and was the first to hold this post in the whole country. His job was to assist in the training of NAAS county staff in farm business management and act as a specialist in giving help in the field. He retired in 1959, and was succeeded by Tony Giles, later to become Professor A.K.Giles OBE.

Tony was the greatest help to me. We dealt with many cases together over a period of years, and I have been fortunate enough to enjoy his friendship ever since. This happy arrangement came to an end when NAAS set up its own Farm Management Department in the Provincial (later, to be termed Regional) Headquarters.

We started in-service training at Reading in the early 1950s, and were initiated into the mysteries of comparative account analysis, fixed costs/gross margins, system, partial and cash flow budgets.

At first, the volume of demand for farm business management advice was minimal, confined in South Warwickshire almost entirely to businessmen/farmers whose accountants had told them that their farming losses were such that they could not be sustained.

One of the first of such cases comes to mind. Farm losses were running at £6,000/year, a very substantial figure in those days. After going through the accounts, it was clear that £4,000 of this was accounted for by the expenses attributed to the horses: the groom's wages, running the horse box, feed, and not to mention the gardener's wages and the costs of running several cars.

Not surprisingly, the Inland Revenue were taking a dim view. The actual farm loss was due mainly to the poor performance of the dairy herd. Yields were low and concentrate use high. This latter was partly due to the practice of smothering the farm in the winter months with store lambs bought at Honeybourne. These regularly made a profit of a several pounds a head but in consequence there was little grass neither for grazing until the second half of May nor for a decent crop of hay later.

But demand for farm management advice grew. The banks cottoned on to the fact that this had the potential to be of great value to managers. The publication of *Farming for Profit* by Barber and Dexter (1961), stimulated great interest and had an impact as great if not greater, than the *Farming Ladder* (1944) by Henderson. The first edition of *The Farm Management Pocketbook* by Professor John Nix ,of Wye College, appeared in 1966 and is now the standard source for facts and figures.

The number of farm secretaries proliferated to prepare management accounts. Their analysis by NAAS/ADAS became computerised. Banks started to appoint their own agricultural managers and private consultants began offering their services. In the case of the latter, the top firms of national estate agents started their own farm business management departments. In short, a whole new profession had been created.

But it should never be forgotten that the university departments of agricultural economics were the original driving force, and the NAAS county staffs the first practitioners.

Schemes

From the 1950s onwards, there were various schemes to assist farmers to increase productivity and profits. With all of these, District Advisers were heavily involved. Most of them would have been impossible without farm business management data and techniques.

The first, the Silo Subsidy Scheme, was the exception. This was introduced in the early 1950s to encourage silage making, improve its efficiency and the quality of the end product.

It was based on the erection of silo barns, or the conversion of existing Dutch barns by constructing solid side and back walls, concreting the floor and an apron on which to dump the grass fresh from the field.

Standard costs were calculated for each item. For instance, so much per square yard of roof, of concrete, or hardcore floor, of sleeper or concrete side walls, or yard run of drain and so on. Needless to say, the vast majority of applicants were dairy farmers. It was a good scheme and simple to administer by District Advisers.

Finally, it has to be admitted that some new silo barns never saw any silage; it was a good way of obtaining a Government grant to erect a new Dutch barn in the days before of the Farm Improvement Scheme, of which a passing mention must now be made, although District Advisers were not directly involved.

The Farm Improvement Scheme was introduced in 1957 and was for the erection of new buildings or the conversion of existing ones and other items of fixed equipment. Happily, in those days, no planning consent was needed from the local authority, as farm buildings were, at that time, exempt. This was fortunate, since the whole process would have been extended even further. It could be bad enough as it was, when others were involved, and had to be consulted e.g. the milk adviser, the River Board (as it was originally called) and so on. As the years went by, the number of other agencies involved proliferated, leading to even more delay.

The administration was slow and cumbersome, being the responsibility of the Lands Arm. If, for example, one decided to have a new grain store for the harvest of, say, 1965, you would have to start putting the application together no later than the early autumn of 1964.

Estimates for every piece of work had to be obtained and these, along with the necessary plans, had to accompany the application form. No work could start before formal approval had been given. Even the delivery of material to the site was deemed to be the commencement of work, thus rendering the application void.

Arguments over siting, design, materials etc. could drag on for weeks. Grant rate was normally 40%, but the Lands Arm often wanted a 100% say in matters in which the Ministry had only a 40% interest. Local experience indicated that the officials responsible had no sense of urgency, nor, apparently, the practical knowledge to appreciate that work had to be completed by a certain time, such as a grain store ready for harvest.

All payments had to be made and receipts submitted before the grant was paid. The certification could be a lengthy process as well. The fact that bank interest was ticking up, week by week on 40% of the costs did not register, or was not regarded as significant if it did. Small wonder that some members of the Lands Arm operating in South Warwickshire were heartily disliked.

The Small Farm Scheme was introduced in 1958, with the first applications to be made from January 1st. 1959. By the mid-1950s, it was recognised that those on the smallest holdings, i.e. below 100 acres, faced very real problems in making a decent living. To cut a long story short, this scheme was devised to inject capital by means of grants to enable the farm business to intensify by whatever means suitable to each case. This often meant increased specialisation, or the introduction of a non-land using enterprise such as a flock of hens on deep litter, or a number of sows, the weaners usually being sold on for somebody else to finish.

To be eligible the farm had to be between 20 and 100 acres of crops and grass, and it was amazing what acreage one could 'lose' to buildings, roads, woodland, etc., if the holding was marginally over 100 acres. The intensity of the business was measured, ingeniously, by the labour requirement in terms of standard man days. These had to lie between 250 and 450. A farm plan, covering three to five years, had to be submitted and approved by NAAS. It was normally drawn up by the District Adviser and approved by the County Adviser. It had, of course, to result in an improvement to the farm business, again measured in terms of standard man days.

There were two kinds of grant, the total of which should not exceed £1000. The farm business grant was at the rate of £6/acre, payable over three years in four instalments. Other husbandry grants included an additional ploughing up grant.

In 1965, the scheme was extended to include farms of up to 125 acres with maximum standard man days of 600. Keeping farm records was obligatory. Applicants were provided with a farm record book, based on the NFU version, a copy of which lies beside me as I write.

The small farm problem received a great deal of publicity in the media. This induced, in those directly concerned, some resentment at being regarded as 'the deserving poor,' or an inferiority complex, or both. In some, this resulted in a slightly aggressive attitude. For instance, I received a letter from an applicant in Long Compton parish, 'I demand my rights under the Small Farm Scheme,' or from another, 'I want the money, but I am going on just as I have been before.'

I soon learnt that other, more diffident types, did not wish to appear to be applying for the bounty. They would ask you onto the farm for, apparently, an entirely different purpose. It was then up to me to broach the subject, suggesting an application might be of benefit, outlining the scheme and offering help in drawing up a farm plan.

In my opinion, those in the second category were to be preferred to those in the first and I made many friends with these and enjoyed helping them.

In my district, I had some sixty-eight farmers in the Small Farm Scheme. In practice, it failed to meet its objective in the vast majority of cases. It provided a welcome temporary addition to farm income, but no lasting benefit. Of the sixty-eight, few survive as separate units. With one exception, these are all County Council tenants and, even these, in most cases, farm additional acres, their present holdings having been amalgamated with one or more adjoining ones.

The Agricultural Credit Corporation was set up at much the same time as the Small Farm Scheme. It was an organisation independent of MAFF and acted as a guarantor of overdrafts at the Bank. For this service it charged a percentage of the amount involved. If my memory serves me correctly, its liabilities as a guarantor, in the event of the overdraft being called in, were underwritten by the Ministry. This proved expensive.

The whole idea behind this scheme was to provide the Bank with security in cases where its farmer/customer had none, or insufficient, to offer for modernisation or expansion. Obviously, the applicant had to be competent and put forward proposals which made sense in the form of a farm plan with, normally, system and cash flow budgets. It was, in short, to make credit available to deserving cases who, otherwise, would be unable to obtain finance. Overall, 40% of applications were for the purchase of additional livestock, 25% for buildings and machinery, and 35% for working capital to transfer hire purchase commitments and merchant debts to the Bank. Needless to say, the majority of those applying were tenants.

Fortunately, I was not much involved, having only one applicant. But some of my Warwickshire colleagues were not so fortunate. Once all the paper work had been completed, the application was submitted to the ACC and either approved for a guarantee or turned down.

My colleagues, who had more experience of the matter, were amazed at the somewhat eccentric behaviour of the ACC in the early stages. Applicants who they considered worth backing were turned down, while those who came into the category of being amongst the lost causes of British agriculture were successful.

Nationally, some 90% of plans and budgets were prepared by NAAS District Advisers. The Agricultural Credit Corporation was God's gift to bank managers. Very often, the bank manager was the one who took the initiative, suggesting fairly forcibly to his client that an application should be made. It must be remembered that when the ACC was set up banks, as a general rule, were less keen to lend to farmers than they became a decade later. The view taken was that, in principle, banks should be a source of short-term finance only. It was only in the early 1960s that The Midland became the first bank to lend long-term for the purchase of farms, with disastrous results for two or three local farmers during the credit squeeze at the end of that decade.

The 1960s saw the introduction of the Farm Business Recording Scheme (FBRS). When, in the early 1950s, we, in NAAS, were being instructed in the art and mystery of farm business management, it was thought that farm accounts prepared for tax purposes by accountants could be used as the basis of comparative analysis.

In the event, when one got out into the field, or rather onto the farm, this proved to be optimistic. For example, accountants invariably lumped fertilisers, feedingstuffs and seed together as one item. Insurance was one item which included car and machinery premiums, along with those for general insurance. Such omnibus entries had to be analysed out with reference to the relevant invoices.

In defence of accountants and their clients, in the mid 1950s, we have to remind ourselves that it was only since 1940 that farms of any size were forced to present tax accounts. Previous to that, liability for income tax was assessed on the rent paid, very often a matter of shillings/acre, rather than £s. Few, in fact, paid any tax. The impression, and it was only an impression, that I gained was that accountants as a profession did not, at that time, actively seek farmer clients. They involved a lot of work for comparatively modest fees.

Given that tax accounts were, naturally, prepared to obscure the issue, rather than clarify it, District Advisers were often in some difficulty in using them for management purposes. This was compounded by the fact that their clients often had little idea of even the fundamental rudiments of their farm business.

In reply to a query on the rent paid, or the weekly wage bill, one was informed that, 'the missus does the booking,' or alternatively, 'I am more of a practical man.' Not helpful!

The upshot of this situation was that, during the 1960s, it was possible for farmers to get a grant for three years under the FBRS for paying a farm secretary to keep the necessary records and accounts. Incidentally, Studley College, in South Warwickshire, was the first establishment to offer a one year course for those girls who wished to become farm secretaries. Needless to say, many other colleges quickly followed suit.

The National Farmers' Union produced a farm record book in loose leaf form the use of which became almost universal. It contained cash analysis sheets, feedingstuff, crop, monthly livestock numbers records and so on. It also had sheets on which gross margin accounts could be kept. At the end of the year, all the information was there to complete accounts both for tax and management purposes.

It was a good scheme. Apart from producing excellent records and accounts, it stimulated the employment of farm secretaries. It was very unusual, in my experience, for farmers to dispense with the services of a farm secretary once the three years was up.

Needless to say, District Advisers were heavily involved in the administration of FBRS. By now, the farm management accounts were being processed centrally. Once these reports were returned, the District Adviser would take them to the farmer, with notes commenting upon them.

Without doubt, the 1970s were the decade of the Farm and Horticultural Development Scheme (FHDS). This was an EU-funded scheme. Its core was the drawing up of a plan, with budgets and so on, for the modernisation and development of the farm business. Grants were available, not only for fixed equipment but also for plant and machinery, the rates varying according the item being grant aided. The proposals put forward had to be detailed and comprehensive, and could be drawn up by private consultants or by the District Adviser, but had to be approved by ADAS in any case. Invariably, before approval, plans had to go to the Lands Arm, Milk Advisers and so on. Although worse was to come, bureaucracy was beginning to exert its stranglehold.

The take-up of FHDS in South Warwickshire during the 1970s was good, and a great deal of time was spent in helping to draw up plans, reporting annually on the management accounts and so on.

The scheme was particularly timely for dairy farmers. Many owners of herds which had been expanded to fifty or sixty cows, changing from cowpens to a yard and parlour system in the process, ten or fifteen years previously, now found they had to double up once again. FHDS provided funds for new parlours (milking equipment was now grant aided), new grass silos and increased yarding, etc.

Some applicants now held the view that the intensity of their growing of combineable crops had gone far enough, and they wished to make a return to a system of ley farming. Grant aid was directed to better fencing and water supplies, the provision of cattle yards or in-wintering sheds for the ewe flock, along with the purchase of additional livestock.

Those that were taking the other route towards all-arable farms were glad of assistance for additional grain storage and drying equipment. It was a good scheme, helping many in South Warwickshire to expand and modernise.

Clearly, expansion and modernisation had been a feature of farming since the 1950s. The various schemes described above, starting with the Silo Subsidy, all played an effective part in this process, with the possible exception of the Small Farm Scheme. As time went on, the schemes got progressively more complicated but, with the exception of the Farm Improvement Scheme, District Advisers played a key role in every one.

In short, both NAAS and then ADAS proved to be very different advisory services from that which my generation fondly imagined we were joining in 1946. From the 1970s onwards, the trade and agronomists in private practice took on much of the crop husbandry advisory work, and consultants in farm business management began to offer a wide range of business services. ADAS, itself, eventually became a fee-charging service, withering away in the end to a mere shadow of its former self. Of course, farming itself had changed out of all recognition in fifty years or so. It was, in fact, becoming increasingly difficult, and then impossible, to justify an agricultural advisory service financed from public funds.

30. AGRICULTURAL CO-OPERATION

It could be claimed that South Warwickshire is one of the cradles of agricultural co-operation, and that South Warwickshire farmers have been particularly forward looking in this respect. Not only have they initiated co-operative ventures over the years, but have also supported those that originated elsewhere.

Amongst the latter must be counted the Avoncroft Artificial Insemination Centre, situated at Stoke Prior, near Bromsgrove. This was started by the Cadbury Trust, but was run by farmers for farmers. Not only have the services of this centre been widely used in South Warwickshire over the years, but some of our local livestock farmers have played a prominent role in the organisation. The names of Ken Smith, of Walcote, and Bertie Watts, of Willicote, amongst others, spring to mind.

Arable Research Centres (ARC) is another co-operative, which is supported by some South Warwickshire farmers, has its local trial centre on a farm at Hatton, near Warwick. The first centre was started in the Cotswolds in 1979 and, at the last count there were fourteen centres now operational. These are all locally managed, with overall co-ordination provided by the Centre based on the Royal Agricultural College, Cirencester.

ARC is a unique trials organisation funded predominantly by farmer subscription. Its purpose is to provide progressive farmers with the latest technical information to enable them to maintain and improve the profitability of their combineable crops.

These, then, are two co-operatives which, although originating outside the county have received valuable support from South Warwickshire farmers. We now have to turn to our native-born co-operatives.

The NFU Mutual Insurance Co.

This must be considered the doyen of them all. It was founded in 1910 as the Midland Farmers' Mutual Insurance Society following a meeting of a few prominent local farmers in a tea-room in Stratford-on-Avon.

In passing, it is worth noting that this was a year after the founding of the Stratford-on-Avon Branch of the National Farmers' Union. This was followed by the formation of Branches at Warwick, Henley-in-Arden and Shipston. Representatives of these met monthly, in the Free Library in Stratford, to discuss matters affecting farmers and farming in South Warwickshire. This was, in fact, the precursor of the Warwickshire NFU County Executive Committee.

Incidentally, the Branch membership peaked in the 1950s at 500. Today, it is half that number. Countryside members who have 'larger than a garden but smaller than a farm' now exceed the farmer members at 300.

Among the first Directors of the Mutual were South Warwickshire farmers James Henson, John William Lowe, Arthur Henry Pearce, J.R.Black and John James. The latter was the first member of the Stratford NFU Branch to have a policy issued, No. 501.

J.R.Black married a daughter of John James. He became the first Secretary of the Mutual, then its Managing Director, and continued to serve as a Director until his death in 1952. I can well remember him and Mr. Pearce, the latter driving around the town in his Rover.

NFU Branch Secretaries also act as agents for the Mutual and for its sister company, the Avon, which caters for non-NFU clients. This seems to me to be an ingenious arrangement, as the Branch secretaries derive much of their income from commission. Also, with farmer numbers falling year by year, the creation of the Countryside membership was a brilliant stroke. While such members have no voting rights on NFU matters, they enjoy all the other benefits of membership such as insurance rates, legal advice and, of course, the service provided by the Branch office.

The NFU Mutual is now a large and very well run organisation, and provides a wide range of financial services and investment opportunities, as well as insurance.

From little acorns great oaks grow.

Warwickshire Farmers Ltd.

This was a farmers' co-operative formed in the early 1920s and, like many others across the country, supplied a wide range of farm inputs such as seed, fertilisers, feedingstuffs and many other sundry items. Like many others, Warwickshire Farmers manufactured its own range of feedingstuffs, eventually purchasing the premises of the MMB grass drier at Bearley in the 1950s for this purpose not long before it merged with Worcestershire Farmers to form Midland Shires Farmers. Over the years, other mergers took place and the combined co-operatives now trade under the name of Countrywide, which is now the largest organisation of its kind in the country. Thus, Warwickshire Farmers, established all those years ago, can claim to be a founder member of Countrywide.

Both the NFU Mutual and Warwickshire Farmers were well established before the outbreak of war in 1939, and we must now describe the formation of the other South Warwickshire co-operatives during the second half of the twentieth century. It also has to be recorded that Midland Shires Farmers, as it then was, played a vital role in the establishment of these, providing expertise, management services and, in some cases, office accommodation as well.

Arable Crop Marketing

Arable Crop Marketing (Midlands) Ltd. was set up in 1973 by a group of Midland farmers. Their objective was to start a trading organisation which would deal with every aspect of marketing from sampling through to selling, with a suitable administrative set-up. The co-operative would also be able to negotiate advantageous financial arrangements, so that interim payments could be made to members throughout the marketing year. Over the years all these objectives have been achieved successfully.

In 1979, a sister co-operative was formed, Arable Crop Storage Ltd. With assistance of grant aid from both UK and EC sources, a 20,000 tonne grain store was built on the old aerodrome at Atherstone-on-Stour, near Stratford-on-Avon. This was equipped with a modern grain assessment laboratory to carry out the necessary tests so that cereals, legumes and oilseed rape could all be marketed to the best advantage.

Members of ACM had to agree to sell all their grain through the co-operative, with the exception of that grown on seed contracts and for farm use. Over 90% of the grain is sold through the pool system. This provides a structure for making advance payments to members and enables grain of the same quality to be marketed in a common pool. The resulting average values are then distributed amongst members. ACM have been able to obtain finance on very good terms to make interim payments possible.

It has been a fundamental principle that grain should be sold at a time determined by marketing judgement, as opposed to when the cash flows of members dictated. To ensure that every member was able to receive payments when required, there is a comprehensive range of pool payment options to meet most needs, arrangements which have stood the test of time.

ACM was incorporated on July 9th. 1974 with J.R.Reeve, F.J.Bennison and D.V.F.Thomson as Directors. By the second year, ACM consisted of the Warwick, and the Ouse and Cherwell groups, to be joined the following year by Croplink. By then 17,000 tonnes of grain were being marketed.

In 1982, UGP Exports (Southern) Ltd. was formed and the Southampton silos opened, ACM taking shares in the new organisation. Further mergers took place with Craven Grain Ltd., Hereford, in 1992, to be followed by Eagle Grain Ltd., Stafford, in 1994, and with Hampshire-based GCS a year later. Before this last merger, ACM was marketing 156,000 tonnes of grain from 320 members. By 1997-98 the combined groups were trading 560,000 tonnes from 772 members.

Over the years, the store at Atherstone-on-Stour has been expanded and the equipment improved. ACS Ltd. remains an independent organisation, its status being unaffected by ACM's merger with GCS Ltd.

In short, from small beginnings this South Warwickshire grain marketing co-operative can claim to be a resounding success. As in all other organisations, mergers have been the name of the game. There has been a steady expansion in the tonnages of grain traded. While average pool prices have always exceeded those published by the Home Grown Cereal Authority (HGCA).

Warwickshire Quality Calves

This was formed by Warwickshire farmers in 1981, and the aim was to provide an efficient, independent marketing service for calves mainly from dairy herds in the county. Today, WQC has expanded its services far beyond South Warwickshire and is now the leading calf marketing co-operative in the country with some 600 shareholding members.

Growth has been steady over the years. In 1982, some 5,000 calves were traded. In 1998, sixteen years later, this figure had risen to approximately 42,500.

Calves are purchased from dairy farmers and sold on to beef producers as rearing or reared calves, mainly the former. All stock is marketed with a seven-day health warranty and full traceability. WQC has unique contacts between calf producers and buyers. This has been used to produce calves to customers individual requirements and dairy farmers receive a cash bonus for producing calves by specific breed sires.

Among South Warwickshire farmers on the original Board were: John Wyatt of Rollright; Nick Taylor, Tysoe; John Fox, Goldicote, and George Steele, Studley. Also special mention must be made of David Slatter, Lower Clopton, Quinton, who served on the board for fifteen years. In the early days, much help and support came from the Warwickshire Branch of the National Farmers' Union. Midland Shires Farmers supplied management services and provided office accommodation on the site at Bearley. For nine years, Frank Bennison of Little Wolford, who has played such an important role in agricultural co-operation in South Warwickshire, was the MSF representative on the Board of WQC.

The first lairage was at Rectory Farm, Whatcote, where the calves were collected, weighed and vetted before being despatched to the farms of their purchasers. Later, a much larger lairage was built on the old Snitterfield aerodrome, close to the offices at Bearley.

Meadow Valley Livestock

Meadow Valley Livestock (MVL) originated in the neighbouring county of Worcestershire in 1975, when a group of cattle sheep and pig producers marketed their stock together through a local abattoir, owned by the co-operative. In 1983, they decided to expand their activities and asked Midland Shires Farmers to supply management services to them in the same way as MSF had assisted Warwickshire Quality Calves. Similarly the co-operative's base moved to Bearley, where it remains to this day.

The history of MVL has been one of steady expansion, not only in the numbers of finished stock marketed, but also into trading in breeding and store stock. In all this, David Slatter, has played a prominent part.

In the case of finished cattle and lambs, field staff advise on finishing and outlets, and help select cattle and draw lambs. Producers are advised on identified, and niche markets, and also on future requirements. For example, a Yorkshire abattoir pays a premium and the additional transport costs for Hereford and Hereford cross cattle. Stock is transported direct from farm to abattoir, carcase information is returned promptly to the producer, and carcase grading is checked regularly by experienced staff.

MVL market cull stock, which include cows from dairy and suckler herds, stock bulls and ewes and rams. These are sent direct to abattoirs, mainly in the Midlands. Field staff can advise on selection, and there are regular collections and careful handling.

The co-operative also deals in breeding stock and can supply MLC recorded rams, breeding ewes and all types of breeding cattle from quality-assured farms – stock bulls for dairy and suckler herds, suckler cows in calf or with calves at foot, and quality heifers. Store stock can be supplied on a direct farm-to-farm basis. Finished pigs, both pork and bacon weights, are marketed on behalf of members, as are cull stock. MVL can supply quality store pigs and are agents for selected breeding companies.

Meadow Valley Livestock is certainly another co-operative success story with a history of steady expansion in stock numbers traded over the years.

Conclusion

Finally, it must be pointed out that co-operatives' financial results have suffered, along with farmers, during the years of recession in the closing years of the 1990s and into the 21st century.

The history of agricultural co-operation during the 1920s and '30s, but up to the present time, to some extent, has not been a happy one. This has been due to a number of reasons. First, and this applies particularly to the old school, a supreme confidence in the individual's ability to drive a hard bargain is a characteristic of the farming community. But success is not always assured, and I can well remember leaning on a the wall of a partly open yard one winter's day looking at a dejected, scraggy bunch of cattle up to their bellies in muck. Their owner came out with the traditional and classic remark, 'They are sure to grow into money,' which when translated means, 'I gave too much for them in the first place, if they all live I might break even.'

Secondly, particularly during the inter-war years, there was a reluctance to pay for first class management in the case of merchanting co-operatives. The principle was that those whom farmers employed should not enjoy a higher income than the farmer co-op members. Those co-operatives that did flourish were those which employed good management.

Thirdly, the inability to take a long term view. It is a fact of life that on some occasions during the year, stock will make more in the local market, or there may be better offers from the corn merchant than the co-operative is currently paying. This shakes the faith in the system, regardless of the fact that, at the end of the day and taking everything into account, the co-operative is likely to have the edge. This is certainly true of selling grain. The individual is up against merchants who know a great deal more about the trade than he, or she, does. Over the season, and over a run of years, a corn grower will do very well to consistently beat the HGCA average prices. Co-operatives employ professional grain traders, like ACM'S David Edge and, with the annual pool system, do just that.

In the fourth place, many feel that committing the marketing of the whole production of a commodity entails a loss of independence, which they are not prepared to countenance.

In these difficult times, the pundits are constantly urging farmers to 'improve their marketing' as one method of going some way towards mitigating the effects of the current recession. It is to the credit of so many South Warwickshire farmers that they got the message many years ago.

31. MECHANISATION

Fig. 15 John Deere articulated tractor. (John Deere)

Underlying all the changes that have been recorded in previous chapters, both in crop and livestock husbandry, is increased mechanisation. A full description of the mechanisation of farm work would fill a large volume, and the following is but a series of random memories of, and thoughts on, the developments which have taken place since 1940. And these could take many forms.

The humbler and less spectacular, such as the stationary engine and the electric fence may not spring immediately to mind in this context, but nevertheless played their part in their day. Electric fences are still in daily use on many, if not most, livestock holdings. During the 1940s, the main power sources on any farm were provided by the muscles of men and horses. Locally grown, as it were, on the farms and in the villages of the countryside.

This is in sharp contrast to this day and age, when farming is dependent entirely upon oil, much of it from distant lands. It is a painful fact that supplies can, only too easily, be disrupted by industrial action of one kind or another, by terrorism, or by acts of war. This is the price which has to be paid for progress. This dependence is not confined to fuel for machinery of all kinds, but extends to the manufacture of crop protection chemicals and fertilisers, not to mention the transport of materials to, and produce from, farms. In common with most modern activities of every kind, agriculture has become to rely almost exclusively on oil.

In the 1940s, there were many farms in South Warwickshire which were without a supply of mains electricity. Some, a small minority, would have a generating plant of some sort. But this supplied electricity for lighting only. For the rest, candles and oil lamps in the house and around the farmstead were the order of the day. Central heating in farm houses was almost unheard of; fire wood was in abundance, and open fires provided heat. Solid fuel kitchen ranges, Rayburns and Agas (before they became *up-market*), supplemented with oil stoves, were the means of cooking.

How many of those advocating a return to traditional, sustainable, farming today would take readily to the time consuming, daily chores of filling oil lamps and washing and polishing the glass chimneys and shades, sawing and carrying wood, and humping coal and coke? But there were advantages. Providing there was a large stack of firewood by the back door, a good store of coke or anthracite and a tankful of paraffin, domestic comfort and convenience, such as they then were, could not be threatened by urban malcontents or other trouble makers.

Incidentally, before paraffin produced from mineral oil became available, oilseed rape (then known as colza), which was home-grown on English farms, provided the oil for lighting. Indeed, oil lamps were sometimes referred to as colza lamps.

Stationary Engines

Before electricity was laid on, many of the tasks now performed by electric motors were carried out by small, petrol or paraffin driven stationary engines, which were maids of all work. Perhaps their most common function was to drive the vacuum pumps of milking machines. These small engines, of usually 2 to 5 horse power, were also used for a variety of other jobs, such as pumping water, driving barn machinery, or taking the place of the horse gear to drive the old wooden elevators, and so on. They were a common enough sight on many farms for well over half a century.

The 1908 edition of *Fream's Complete Grazier* mentions and illustrates a Hornsby while by the 1920s, R.A.Lister, Pegsons and Wolseley amongst others were well known makes. During the 1940s, when food production had a high priority, there was a drive to connect farms to the main electricity supply, normally single phase. This posed problems later when three phase was needed to drive grain driers, so many of which were installed in the 1960s onwards.

Electricity

But not all farmers were enthusiastic when offered connection to the main supply. Harold Ward, himself an industrial electrical contractor, of Grey Mill Farm, Wootton Wawen, approached his neighbour, a farmer of the old school, to join him in installing a joint supply, the cost to each being £700 – admittedly a substantial sum in those days, the second half of the 1940s. He declined the offer with the remark 'You can buy an awful lot of paraffin for that money.'

By the end of the 1950s, there were few farms in South Warwickshire without a mains supply of electricity. Electric engines of every size and power could now be put to a multitude of uses around the farmstead driving grain driers, elevators, conveyors, grain milling and feed mixing machines to name but a few. They took over milking machines from the stationary engines and an electricity supply was essential when refrigerated bulk milk tanks were introduced.

Electricity was an essential power source for heating and lighting in intensive pig and poultry units, not to mention the transformation in the farmhouse with electric cookers, refrigerators, washing machines, dishwashers and so on. In short, it is impossible to imagine a modern farmstead without a supply of mains electricity, which was very far from being the case in the 1940s.

There was, of course, a downside. Stand-by generators had to be provided against the possibility of a power cut. Livestock units were particularly vulnerable. For example, no modern dairy unit would be complete without one, usually driven off a tractor power take-off. Some generators were driven by a petrol engine.

The Electric Fence

This is a comparatively simple and inexpensive piece of equipment introduced in the 1940s. Usually run off a battery, but sometimes connected to the mains supply via a transformer, it revolutionised grassland management and, indeed, the utilisation of root crops. It enabled the bred strains of grasses and clovers, which became widely sown for the first time in the 1940s, and the increased use of fertilisers, notably the nitrogenous variety, to realise their full potential in improving stocking rates and achieving economy in feeding by greater reliance on grazed grass.

The Tractor

The tractor is probably the first farm machine to come to the mind of the layman pondering (or decrying) increased mechanisation in the countryside. Tractors first made their appearance on UK farms towards the end of the 19th century, but were few and far between and not considered practical by the majority of the farming community.

But during the First World War, significant numbers of tractors were imported from the USA to help in the food production drive. The production of tractors in quantity started in the UK at Dagenham in 1933, when the first blue Standard Fordson began to be manufactured. They were described as 'costing no more than three horses and doing the work of eight.'

In 1937, the colour was changed to orange and then to green at the outbreak of the Second World War. In those days, ploughs and implements were pulled behind a tractor by means of a tow bar, and many tractors had a pulley for a belt drive and some had a power take-off as well.

Fig. 16 Fordson and trailer plough. Early Ferguson with direct mounted plough. (1950s)

Self starters were, of course, something very much in the future in the 1940s. On many a cold winter's morning, a good sweat would be got up swinging the starting handle. For these machines ran on paraffin when the engine had reached the necessary temperature, but had to be started on petrol. By 1939, there were something less than 55,000 tractors on British farms, three quarters of which were Fordsons. In the same year, there were still 700,000 working farm horses. By the end of the Second World War, there were no less than 170,000 tractors in use. Many were imported, but the Standard Fordson was still very much in evidence until it was replaced by the Major in 1945.

Perhaps it could be argued that the tractor revolution really began with the introduction of *The Little Grey Fergie*, as it was affectionately known . This was manufactured in Coventry by the Standard Motor Company and production started in the summer of 1946. This reached 5,500/month two years later, many, of course, being exported. It was revolutionary in design. The implements were no longer towed but became an integral part of the tractor, being lifted in and out of work by a hydraulic system that also controlled the depth of working. A whole range of implements and other tackle were developed for use as part and parcel of the new system, from a plough to a saw bench, or from a seed drill to an earth moving bucket.

The flexibility and adaptability of the Fergie was well illustrated by an incident which took place in July, 1955. This was a very dry year, so much so that those trying to break out a ley for a half fallow in mid-summer had difficulty in getting a plough into the hard ground. One Tuesday, in Stratford market, Ken Smith, then of Manor Farm, Walcote, came up to me saying, 'You're a clever man. Mike. How do I plough out a ley with the land like concrete?' He thought, of course, that this was an impossible question to answer. 'Stick a sub-soiler on one Fergie and follow on with the plough on another,' I suggested off the top of my head, with fingers crossed behind my back. The following Tuesday in market Ken came up; 'It worked!' he said. 'Of course,' I replied, loftily. What a lucky guess!

Incidentally, the drill had a design defect when used on ridge and furrow, which could not possibly have been foreseen. In the 1940s, fields in ridge and furrow which had been ploughed out of grass had yet to be levelled, as they became in the fullness of time with continuing cultivation. If such fields were drilled across the ridge and furrow, the Ferguson drill was thrown out of gear as it moved over the crest of the ridge. This gave rise to narrow strips of unsown land right across the field which were something of a mystery at first. The design was such that increased draught was transferred to the rear wheels and gave increased traction. Thus, it was said, that if wheel slip occurred when ploughing, the remedy was to stick on another furrow. Sets of spiral steel strakes were available for the rear wheels. When these were fitted traction was certainly remarkable.

At first, Fergies were not too popular with drivers in some cases. With Fordsons, it was always possible to ease one's position during a long working day by standing on the steel deck between the rear mudguards. But there was no such thing on a Fergie; you sat astride the gearbox and transmission casing, with feet on rests fitted each side, and there you stayed in one position all the day.

There is no doubt that the Fergie was a brilliant innovation both in concept and execution. It revolutionised tractor design and practice.

But, as the years went by, it became clear it had one drawback. This was epitomised by the sight of three, four, or sometimes even more, of these little grey tractors ploughing in one large field, just as one might have seen, in days gone by, the same number of horse teams which they replaced. In short, by the 1960s, it began to become apparent that the output per man, which by then was starting to become all-important as the farm work force dwindled, was sadly lacking. As the years went by, more powerful tractors became available with a greater output per hour. Many other makers besides the Standard Motor Company and Fords entered the market. David Brown, Nuffield, Case, John Deere and many others competed for the custom of UK farmers.

During the 1950s, diesel engines started to replace the now outmoded petrol-paraffin type and, before very long, became universal, along with electric self-starters. In short, tractors became more powerful, larger and, of course, more expensive. In the 1970s, horse power started to run into three figures. The imported Steiger, of over 300 hp, was, if my memory serves me correctly, the first mammoth tractor to appear in South Warwickshire and, needless to say, became something of a status symbol amongst the new breed of arable farmer. In the 1960s, four wheel drive tractors became available. Locally, it could be argued that they transformed the farming of Larkstoke and Brailes Hill farms with their banky fields and somewhat abrasive soils, which increased track wear so much on the only alternative, crawler tractors.

Increasing emphasis was being put on driver comfort. By 1946, an all weather tractor cab for a Fordson was being advertised by S.E.Opperman Ltd. This came complete with glass windscreen, manually operated wiper and a sliding glass side window. The price was £19/10s (£19.50); a canvas back apron could be had for an extra 23/6 (£1.175). Today, of course, tractor cabs are air conditioned, with fitted radio and upholstered, sprung, seats. All a far cry from an old sack stuffed with hay on a pan seat and an ex Home Guard overcoat! Hydrostatic steering, electronic controls and change-on-the-move gearboxes have all made the drivers' lot that much easier.

Crawler tractors had always suffered from the disadvantages of slow speed and unsuitability for use on roads, but, nevertheless, played an important part in farming the Warwickshire clays. With the coming of rubber tracks, introduced by leading makers in the late 1980s, all this changed. With multi-furrow ploughs and other tackle to match, the output per man reached levels unthought of in the first days of the Fergie. Another innovation in the 1980s was the high speed tractor. The first was the Trantor, which appeared in 1979, followed by the JCB Fastrac. Eventually, these were developed to do field work, just as well as high speed haulage on public and other roads.

Such tractors are now a familiar sight on roads in South Warwickshire, and are extensively used by Bomford Ltd. in connection with their horticultural growing and packing business.

Cultivators

Needless to say, the size of all field equipment increased along with the power of tractors available to work them. This applies equally to ploughs, cultivators, rolls, drills and the rest. Mention has already been made of the development of minimal cultivations, or no-plough seed bed preparation, and the role that the NAAS Experimental Husbandry Farm at Drayton, near Stratford-upon-Avon, played in this development. Manufacturers were quick to jump on this bandwagon, introducing a whole range of combined cultivators, all designed to make the production of a seedbed from stubble as rapid, and as efficient, as possible and, after burning was banned, to incorporate straw and stubble.

To this end, many makers combined discs, cultivator tines, harrows, crumblers, and so on, in an almost bewildering array in some cases. The final step was to add a seeder to the outfit, making possible the preparation of the seedbed and sowing into it in one pass – something that was considered the Holy Grail of arable farmers for very many years. All these developments were taking place approximately from 1970 onwards, and thus coinciding with a renewed interest in what became known as *soil management.* This came about owing to the very difficult conditions arsing from the high rainfall in the second half of the 1960s.

These developments were accompanied by an upsurge in the practice of subsoiling, which came to be regarded as an integral part of minimal cultivations and, in some cases, a method of rejuvenating old tile drainage systems. Thus, in the 1970s, the conventional subsoiler sprouted wings to increase earth shatter. Novel designs appeared on the scene, amongst them the Howard Paraplow, the power-driven Shakerator, and the Flatford Progressive Soil Ameliorator, amongst others. The latter, incidentally combined a cultivator with subsoil tines and needed a 200 hp. tractor to pull it. Rotary cultivators, both pedestrian controlled and tractor mounted, had been with us for many decades, but even the tractor-mounted versions had slow rates of work.

The introduction of power harrows superseded rotary cultivators for farm work. The first model was introduced by Lely in 1968. These quickly became very popular with arable farmers in South Warwickshire, their possession in the early days being a subject of some pride on the part of their owners. In short, more powerful tractors opened up a whole range of possibilities for increasing output/man/hour and more rapid seedbed preparation.

In South Warwickshire drilling cereals has always been the main seed sowing operation. The combine drill, which sowed seed and fertiliser at the same time, was in almost universal use during the 1940s, and well into the 1950s. There were, of course, many other makes but Sunshine corn drills, imported from Australia, were widely used in the district. In fact, the *War Ag* machinery depots were equipped exclusively with these, to the best of my recollection. These Sunshine drills, in common with most other combine drills, had spring loaded disc coulters. Perfectly serviceable in a good tilth, but inclined to bounce and sow unevenly in a cloddy seedbed, which was all too often the case on the clays in a dry autumn, and which was made a good deal worse if the tractor was driven in too high a gear.

Sowing

Fig. 17 Tillage train. One-pass seeding.

This was brought home to me one autumn, and the fact that disc coulters could be inferior to the shoe coulters fitted to the old Smythe, or Suffolk, drill. These were not spring loaded and the mechanism forced them into the soil, more or less, whatever the conditions, and held the coulters at the set depth. I was on Crimscote Fields Farm, then owned and farmed by 'young' Tom Canning (to distinguish him from his father). One day in early winter, a field opposite the house had been drilled to winter wheat, which was well up in the row, the right hand side looking more forward and prouder than the other half.

The difference was simply that the better half of the field had been sown with a Suffolk drill and the other with a Sunshine. Cup feed drills, such as the original Smythe's had their disadvantages and this mechanism was replaced by force feed drills of various makes. Fergusons produced a multi-purpose drill that could sow seed of a number of crop species. With horse drawn drills, it was common practice for a second man to walk behind to see that all coulters were sowing.

With the advent of tractor-drawn drills, a platform was fitted for the second man to ride on who could put the drill in and out of gear when turning on the headland. Later, of course, a second man became a luxury and drills were put in and out of gear by means of hydraulic rams. Combine drilling gradually went out of favour and, by the 1960s, the practice had all but ceased. There were several reasons for this. First, and even in the case of the Lias clays of South Warwickshire, the phosphate status of soils had improved to such an extent that there was now little or no advantage in placing fertiliser in close proximity to the seed when drilling. Secondly, combine drilling was painfully slow because of the necessity of filling the fertiliser hopper at comparatively frequent intervals. Moreover, the sheer weight of these drills did put a limit on their width. In the end, corn growers found it was quicker and easier to use a seed-only drill and broadcast fertiliser during seedbed preparation.

Before the days of drills which were capable of sowing a range of seeds of different sizes, root drills were in common use. A Mr. Betteridge, of Wellesbourne, was making these in the 1930s and 1940s, and were much sought after locally. During the 1940s, a small drill made by International was imported, which was capable of sowing all kinds of small seeds. The coulters were at 4" centres and could, of course be blocked off to give any desired row width. The Warwickshire *War Ag* had one or two of these drills, and I used one when direct re-seeding grass and clover seeds on contract. Two passes were made on the diagonal. This, combined with the narrow coulter spacings, gave a very quick cover.

While on the subject of more specialised drills, one might mention the Bomford bean drill. Beans, unless they are ploughed in, need to be sown deeper than cereals, and not all corn drills were satisfactory in this respect. Bomfords developed their Superflow chisel plough, in reality a heavy duty cultivator. Converting it to a bean drill involved clipping plastic tubes to the inside of the cultivator legs, which could be adjusted to give the desired row width. Each tube had its seed hopper mounted on the frame, with a simple drive from a land wheel to feed the seed down the spouts. This, and later variations, proved an excellent tool for bean drilling, once the tine was in the ground at the required depth it stayed there!

Direct drills were developed for sowing into stubble, with, or without, a light cultivation first. Eventually, pneumatic corn drills put in an appearance and also improved root drills, usually now consisting of a number of individual seeding units. All drills, over the years, became wider, in line with more powerful tractors whose output per day would have been unthinkable fifty years ago. For example ten acres per day with two horses and two men, compared with at least 40 acres/day with one man today.

Crop Protection

Once any crop has been established, it has to be protected against competition from weeds, diseases and pests. In the 1940s, at the beginning of our period, weed control (with the exception of sulphuric acid on cereals, see Chapter 15 *Crop Protection Chemicals*) was by mechanical means. Perennial weeds, such as squitch, thistles and docks, were dealt with mainly by means of a fallow or half fallow and, this was especially the case on the heavier soils where the acreage of root crops grown in wide rows was necessarily limited.

On such soils, the plough was the main implement involved, whereas, on the lighter land squitch would be worked to the surface by means of cultivators, drag harrows or whatever – all implements in common use on arable land for seedbed preparation – and gathered into heaps, and then burnt. In the case of annual weeds in cereals, the better arable men would use the stale seedbed technique; working the land down to a tilth, letting the weeds germinate and then killing them by subsequent cultivations, drilling and harrowing-in. In the case of winter cereals, harrowing in the spring to pull out the weed seedlings was common practice, and wheat could take a lot of punishment in this respect. It was not always effective, however, against well-established over-wintered plants, cleavers in particular.

It will be noted that none of these methods involved the use of specialised implements. They were all used at various stages to produce seedbeds, employing either horse or tractor power. However, by the late 1940s, specialised weeders made their appearance for use in potato crops but also in cereals. For instance, the Massey-Ferguson weeder had seventy-one lightweight tines and, it was claimed, could weed 50 acres of cereals in a working day. Although, by the time of its introduction it was made obsolete almost immediately by the selective weedkillers for use in cereals, it is significant that interest in such weeders has been revived towards the end of the 20th century as a means of reducing the use of chemical herbicides. This is regarded as being more environmentally friendly, in spite of the fact that more tractor hours are probably needed for the desired effect, leading to an increased volume of exhaust emissions!

Row Cropping

Root crops grown in wide rows were, quite rightly, regarded as cleaning crops because they enabled inter-row cultivation until the plants met in the row. In South Warwickshire, on the lighter land mainly in the river valleys, the proportion of arable land in root crops such as potatoes, sugar beet, horticultural crops and fodder roots, could be higher in relation to cereals and pulses than on the claylands. On the latter, roots were confined, except during wartime, to mangolds and kale, with some swedes.

Needles to say, row crop work needed special implements and, indeed, tractors, when these began to replace the horse. In the 1940s, the horse hoe was still in universal use. In *Agriculture,* by Watson and Moore, two types are illustrated. First, the steerage horse hoe which consisted of a wheeled fore-carriage, to which was attached a trailed body carrying the tines and steering handles. A man, or boy, might lead the horse with a second walking behind and steering the hoe body. This would be capable of hoeing several rows at once. Then there was the expanding horse hoe, the side members of which were hinged and clamped in front to give any desired width of working. There was also the simple, single row, horse hoe, and a man, or boy often had to lead the horse.

Some horses were quite capable of walking, steadily between the rows without stepping on a single seedling. Today, much electronic gadgetry is employed in multi-row tractor hoes to achieve precisely the same accuracy of working. Such is progress! By the 1940s, and into the 1950s, before herbicides for potatoes, sugar beet and other root crops made them redundant, there was a whole range of tractors and tractor mounted multi-row hoes designed for row-crop work.

Steerage hoes were popular as making for more accurate work. Although two men were needed there was less strain on the tractor driver. Row-crop tractors, wasp-waisted with high clearance and narrow tyres were ideal for mid-mounted hoes. The Allis Chalmers B was typical of such machines, and much sought after by South Warwickshire farmers. It must be remembered that in this district, in the 1940s, row cropping was by no means confined to cash and fodder roots. For example, significant acreages of cocksfoot and timothy grasses were grown for seed production, and these were kept clean of weeds in the year of establishment by horse or tractor hoeing. Subsequently, such crops were cultivated between the rows in the spring each year.

Field beans were a notoriously fouling crop due to their open habit of growth and, before the advent of the herbicide, Simazin, which revolutionised the growing of this crop, beans were regularly hoed by horse, or tractor, until the plants met in the rows. In South Warwickshire, substantial acreages of horticultural crops were grow in the valleys of the Avon and Arrow.

Normally, these were, of course, to be found on market garden holdings, but crops such as sprouts and winter and spring cabbage were grown on farms on a field scale. These were then sold by the acre, or land was taken by the season on farms by market gardeners. When one takes all these crops into consideration, and the fact that inter-row cultivations and hoeing had, usually, to be supplemented by hand hoeing, and singling, or chopping out with some root crops, the number of man and horse hours involved every season in South Warwickshire was prodigious.

Certainly in the 1940s, and even later, these man hours were provided by a labour force that was, only too often, poorly paid, poorly housed with too few amenities and with their children often deprived of educational opportunity.

How many of those now deploring the use of modern chemical weedkillers on environmental grounds would have been willing to take the place of these workers?

The benign social effects of the introduction and continuing development of selective herbicides are something that, to my knowledge, has never been mentioned, being, no doubt, politically incorrect to do so.

Sprayers

The first sprayers for agricultural use were just wooden barrels on wheels, with a pump driven off one of them and a spray bar. Originally horse drawn, these had become converted for tractor use by the 1940s. The first precursors of the modern sprayer were introduced in the late 1940s to apply the new so-called *hormone* weedkillers, MCPA and 2-4D. One of the first was a Ransomes, with a blue vertical tank, power take-off driven pump, filters and a spray bar about 16 feet wide with nozzles. This was raised and lowered by means of side handles, operating the two halves of the spray bar.

There were other makes with square tanks of similar design, with tank capacities of around forty gallons and all mounted on the hydraulic lift. Of course, over the years, sprayers were developed and finally became almost the most used tackle on the farm, applying not only herbicides but also fungicides, insecticides, growth regulators and so on. Tank capacity grew to hundreds of gallons, spray bars increased in width to eighty feet or so, trailed sprayers became commonplace, only to be succeeded by self propelled machines.

By the 1990s, these were monster machines bearing little resemblance to the watering cans on wheels of fifty years previously. Tank capacity was 500 gallons plus, boom widths of 70 to 80 feet became commonplace, cabs were air conditioned, there were electronic systems for control and monitoring the whole spraying operation, and engines needed for the propulsion of all this ironmongery were in the 120 to 150 horse power range.

No description of modern crop spraying would be complete without mention of tramlines and aerial spraying. Tramlines are wheel marks in the crop which facilitated accurate fertiliser spreading and spraying. In farm practice, the widths of the fertiliser spreader and the spray booms were married up so that all the driver had to do to ensure accuracy was to follow the tramlines through the crop, whether spreading a top dressing of fertiliser, or making a pass, probably one of several or more, with the sprayer.

Both fixed wing aircraft and helicopters were used both for top-dressing with fertiliser and the application of crop protection chemicals. The hey days of this practice could be regarded as the 1960s-70s. It had one grave disadvantage. It was an overt expression of the use of pesticides, and this was a bad public relations exercise, given the consumer hysteria engendered by their use and whipped-up by single interest groups.

In the end, aerial spraying was regulated out of existence and, in South Warwickshire at least, the practice had all but ceased by the 1990s. Nevertheless, the modern ground crop sprayer is the basic tool of the new farming, providing the means of weed, disease, insect control and the regulation of plant growth, unheard of and undreamt of fifty years ago. It, along with the materials it was used to apply, revolutionised crop husbandry. Growing crops in wide rows to allow inter-row cultivations as a means of weed control became a thing of the past, as did the full or half fallow used to keep perennial weeds in check.

Harvesting

As potatoes and sugar beet have always been minority crops, taking South Warwickshire as a whole, the development of mechanised harvesting of these will be given only the briefest of mentions. As already pointed out, the fact of the matter is that when the point had been reached at which the growing and harvesting, particularly the latter, had to be mechanised, with the considerable investment that this involved, many South Warwickshire growers gave up growing these crops.

The acreages that they could devote to them were not large enough to warrant the necessary capital expenditure on machinery and storage, grading, and so on, in the case of potatoes. The same applied to harvesting sugar beet. For these reasons, but with a few notable exceptions, the full mechanisation of the harvesting of these crops has not been a feature of South Warwickshire farming.

Balers

These, of course, were used to deal with straw, a by-product of the corn harvest, and also in harvesting the hay and silage crops. At the beginning of our period, hay (then almost all grass was conserved in this traditional manner, silage making being in its infancy) was usually stacked loose in rick or barn, having been gathered from the field either by wagon and loader or by sweep.

In the winter months, hay was cut from the rick by hand, loaded and carted to wherever it was to be fed. If it was to be sold off the farm, either for feeding farm stock on other holdings or to town horses, it was usually trussed; loose hay takes up much volume and is thus expensive to transport any distance.

Owing to the increasing volume of goods being transported by rail during the second half of the 19th century, the national horse population increased very considerably during this period, reaching its peak of 1.2m in the early 1900s. The majority of these were town horses, which were dependent for much of their keep on hay. This provided a lucrative market, which was supplied from farms nearest to the largest centres of population, amongst them Birmingham and Coventry.

The sale of hay from South Warwickshire farms to these cities and other towns became a useful source of income, and there are figures relating to one or two South Warwickshire parishes to show by just how much this trade increased onwards from 1850, or thereabouts. The hay trusser was the precursor of the baler. In was, in essence, a press operated by a long wooden lever, still, in fact, a manual process; the hay still had to be cut from the rick by hand, loaded into the trusser, pressed and tied by hand.

Old hay, that sold between August 31st and June 30th , weighed 56 lb./truss, and *new* hay traded between June 30th and August 31st weighed 60 lb./truss. A *load* of hay, and it was usually sold by the load, consisted of 18 trusses, or 18 cwt. of old hay. In South Warwickshire, hay was still being trussed in the 1940s, although by then much would be baled with a stationary baler for transport off the farm. In my mind's eye I can still recall two men, on a frosty winter's day, trussing hay from a rick in a field beside the main Alcester road at Oversley.

There was another type of mechanical trusser which was attached behind a threshing box, and tied the straw as it came off the straw walkers behind the drum. It produced a bundle, rather than a bale or truss, which it tied with two lengths of twine. These were known as *boltins*, at any rate in the Cotswolds. They were not heavy, weighing about 30-40 lb. You stuck a fork into the middle, and then carried them on your back into the yard or loose box when littering down. Mechanical trussers producing low density, lightweight, bales duly made their appearance. By the early 1950s, pick-up versions were evolved, the Class LD was typical, driven from the tractor power take-off. These might be regarded as the precursors of the pick-up baler, of which more later.

But in passing, it might be noted that the round bale was not an innovation of the 1970s. The Allis-Chalmers Rotobaler was imported from the USA in the 1940s, and was later made in this country. It picked up hay, or straw, from the swathe, elevated into belts which formed a round bale, and then tied with twine. The tractor had to be stopped when the latter operation, and ejection, were in progress. These Allis-Chalmers round balers, driven by the tractor power take-off were a common enough sight in South Warwickshire in the 1950s. One advantage was that these round bales would shed rain if they had to be left in the field – an improvement over conventional rectangular bales.

At least two serious accidents with these balers occurred in this district, the one at Ilmington proving fatal and the other, at Studley, causing serious injury. Eventually, these balers disappeared from the farming scene, and were superseded by the conventional pick-up baler.

All the machines mentioned above produced trusses or, what we would call today, low density bales. High density bales had been produced by stationary balers for very many years. The first models were about in the early 1900s and were driven by steam engines. These were used to bale straw behind a threshing drum, but could also be used for hay. Over the years, these became common enough, and this was certainly so in the 1940s, by which time they were driven by belt and pulley by a tractor and, of course, baling both straw behind a drum or hay. In the case of the latter, stationary balers could take the place of the hand trussers, baling hay from the rick. There was one available for use on contract from the *War Ag* machinery depot at Alcester, which was certainly used in the field, hay being swept to it from the swathe and loaded direct on to a flat trailer, and doubtless this was practised elsewhere.

These bales from stationary balers were heavy and wire tied, and hand hooks were used to move them about. Wire tying was mainly a manual operation, and these balers needed quite a gang to work them. There had been pick-up balers working in the 1930s, but these were few and far between. In the 1940s, a limited number were imported from the USA. Manufacture in the UK started in the early 1950s, and very soon they became the usual method of handling both hay and straw from the field. The earlier models were powered by their own engine, but later were driven by the tractor power take-off. They produced rectangular bales: barley bales typically weighed about 28 lb., wheat a little more and hay 40-50 lb.

Until the coming of the big round bale, bale handling was about the last of the heavy manual tasks left on the farm, with the possible exception of humping bags of fertiliser and seed corn. Tanker combines had made sacks of corn a thing of the past. Many attempt were made to devise mechanical means of collecting and conveying pick-up bales from field to stack or barn. These included bale sledges and collectors towed behind the baler, flat 8 bale loaders, bale elevators and, possibly the ultimate, the bale packer which tied bales in 20s to be carted away by a forklift truck. Even when the bales had been transported to the barn or rick, they had to be stacked by means of elevators and this invariably involved hand work.

Nevertheless, the pick-up baler remained the standard machine for handling hay and straw from the field for some three decades, and, of course, great numbers are still being used today. The Howard Rotavator Company was responsible for introducing the big bale and big bale handling into the UK. The Howard big baler became available commercially in 1972. It produced round hay bales weighing around half a ton, and those of straw, 7 cwt.

Like the Allis-Chalmers Rotobaler, the Howard Big Baler had to be stopped to discharge the bale, but this was necessary only a few times/acre, the bales being tied with three knotters using thick twine. The big bales were handled and stacked by means of a Big Bale gripper mounted on a tractor foreloader. Thus began a whole new era in the harvesting of hay, straw and, indeed, silage.

Needless to say, other manufacturers quickly followed suit and many developments and improvements were introduced. These included big balers which made square or rectangular bales, which were more convenient for transport and stacking, balers which wrapped silage bales and so on. The profound effects which big bales had upon straw handling, and thus cattle housing, and upon silage making, have already been described in the Chapter 4, *Dairying*, not to mention the elimination of hand humping from the hay harvest.

The Self-Binder and Threshing Box

A faire feeld full of folk... (The Vision of Piers Plowman)

In the 1940s, by far the greatest proportion of the corn acreage was harvested by binder and later threshed with a drum. In modern parlance, the corn harvest was labour intensive. Sheaves had to be stooked, usually in sixes or eights. The trick was to ram the butts into the stubble. It was hard work with sleeves rolled down to protect the arms from being scratched raw on the insides. But, no mater how thick the shirt, there were invariably sores at the end of the day and, doubly so, if the crop was dirty with thistles. Moreover, in a wet time, the sodden stooks had to be undone, with the sheaves thrown on the ground in an effort to dry them out and then the whole process gone through again.

After a week's stooking, even the most vocal of the critics of modern farming and advocates of a return to traditional, sustainable, methods might well have second thoughts. Then, of course, the sheaves had to be loaded onto trailers or wagons. Hard work again, involving a quick twist of the fork handle, so that the sheaf fell away from the prongs. When the crop was safe in stack or barn, the job was only half done.

Threshing was usually a winter job, unless winter corn was needed for seed or the crop had to be sold as soon as possible because the Bank manager or the merchant was pressing. Only the largest farms had their own drums, certainly in our district; the vast majority depended upon the threshing contractor. Drums produced *firsts*, the best corn, *seconds,* and *tail* which contained the smallest and broken grains and weed seeds. One of the criticisms of combines was that the latter were returned to the soil!

Corn was usually handled in Hudson or Railway sacks, which were hired, and carried two and quarter cwt. of wheat. Humping these about for a week or two might well dampen the enthusiasm of the whingers for the old ways of farming. Originally horse drawn, by the 1940s, at any rate in South Warwickshire many, if not most, binders had been converted for tractor use. The drive for the mechanisms, the knife, the sails and the knotter, was provided by the big land wheel, which also supported the weight of the whole machine.

By the late 1930s, binders specifically designed and built for tractor use had appeared on the market. These were of a more robust construction and, even more important, the power take-off drove the knife, sails and knotter. This ensured that the rate at which the knife was driven was no longer dependent upon the forward speed of the binder, which was of the greatest advantage when dealing with laid crops.

Fig. 18 Steam driven threshing drum. Wartime corn ricks at Crimscote.
(Joan Hughes)

During the war years, these, the ultimate in binders, were few and far between in South Warwickshire – so much so that when Harry Whetter, of Thelsford, acquired one, it was considered something of a novelty. There might well have been further refinements and developments to the self-binder, who knows?

But by the mid-1940s, it was rapidly being superseded by the combine harvester. However, on a visit to East Anglia in the 1950s, I was amazed to see that far more corn was still being cut by binder than in South Warwickshire. The reason, so I was told, was that men were still needed for the sugar beet harvest, which had yet to be mechanised, and, that being the case, there seemed little point in investing in combines and grain stores, so the older method of harvesting continued for some time.

Fig. 19 Hay Trussing. (Rural History Centre, Reading University)

Combines

In 1940, there were only one hundred combine harvesters in the whole country. By 1942, these had increased ten fold to 1,000. In 1946, the first year of peace, their numbers had risen to nearly 3,500.

The first combines were tractor drawn, sometimes with their own engine mounted on them, or driven by the power take-off from the tractor. They delivered the corn into sacks, and by now the 1 cwt. size was favoured. A second man rode on a platform, removing the bags from the corn chute when full, tying them and then pushing them down a slide onto the ground. From there they were loaded onto trailers and so to the farmyard.

One particular combine was much favoured in South Warwickshire, especially by seed growers, of which there were then, in the '40s and '50s, a considerable number. It was the Allis Chalmers All Crop 60, the makers claiming that it would harvest and thresh no less than 60 different crops. It had a five foot cut, and was a trailer model driven by its own engine. It certainly lived up to the maker's claims, for it had an excellent threshing mechanism with rubber coated beater bars.

In South Warwickshire it made a very good job of harvesting grass and clover seeds in particular. Elsewhere in the county it was used for vegetable and sugar beet seed. No other combine available at that time could make such a good job of these crops. With cereals and beans, it also produced an outstanding sample. But, of course, its output/hour, even under ideal conditions was abysmal by modern standards. It was originally made in the USA, the first in 1935 and was manufactured in this country in the 1950s.

Fig. 20 Combines, old and new. (John Deere)

By the middle of that decade, contractors and farmers on the broader acres were mostly equipped with self-propelled combines, although these had been available in the 1940s. Trailer models were still considered adequate for the smaller acreages. Bagger combines, by then, were giving way to tankers with all grain being handled in bulk. However, the drivers were still exposed to the elements, in a miserable cold summer sometimes driven to wearing an overcoat!

Dust was the worst thing that had to be endured; combining a laid crop on a hot dry day on those bouts with a following wind was not a happy experience. It was not until the late 1970s that air-conditioned cabs made their appearance, and then only on the largest and most expensive machines. By the end of the century such cabs were standard equipment.

The story of the development of combines since the 1940s is one of increasing cutter bar width, with threshing mechanism to match. Axial flow combines made their appearance in the 1980s; the top-of-the range combines in the 1990s were monsters indeed. These were up to 22 ft cut, with engines of 300 hp. and they bristled with electronic gadgetry. Amongst other refinements was the automatic height control for the cutter bar, a far cry from the manual control by means of a handwheel in the 1940s.

Grain Strippers

Finally, grain strippers, or the 'alternative combine' must be mentioned in passing. These were invented in Australia in the 19th. century. The Wild Harvester Thresher was imported in the second half of the 1940s into the UK. I well remember going to Grove Fields Farm, Hampton Lucy, with Ernest Bomford and Harry Whetter one summer's evening to see one working in a crop of wheat. Long fingers guided 4ft. of the crop into the stripping mechanism, the grain was stripped out of the ears, the chaff being blown out through tall, rather curiously shaped funnels and the headless straw left standing to be dealt with later. A man rode on the machine to bag the corn. The whole affair was drawn by a tractor, and the stripper mechanism being driven by a small engine mounted on the machine.

Its rate of work was impressive compared with comparable combines of the day, but, of course, the straw had to be cut and baled as a separate operation. Nor was the sample very good.

This model never caught on. But there was a sequel as far as I was concerned. In the 1980s the Manpower Services Commission ran a workshop for the unemployed in the Old Dairies at Clifford Chambers with Sue Comber its enthusiastic manager. One of the main activities was the restoration of old agricultural machinery and tools. The Commission needed an insurance valuation of those items being worked upon, or awaiting restoration. Sue contacted me when I was at Sheldon Bosley in Stratford to do this.

'Nobody can tell me what that lot is, not even visiting farmers.' complained Sue, pointing to what appeared at first sight to be a load of scrap. One characteristic funnel (the other was missing), to my mind reminiscent of a bishops' mitre, was the clue. The frame, the engine and most of the stripper were all there. In an instant I was transported back to that warm summer's evening nearly forty years ago, standing in that big, flat field by the River Avon with my two mentors watching what was probably this same machine working away in a crop of wheat.

Agriculture has much in common with that mythical bird that flies in ever decreasing circles until its inevitable disappearance in the traditional manner. For some forty years later there was, in an updated form, renewed interest in stripper harvesters. Shelbourne Reynolds Engineering produced several grain strippers for the 1988 harvest. Later, in 1990, Kidd Farm Machinery produced a prototype trailed stripper for exhibition at the Smithfield Show. But, to the best of my knowledge, all these alternative harvesters have been sunk without trace, amongst farming dead-ends.

Grain Drying and Storage

As the old gave way to the new – self-binder and threshing drum to combine harvester and the bulk handling of grain – so the practice and problem of grain drying and handling had to be addressed.

As far as grain growers in South Warwickshire were concerned, their experiences with the Ministry of Food grain silos in Old Town, Stratford-on-Avon were enough to convince them that communal facilities were not the way forward, and who could blame them ? Co-operative ventures for processing and storage were, in the 1950s, many years in the future, although South Warwickshire farmers were to lead the way eventually in co-operative storage and drying with the plant of Arable Crop Storage on the old aerodrome at Atherstone-upon-Stour, and with co-operative marketing by the sister organisation Arable Crop Marketing.

There was also an ingrained suspicion of 'The Trade' and a reluctance, amounting to a refusal, to rely on merchants for central drying and storage facilities. The upshot was that the development of grain drying and storage facilities became essentially and completely an on-farm operation. This was not necessarily pre-ordained and in contrast to practice on the Continent. However it became a fact of farming life here for the reasons outlined above.

While the output of combines was relatively small and bagger machines the order of the day, in-sack driers were the vogue for a short time. These, in essence, were concrete platforms with grids incorporated into them, over which sacks were laid and through which warm air, produced by an oil furnace and fan, was blown. This was a slow, labour intensive process, but had the advantage of being capable of dealing with herbage seed crops.

However, its day was short lived. Blown bins came into favour. But those blown through air bricks in the floor had the drawback that, in a wet harvest, only a limited depth of damp grain could be dried at a time. Too great a depth simply meant that moisture was blown from the bottom layers to the top, making for mouldy grain in the upper part of the bin.

This problem was overcome by the Simplex bins which had a central air duct, the warm air being blown through the grain from the centre outwards. These were built on a concrete base, incorporating a wind tunnel, shutters being provided to direct the air flow into individual bins. The best practice provided a drying bin of lesser diameter than the main storage bins to allow of comparatively rapid drying of the wettest corn.

Continuous flow or batch grain driers attracted no grant, but bins and their associated structures did. Thus blown bins had this added attraction. Moreover, in South Warwickshire the Simplex company was vigorously and ably represented, providing an excellent sales and technical service. A further advantage was that the source of heat could be provided by the power source used to drive the fan, either a tractor in a 'kennel,' or a Lister or similar fan. Otherwise an electric fan was used fitted, with a bank of heaters. For a number of years, in the 1950s and '60s, these blown bins became almost the standard method of storing and drying grain in our district.

The reception pits and bins were served by a system of conveyors of varying sophistication, from those which could be moved along a row of bins to fixed installations. But they all had one defect in common, whatever type of bins, with or without a continuous flow drier. Once installed their capacity was fixed and could not be increased, except at great expense, to cope with the ever rising outputs of new generations of combines. In short, the conveying capacity of many grain plants became a bottleneck , especially on those farms where the corn acreage had increased substantially for reasons which have already been described.

Thus the next phase in grain drying and storage was the on-the-floor store with a wind tunnel and side ducts through which warm air could be blown. Such stores sometimes incorporated a continuous flow drier.

These stores were filled with a grain bucket on a tractor foreloader or one fitted to a JCB or similar machine. Sometimes high capacity portable elevators were used with a grain thrower attachment. Whatever method was employed it was more flexible and often with a greater ability to cope with high volumes of grain as they came off the bigger combines. When not filled with corn these buildings were essentially general purpose. They could be used for storage of seed, fertiliser, or what-have-you, and even serve as lambing sheds.

On-floor stores had two potential disadvantages in practice. First, care had to be taken not to create 'hot-spots' with loads of high moisture corn. Secondly, while moveable walls could be used to separate different grain crops or different varieties of one crop, it is more difficult to do so than is the case with a bin installation. In passing, it is now more important than ever, when it comes to marketing, to keep separate different varieties of wheat, for example.

Material Handling

The great strides that have been made in the handling of the grass, forage and grain harvests have already been described, in addition a passing reference has been made to the mechanisation of the lifting of both potatoes and sugar beet. We are, therefore, primarily concerned under this heading with the handling of farmyard manure, feedingstuffs, fertilisers and seeds.

Farmyard Manure

The older generation will remember only too well, the back- aching, gut-rending job it was cleaning out yards and loose boxes at the end of the winter, loading the heavy, tightly packed, sodden manure into carts, making the 'muck buries,' then in due course, into carts again, dragging the well rotted manure into small heaps across the field, which, in turn, had to be spread by hand. In the old days, before the widespread use of fertilisers became commonplace, FYM was almost the sole source of fertility for arable land, along with the folded sheep flock and the ploughed out ley. Its handling, making and spreading was one of the kingpins of successful farming and the maintenance of the virtuous spiral of 'more muck, better crops; heavier crops more stock, more muck,' and so on.

The first mechanical farmyard manure spreader was shown in this country in 1907-08. It was a four wheeled wagon, low slung, with a revolving drum at the back, the manure being fed into it by a moving belt, the drive being obtained by chain from one of the back wheels. This basic design remained unchanged into the 1930s and is described as needing 'three horses or a tractor' to pull it. But manure still had to be loaded from the yard, carted to the heap to rot and then loaded into a mechanical spreader by hand. The four tined fork was still the prime mover of farmyard manure.

In the 1940s some effort was made to mechanise the manual work. A weird and wonderful machine for mucking out yards and, indeed, loose boxes appeared. It consisted of a king-sized fork, almost like a mini buckrake. This had a handle for the unfortunate individual on the business end. The fork was attached by cable to a drum which was driven by a small engine, the clutch being operated by a second man. The first worker dug the fork into the manure, the second put the drum into gear pulling the forkful of manure out, ready for loading into cart or tipping trailer. Needless to say this contrivance was a nine day wonder.

The task of spreading the field heaps was mechanised more successfully by the Wild-Thwaites spreader. This spreader was a success and undoubtedly served its purpose as long as this method of dealing with farmyard manure persisted.

During the 1950s and '60s many companies were manufacturing manure spreaders still based on the original design which had made its debut in the early 1900s. This new generation of spreaders were, of course, tractor drawn. But many still derived their driving power from the rear wheels, albeit now fitted with pneumatic tyres. But the principle was the same with much improved beater bars and auger spreaders, with chain driven slats feeding the manure into them.

Before long the mechanisms were driven by the tractor power-takeoff. Howard Rotovators introduced a rotary spreader based on an entirely different principle, flail rotors spreading solid manure or slurry from the side of the machine. These became very popular.

Rear discharge manure spreaders increased in size, along with tractor power. By the 1980s their capacity had increased into the 7 to 12 ton range.

The advent of front or rear mounted tractor loaders in the 1950s enabled the handling of farmyard manure to be fully mechanised.

Finally, as manure spreaders and loaders became larger and more sophisticated, the cleaning out of yards and the spreading of manure became jobs which were often carried out by contractors using the high capacity, and very expensive, equipment which is today available.

Loaders

Mention has already been made above of tractor loaders. Tractor mounted fork lifts came into use in the 1960s and were useful for handling potato and fruit boxes and, of course, pallets. Ten years later rough terrain fork trucks appeared on farms. In due course these became available in four wheel drive form and with telescopic arms. All these loaders could be fitted with a wide range of attachments for the handling of many materials. These included grain buckets, manure forks, silage block cutters, pallets and half ton bag handlers and so on. It is no exaggeration to state that these loaders, in all their shapes and sizes, revolutionised materials handling on farms.

Fertilisers

In the 1940s the amount of fertilisers applied to cereal crops was minimal compared to modern practice. The more accomplished growers would put 1 cwt./acre of triple supers 'down the spout,' followed by a top-dressing of not more than 2 cwt./acre of Sulphate of Ammonia or Nitro-Chalk in the spring, or 3 cwt./acre in all at most.

As combine drilling gave way to broadcasting, a seedbed dressing of 2 cwt./acre became usual and the rate of top dressing rose to as much as 4 cwt./acre in some instances, and usually at least 3 cwt. , the tonnages involved becoming significant. This is not to mention the greatly increased use of nitrogenous fertilisers on grassland. Thus on both mixed and arable farms in South

Warwickshire and elsewhere the tonnages of fertiliser which had to be moved around the farm became considerable.

For example, the growing of, say, 250 acres of cereals, could involve handling and spreading 62. 5 tons of fertiliser, which is starting to be serious weights. With substantial acreages of potatoes and sugar beet, with typically heavier dressings per acre, the problem was compounded.

Fig. 21 Handling fertilisers in half-tonne bags. (Kemira)

Each bag of fertiliser had to be handled several times. First from lorry to where it was to be stored before use. Then onto a trailer for transport to the field and again from trailer into the distributor, three times in all.

The more ingenious and forward thinking devised various means of reducing the humping to a minimum. For example, if delivery took place shortly before use, bags could be stacked from lorry direct onto trailer, cutting out one handling. Ron Godfrey of Manor Farm, Aston Cantlow, had another approach. He had a large loading deck built in a Dutch barn sheeted down at the back and partly at each side. Bags could be wheeled by sack truck straight onto the deck where they could stay until needed, then wheeled again onto the trailer. Before the bulk handling of corn, grain sacks could be dealt with in a similar manner.

But whatever methods were used to reduce the work, the fact remained that handling what had become large tonnages of fertilisers in 1 cwt. bags was a time and energy consuming chore.

Bulk handling was one method tried to overcome the problem. Lime, of course, had, for many years been delivered and spread in bulk by contractors as a matter of course, this service being arranged and provided by the merchant. This practice was extended to basic slag when this by-product of the steel industry was available because the quantities per acre, usually half a ton or thereabouts, were substantial. For a brief period, and to the best of my recollection, one firm did offer a bulk delivery and spreading service for granular fertilisers in South Warwickshire. But, while lime continues to be spread in bulk by contract, basic slag has, regrettably, disappeared from the farming scene and the contract spreading of other fertilisers proved to be a nine day wonder.

Liquid fertilisers were very much in vogue at one time; 'pump not hump' was the cry. Chafers was the leading firm in the manufacture of liquids, and in the provision of the necessary storage tanks and sprayers. The latter could, of course, be also used for the application of crop protection chemicals. Liquid fertilisers did have one built-in drawback. Because there was a limit to their concentration (NPK in heavy concentrations came out of solution) the cost per unit tended to be greater that of conventional solids. Against this had to be set the advantage that individual formulations to suit particular customers' needs could be provided. Frank Bennison, when he was managing Weston Park farms' was an enthusiast for liquid fertilisers, storage tanks being sited at strategic points on the estate.

The advent of pallet handling was a great step forward in the handling of not only fertilisers, but also of feedingstuffs and seed. As already mentioned this method was dependent upon the innovation of forklifts, either on tractors or purpose built machines.

Finally (?), the half ton bag made an appearance, which eased enormously the handling of both fertiliser and seed. Again, this depended upon the development of equipment to handle such weights. On one South Warwickshire mixed farm with which the author was closely involved, being responsible for the purchasing of seed and fertiliser, amongst other duties, all fertiliser and seed were eventually delivered in half-tonne bags which, of course, were handled entirely mechanically. The days of humping fertilisers in 1 cwt.. bags were over, at least on a very large number of holdings.

Seed

In the 1940s seed usually arrived in jute sacks which later gave way to paper. These 1 cwt. sacks were eventually delivered on pallets and then, as described above, in some cases in half-tonne bags. This, of course, refers to cereals. Small seeds continued to be delivered in paper sacks, eventually 25 or 50 kg, according to type.

Feedingstuffs

Here again much the same story as seed. When a pupil on that farm in the Cotswolds, I was often sent with horses and wagon to Sherston station to collect feed in 1 cwt. jute sacks, 'straights' such as palm kernel, flaked maize, wheatings and bran, or great slabs of linseed cake which had to be broken up in a hand turned machine before use, and a limited amount of dairy 'cake' which was fed only to the highest yielding cows.

As with seed, jute gave way to paper, and pallet handling eventually became commonplace. In the end, and certainly by the 1990s, feedingstuffs were delivered in bulk. Indeed, when I was dealing with Midland Shires Farmers, now Countrywide, most dairy, pig and poultry feeds were delivered in bulk, a surcharge being made if, for any reason, the customer stipulated bags.

When the dairy unit on the above mentioned South Warwickshire farm was modernised a system of bulk delivery, storage and use was installed and is worthy of a description. A small Dutch barn had been converted into a feed store. Dairy cake was blown into two canvas containers slung within a steel frame. These emptied into a below ground conveyor which delivered the feed under a roadway and then up an elevator, to be conveyed into hoppers above the feeders in the parlour. These were controlled electronically, measuring the pre-determined ration for each individual cow.

In the same Dutch barn bunkers, built of sleepers, had been installed and into these brewers grains were delivered in bulk. Of course, these could also be used for other feeds, such as sugar beet pulp. On the same farm a feeder wagon was used for the out-of-parlour feeding of silage (cut and loaded with a block cutter), brewers grains and anything else that was included in the ration.

All a far cry from cutting silage by hand, loading onto to a trailer to be taken wherever it was to be fed; or doling out concentrates by baler from a feed barrow into mangers in cowpen or parlour.

In short, while to the layman the mechanisation of farming may well be a matter of tractors and combine harvesters, the mechanisation of material handling has been the quiet revolution during the period with which we are concerned. Possibly only those who have worked on farms in the 1940s and '50s, or those in close daily contact with them, can appreciate the sheer amount of hard manual toil that has been eliminated by the means described above.

32. DIVERSIFICATION

Diversification – what might be described as deviations from mainstream agriculture, the growing of staple commodities such as cereals, beef, lamb and wool for example – is an long-standing feature of farming in this country. Possibly the most common form has been the cultivation of new crops. The introduction of oilseed rape, then known as colza, the growing of woad for several centuries and, in more recent times the re-introduction of oilseed rape and linseed, or the attempts to grow soya and sunflower and the cultivation of herbs, are all examples of crop diversification.

Coming nearer home, a prime example of diversification to meet changed economic circumstances is provided by the Bomford family, then farming some 5,000 acres on the Warwickshire-Worcestershire borders. In 1880, the death of Benjamin Bomford coincided with a catastrophic drop in corn and beef prices, their main sources of income, apart from that provided by their contracting business using steam tackle. The business was taken over by his second and third sons, Raymond and Benjamin junior, who started to diversify into the traditional crops of the Vale of Evesham, fruit and market garden crops, which had been cultivated by the monks of Evesham Abbey many centuries before.

The changes to meet the new circumstances were tackled with typical Bomford foresight and energy. For instance, 250 acres of orchards were planted on the stiffer land, while potatoes, peas and other horticultural crops were grown on the lighter soils. A substantial acreage of soft fruit was planted: currants, raspberries, gooseberries, and 15 acres of strawberries. The total acreage farmed fell over the years from 5,000 to 3,000 acres. This is diversification, or restructuring, call it what you will, on the grand scale, taking place over 120 years ago.

Today, the generally accepted meaning of *diversification* is the addition of a non-agricultural enterprise as part and parcel of the re-organisation of the farm business, in order to maintain income in a time of falling product prices.

Sale of Assets

It would be unrealistic to ignore the sale of assets to raise capital to pay off loans and debts, for re-investment or to finance changes in the farm business, including diversification in the usual meaning of the term.

In South Warwickshire, perhaps one of the most common ways of cashing in on farm assets is the sale of farmsteads for the conversion of the buildings to residences. Sometimes the sale includes the farmhouse itself as well as barns, cowpens, cart hovels, granaries or what-have-you for conversion into dwellings, some large and others quite small.

One of the conditions necessary for a successful planning application is that the farm buildings in question have little or no further use for agricultural purposes in this day and age. The vast majority of such farmsteads were built during the 19th century in the cart and horse, or wheelbarrow age. Thus there is little difficulty in proving that they have only a very limited usefulness in the days of mechanisation as described earlier.

Perhaps landowners in South Warwickshire are fortunate, inasmuch as the demand for such conversions in this commuter belt appears to be insatiable, in spite of the fact that the new residents may well be living almost on top of one another. This trend must have started in the 1970s, and the pace of conversions seems to have gathered momentum, year on year, ever since. So much so, that one wonders if there will be any 19th century farmsteads left to serve, in part, their original purpose by the middle of the 21st century, except those specially preserved as historical curiosities!

Examples of such conversions in our district are too numerous to list. They may consist of turning a field barn into a single house standing on its own, as on the southern boundary of Glebe Farm, Aston Cantlow, or the conversion of a whole range of buildings, as at Lower Binton Farm, or the Crofts Farm, Banbury Road, Stratford-on-Avon, into a number of dwellings of various sizes. And, of course, every permutation in between.

There is one interesting case which is worth putting on record. During the planning process, it was recognised that, if the proposed dwelling were used for holiday lets by incomers, or holiday makers, they could only too easily attempt to disrupt farming operations. It was held that these disturbed the 'rural quiet' which they claimed to be their right!

The farm had been purchased by a landowner to let to an existing tenant whose farm had been sold for development. The owners retained the old buildings for sale for conversion into dwellings. The new owner erected additional modern buildings and a farmhouse, a modern cattle yard having been built previously by the original owners in close proximity to the old farmstead. The application for conversion of the old buildings was successfully opposed by the new owner and tenant partly on the grounds that normal farming activities in and around the buildings, which continued to be used for the running of the holding, would give rise to complaints and harassment by the new occupiers. This is something which is only too familiar to those tenants or owners of village farms, and established an important principle which, one hopes, will be of use on future occasions.

Another variation of the trend towards selling farmsteads for development is one which concerns village farms. There are a number of examples of these being sold and the capital raised used to build a new homestead on a green field site outside the, now suburbanised, village in the hope that this would avoid friction with incomers. With uncharacteristic common sense, this process has received the blessing of the planners. Of course, this did not always suit the new countrymen, who objected to the erection of 'unsightly' modern farm buildings on the outskirts and approach to the village. You can't win!

Finally, of course, there is the sale of land for green field residential development. A few acres, perhaps, adjacent to a village are an even a more lucrative proposition involving more land. None of these are diversification within the strict current meaning of the word, but, nevertheless, always play a vital part in the restructuring of any farm business.

The following sections describe the many forms of diversification as it is generally understood today, all of which have the aim of protecting and improving farm income. Some, of course, may well involve the restructuring of the whole farm business, rather than bolting on another extra enterprise to the existing enterprise mix.

The Farm Shop

It is fair enough to assert that these fall into two categories with many variations in between. First we have those shops that sell vegetables, fruit, eggs, table poultry, etc., all, or most, of which are produced on the farm in question. The object of the exercise is, of course, to add value by pocketing the retail value, or a proportion of it, rather than selling wholesale. Many of these smaller farm shops also buy in some produce to offer a wider range.

There is nothing particularly new about this. The author can well recall, as a boy, being driven through the Vale of Evesham in the 1930s and seeing many a roadside stall selling vegetables and fruit, with luscious Victoria plums at 1 penny/lb. (0.4p). The *back door* egg trade has a long history, and an honourable one in maintaining the principle of a free market, in the days of food rationing when this was referred to as the black market.

Examples of the farm shops that fall into this class include Bernard Wilke's 'Veg Shed' in Welford-on-Avon, and the Bluck's shop in a former garage in nearby Weston-on-Avon. Customers at these farm shops are assured of the very freshest produce of the highest quality, the vast majority of which is grown on the holdings concerned. Richard and Phillipa Bluck also sell fresh, farm-reared turkeys at Christmas, as do others in South Warwickshire.

Another South Warwickshire farm shop is at Talton Mill, now run by Mark and Liz Holberton. This evolved from a complete change of farm policy. For very many years Mark's father, Hugh, had run this little holding as a dairy farm, milking Jerseys with great success. But when Mark came home from Australia he did not wish 'to be tied to a cow's tail,' and who could blame him. Instead, he pointed out that the soil was easy working, very fertile, having been under grass for many years, being grazed by cows fed heavily on dairy cake and with the bonus of irrigation. In short, made for market gardening. And so it was that milking ceased in 1974, Mark took himself off to Pershore College to learn the art and mystery of growing vegetables. Back door sales from a brick outhouse started in 1977, and the foundations of a very successful enterprise were laid.

Eventually, a custom-built farm shop was erected which now stocks a wide range of food stuffs. Not only is value added to the vegetables grown on the farm by selling retail, but also a few beef cattle are reared, which are slaughtered. butchered, and the meat sold in the shop – prime Hereford. Similarly with his pigs, selling pork and his own home-bred sausages. He has someone making cakes, he stocks a range of cheeses, 'imports' smoked salmon and kippers from Scotland, sells home-produced free range eggs, chutneys, pates of many kinds, pickles, and so on. Not surprisingly, it is not unusual for the number of customers to exceed well over one hundred in a day.

At the other end of the scale are what might be described as 'shops on farms,' which are very much larger enterprises offering a wide range of food of all sorts, some incorporating a garden centre, a gift shop and, sometimes, a restaurant.

A prime example of this is A.H.Hiller & Son's, at Dunnington Heath. The large shop retails fruit and vegetables of very many kinds in season, some of which are grown on the farm. There is also a delicatessen and locally produced pork, and lamb from Ragley Home Farms has also been available. In addition, there is a garden centre, a gift shop and a restaurant, a speciality of which is home-baked ham salad. Here one can also purchase a range of cakes and the like, all home cooked.

These are simply examples to illustrate the two extreme types of farm shops to be found in South Warwickshire. There are many, many other farm shops in our district, too numerous to mention. Some, it must be admitted, have evolved from the need to add value to what was produced from the farm into enterprises dependent upon bought in goods to a very great degree and, in consequence have become 'shops on farms' rather than shops selling the produce of the holding on which they are situated. Nevertheless, these are still a form of farm diversification. All benefit from their proximity to centres of population such as Birmingham, Coventry, Warwick, Leamington and Stratford-upon-Avon, to name the most obvious ones.

Finally, mention must be made of a shop in Long Compton, which although not on a farm, sells local farm produce exclusively including fruit vegetables, meat, eggs etc. This has been set up through the enterprise of a young couple and clearly is meeting a demand.

Farmers' Markets

These are a comparatively new development in modern times. It must be remembered that in days gone by, and within the living memory of the older generation, the local produce market in the nearest market town was the usual method of selling vegetables, fruit, eggs, poultry, butter, cheese and the rest. Much of the selling was in the domain of the farmer's wife.

In the last few years, the new version farmers' markets have sprung up country wide, usually on one or two days a month, and fulfil the same economic function as the true farm shop, that is, selling direct to the customer and thus adding value in the form of the retailing profit.

Their rapid rise in popularity with the consumer is part and parcel of the emphasis on fresh food sourced directly from the producer, which is, quite rightly, regarded as of better quality. It is, perhaps, a revolt against the supermarket, which is impersonal, sanitised and is not necessarily cheaper than buying direct from the grower or farmer. The personal contact between producer and consumer is something which has come to be appreciated by both parties in very many instances.

Stratford-upon-Avon farmers' market was amongst the first to be established. The range of produce here is wide. Nurseries selling bedding plants, shrubs, perennials and so on, stalls selling vegetables, home produced fruit juices, sausages, pies, bacon, pork, lamb and beef and amongst these one advertising a pig roasting service for village functions and the like. This particular farmers' market is held on two Saturdays a month, and has proved very popular.

Cheese Making

The classic example of this is the old established firm of Fowlers of Earlswood; David and his wife, Pat, are the present representatives of this old farming family. This activity originated in Derbyshire, where the Fowlers produced the local Derbyshire cheese and have revived its manufacture in more recent times.

The Fowlers moved down to Worcestershire and then to Earlswood, at one time running a substantial milk retail business around the south of Birmingham. David re-established the cheese making business, using milk from his herd of Friesians, and now sells a wide range of cheeses for the connoisseur to many retail outlets.

Milk Retailing

Over the years perhaps the most common way of adding value or diversification, call it what you will, has been milk retailing. At the bottom of the scale, as it were, was a character who occupied land, it would be an exaggeration to say he farmed, all of which is now part of Redditch New Town. The grassland would have delighted those who enthuse over the virtues of traditional hay meadows and buildings, and the general level of livestock and grassland husbandry were to match.

The daily routine was as follows. Cows were milked in the morning and a gesture made towards cleaning the buckets, cooler etc. Then breakfast was taken before setting off on the milk round, one churn in the back of an old van, the milk being ladled into the customers' jug, or jugs. Into the pub at twelve noon, sharp; home by 2:30 pm to sleep off the liquid lunch until it was time to milk again in the early evening. Back to the pub again and then to bed in readiness for the next day's exertions.

Maintaining a very much higher standard, in a different league altogether, was Frank Suffield of Home Farm, Aston Cantlow, retailing Channel Island milk from his herd of Guernseys. This was bottled in his dairy and sold in Aston Cantlow and the surrounding villages.

On the farm, kale alternated with a two-year ley of Italian Ryegrass, the other grassland managed to a high standard; silage was made and the cows rationed properly. In other words, a seventy-acre family farm run exceptionally well; such holdings, unhappily now a thing of the past.

Clyde Higgs Farms Ltd operated a multi-round milk retailing business, based on Hatton Rock just outside Stratford-on-Avon. During the depression of the '20s and '30s, Mr Higgs had built up a farming enterprise of some 2000 acres by buying farms in the nearby parishes of Snitterfield and Norton Lindsey. Herds of Ayrshire cattle were milked in bails, the milk bottled in the plant at Hatton Rock and sold through a considerable number of milk rounds covering towns and villages in South Warwickshire.

The method of payment for the retailed milk was ingenious and ensured that the business ran very largely on the customers' money. Each roundsperson, for some girls were employed in this way, had a large roll of green tickets. These had a value of whatever was the going rate/pint at the time. The customer purchased a week's supply of tickets on Mondays, putting out her requirements for the next day with the empties – one ticket per pint. Mr. Higgs had his money every week up front, the customer liked the system and everyone was happy, especially Mr. H.!

Bed and Breakfast

This was a form of diversification which was common enough in tourist areas, such as the West Country and The Lakes, long before the word came into general usage. South Warwickshire, of course, also has the status of a tourist district with Stratford-upon-Avon, with its theatre and river as its centre. But there are other attractions to draw the visitor, for instance the proximity of the

Cotswolds, Warwick Castle, stately homes such as Ragley Hall, Coughton Court, Upton House, and others. In short, there is a lovely countryside to explore, many places to visit and plenty to do.

Needless to say, bed and breakfast enterprises on South Warwickshire farms vary greatly in size and sophistication. But all offer a high standard of accommodation and catering.

At one end of the scale are those who keep their number of rooms below that at which bureaucratic interference kicks in with a vengeance. On these, farming is still the main enterprise. At the other end of the scale bed and breakfast will provide a very high proportion of total farm income, especially on the smaller farms.

One example of this is provided by Mr. and Mrs. Steve Walters, of Dorsington. Their farm is small by modern standards and on heavy clay, at one time, no doubt, run as a small dairy holding. Today, the fact has to be faced that its income-generating potential is not large.

It is now run as a thriving bed and breakfast business. There are a number of bedrooms and a dining room in the farmhouse, and the former cowpen has been converted into a number of family suites, complete with bedroom for the parents and bunk beds in a separate room for children and, of course, en suite with the usual facilities. Moreover, one such unit has been designed specially for the use of the disabled.

Steve mentioned one interesting fact. Their clientele is by no means confined to holidaymakers, but includes regulars who have to travel on business as a matter of course. They appreciate the family atmosphere, the facilities for doing the paperwork at the end of the day and the lower cost compared with hotel accommodation.

Of course, once again, there is every variation and permutation in between these two extremes. On South Warwickshire farms, the very highest standards are maintained and the interesting thing is that demand for such accommodation seems insatiable.

Conversion of Farm Buildings to commercial Uses

This is in contrast to the sale of farmsteads, barns etc. for residential development. In the majority of cases ownership is retained by the farmer, who bears the cost of conversion. This is recouped through the rents, which eventually will provide a welcome addition to farm income. There are many examples in South Warwickshire, and those noted below can be regarded as typical, with some, of course, on a greater scale, such as at Hatton Country

World and Craft Village. Others can be found which are smaller enterprises than these described in the following paragraphs.

James Walton of The Woodlands, Long Compton, originally started with two units, spending comparative small sums on conversion. One unit was occupied by a potter and the other by a carpenter and joiner. Eventually, a considerable sum was invested in converting to first class office accommodation. This is entered through a reception area with lavatories and a kitchenette for coffee making, or what-have-you.

The largest office and one smaller one are occupied by an information technology company, a national firm with an office in London. But the Long Compton office is considered the main base, the occupier living in the village, something which he much appreciates as very preferable to wasting time and money commuting.

The third office is let to a firm that designs fitted kitchens, bedrooms, bathrooms and so on. Although a separate company, these are manufactured at The Woodlands in a woodworking workshop which was originally the tractor shed. Now fully insulated, heated and equipped, the plant now turns out the highest quality fitted room furniture. A further similar farm building is, at the time of writing, the subject of a planning application for a meat processing and butchering enterprise. The fourth office has become the farm and estate office, and a very spacious one it is too.

In passing, one might add that, some years ago, a building was converted to a holiday cottage. This structure has had a somewhat chequered history, having been originally built as a chapel and then being converted and used for many years as a grain store until James converted it into a very attractive cottage. It is now no longer let for holidays, but for longer periods.

It might also be mentioned that, several years ago, James diversified into the provision of corporate hospitality offering clay pigeon shooting, quad bike riding and so on, as well as providing lunches and other refreshments. The industrial recession reduced demand, however, and this enterprise was closed down.

So The Woodlands has a history of diversification stretching back over a number of years. The present tenants in the offices can, of course, offer higher rents than the potter and joiner. Although the investment for conversion has been considerable, the rents provide a satisfactory return on capital.

Like the Waltons of Long Compton, Ned Hutchings and his sons, John and Michael, are the present representatives of old established South Warwickshire farming families. In fact, in days gone by, the Hutchings were men of many occupations: amongst their trades were coal merchants, iron-founders and makers of agricultural implements.

In the 1970s, a farm at Blackwell was purchased and a dairy unit was established there, run by Michael. For a number of years this was very successful, but the collapse of the milk price in the late 1990s was the stimulus for a change of direction and diversification.

The herd and the milk quota were sold, happily before the bottom dropped out of the market for these. It just so happened that a neighbouring farmer was looking for more land and the Blackwell farm was sold to him. Michael retained the house, a field surrounding it, and the very extensive buildings. Ned had retired from active management, but even after the Blackwell land had been sold, John and Michael were still farming some 700 acres, either owned or on a farm business tenancy.

Planning consent was applied for conversion of these former dairy buildings into business units, an application which was supported by ten locals and opposed by fourteen Nimbys, but was granted. Michael then proceeded with the conversion which was carried out to the very highest standards; pleasing brickwork, coloured plastic-coated steel sheeting and brass door furniture were the order of the day. 'I am looking for first class tenants and thus I must offer first class accommodation,' is Michael's philosophy.

Cotswold Teak have a showroom for their high quality garden furniture. Wright Wrought Iron are specialists in handmade metal beds, curtain poles, garden furniture and dining suites, all designed and made at Blackwell.

Other tenants at present include Lighting and Home Automation and financial consultants, Asset Direct Central. As I write, a further unit is being built for Meg Rivers Cakes, a firm based at Tysoe, which will be moving their operation to the Blackwell Business Park. Their premises will include kitchens, store rooms and an office, all designed and specially constructed for their needs.

Further units will be built and there is already interest in these. Not only is the Blackwell Business Park a farm diversification of the first order, but it also has the potential to provide local employment and, indeed, already does so.

Richard and Philippa Bluck of Weston-on-Avon, have already been mentioned in connection with their farm shop and farm turkey business. They have also carried out a programme of converting a range of single storey farm buildings into a number of holiday cottages over a period of years. These are grouped round what was the former farmyard, and are very attractive with hanging baskets etc. providing colour during the summer months. The interiors have been carpeted, curtained and furnished with everything new. The kitchens are fully equipped, down to the last potato peeler.

Weston is an attractive hamlet on the banks of the Avon. This, along with the high quality of the accommodation and its proximity to Stratford, has ensured that the project has been very successful. There is also a touring caravan site, licensed by the Caravan Club on the farm.

Finally, under this heading, Yew Tree Farm Craft Centre, Wootton Wawen, must be described. The Haimes family came to Yew Tree Farm with the melting snow and floods of that disastrous winter and spring of 1947. John, of the second generation at the farm, started to diversify in 1991.

Fig. 22 Weston Farm, Weston-on-Avon. Before and after: conversion of redundant farm buildings into holiday cottages. (Richard and Phillippa Bluck)

The main block of farm buildings, and also the farmhouse, were built in the early part of the 19th century in the then traditional manner around a yard roughly square in shape. Other buildings have been added, notably the cow byre in the 1930s and the silo barn in post-war times.

One of the very pleasing aspects of this farm building conversion, which has taken place over a period of eleven years, is that each unit has a small plaque noting its original purpose. Corn was stored in the Granary and ground in the Milling Shed below. This was fed to the cows in the byre, today called the Herons' Nest, now a restaurant, also a restorer of antiquarian books, using the finest materials and original techniques. The Cart Horse and Pony Stables are self explanatory, while the Pigsty houses a second-hand bookshop. The Old Bull

Pen is now home to an antique shop, The Dairy is, today the Jolly Farmer Farm Shop, and was the first building to be converted to its present use.

The former silo barn has been converted to a spacious showroom for garden furniture and claims to have on display the widest range in the Midlands.

Space does not permit a full list of all the goods or services which can be purchased at the Yew Tree Farm Craft Centre. They range from the most delicious quiches in the Farm Shop to soft furnishings, high quality cut glass, picture framing and so on. Without doubt Yew Tree Farm is a prime example of the conversion of a farm building to commercial use and is a great credit to John Haimes and his family.

Organic Farming

As the income from mainstream farming declines at an alarming rate, farmers are, naturally enough, looking to ways and means of maintaining income, some of which have been described above. Some, looking at the premium being paid for produce grown organically, are attracted to the concept.

There are, however, serious snags. First, the more successful the advocates of organic farming are, the greater the supply of so-called organic food, and thus the lower the premium upon which the economic viability of such an enterprise depends. We have already seen this process operate in the case of organic milk, the supply of which now exceeds the demand. The consequence is that organic milk producers have to accept the ordinary price for a proportion of their production which, in consequence, must be produced at a loss.

The case for an increase in the production of organic food from UK farms, as made out by the Soil Association and others, rests largely on the fact that a high proportion of organic food is imported, apart from their assertion that an increase in organic food is desirable on health grounds. Import substitution comes up against two main difficulties. First, at the time of writing, the strength of the sterling in relation to the Euro, is putting domestic producers at a disadvantage. Secondly, organic farming is very much more heavily subsidised by continental countries than by the UK government. Thus UK organic farmers have to compete, not only against the economic conditions imposed by a strong currency, but also against heavily subsidised imports. This situation, according to the Green lobby should be corrected by giving increased amounts of taxpayers money to organic farmers.

Secondly, the whole exercise depends upon the consumer being willing and able to pay the premium for organic food, which will always cost more than that grown by conventional methods. It is significant that the consumption of organic food is highest in the more prosperous parts of this country. At the present time, consumers are spending as if there was no tomorrow. As soon as the present boom is over, which is inevitable, housewives will start looking at the pennies. They may be unwilling to pay a green premium: for example, at least 80p/half dozen for so-called free range eggs, against 65p for those produced from batteries.

Incidentally, today's free range eggs are produced in large units of several thousands of birds, many of which are quite happy to stay in the large, static houses where they have everything provided for their needs – food, water and protection from the elements Small wonder that some never venture outside but they are still on 'free range' if there is a pophole giving access to the great outdoors. Real free range is a situation where laying hens are kept in small numbers, say 50 to 100, in moveable houses in the old fashioned way. The birds spend almost all their time in daylight, literally ranging about, hence the term.

In the third place, there is no evidence capable of rational analysis that organic food is safer to eat or tastes better than that produced by conventional methods. That it is perceived by some to be is due to scaremongering by the Green lobby, which asserts that it is right and everyone else is wrong. A holier than thou attitude that many find irritating, to say the least. A class of product the promotion of which is so heavily dependent upon the denigration of the alternative, could well be suspect.

To take one simple example. In the experience of the author, there are many occasions when a field of wheat can be kept acceptably free of weeds by one pass of a tractor-drawn sprayer in the autumn. The alternative could be three passes with a tractor drawn weeder in the spring to achieve the same effect. Of these two, which is more damaging to the environment, a single application of a herbicide (already approved as safe to use), or three times the quantity of exhaust emissions, contributing, so we are told, to global warming?

While the cynic may proclaim that the gullible are always fair game, the continuing credulity of those consumers who, at present, are willing to pay the premium for organic produce cannot be taken for granted. Apart from their on-going ability to do so, it only needs someone, like that legendary small boy, to shout 'the Emperor has no clothes' and to gain the attention of the media scenting a good story, for the organic market to suffer a sharp downturn. The organic movement may be on the crest of the wave, but waves inevitably break upon the shore, to disappear back into the ocean.

That the writing is already on the wall is evidenced by the surplus of organic milk. Moreover, the organic movement, itself, is divided on the desirability of increasing organic production. Charles Peers, the chairman of the Organic Farmers and Growers, is on record as being alarmed at the idea promoted by campaigners that 30% of farmland should be organic by 2010. 'Unless there is consumer demand, and it is supported by retailer loyalty to home-produced products at fair and sustainable prices, any increase in organic production would be commercial suicide,' he is on record as saying. Needles to say, the Soil Association, divorced from reality, disagrees.

Converting to organic farming is a lengthy process, taking several years and often involving investment in new equipment. Public money is available to assist in this, but there can be no case for the taxpayer to provide further funding for food fads, the justification for which is, to put it as kindly as possible, unproven. In addition, old skills and practices have to be re-learnt with the ever-present possibility of expensive error. In short, it would be a bold, or foolhardy, farmer who would allow himself to be seduced by apparently attractive prices into this form of diversification as a means of countering the effects of the current depression. Happily, there are few to be found in South Warwickshire.

Children's Theme Farms

This may not be a very good description, but it is an attempt to describe two examples of diversification aimed at providing a day out for the family and especially to familiarise children with farm livestock. These are not necessarily open every day of the week but, needless to say, are open on half term and school holidays for much of the time.

The Umberslade Children's Theme Farm describes itself as providing 'Fun time for kids down on the farm.' This is a working farm where children can meet sheep, goats, Shire horses, and even ferrets and bees. Donkey and pony rides can be had, and a ride round the farm on trailer and tractor. The Shire Horse Centre, Clifford Chambers, offers a wide range of attractions. In the spring, lambs arrive thick and fast, along with rabbits, piglets and guinea pigs. Wagon rides, the chance to drive a Shire horse, rare breeds, a country village and a play barn are indoor attractions, along with an adventure playground, all aimed at providing an enjoyable, and instructive, day out. There is also, it must be added, a shop and restaurant.

Obviously, such forms of diversification, have an educational value in, one hopes, familiarising the next generation with the realities of what is involved in keeping and tending livestock of many kinds.

These, then, are the various forms of diversification that farmers in South Warwickshire have adopted in an effort to counter the effects of a disastrous drop in the prices for mainstream farm produce. This list is by no means exhaustive but shows some of the ways and means by which farmers in this district are adapting to new circumstances with enterprise, ingenuity and an ability to deal with the unfamiliar, all of which is entirely to their credit.

33. CHANGE IN THE VILLAGE

The Urban Invasion

In 1939 it is probably true to say that the nature and social make-up of village populations in South Warwickshire were broadly similar to those at the end of WWI, although in the 1920s and '30s the writing was already on the wall. For the week-end habit, which became such a feature of urban life in the years between the Wars, had already taken root.

A. G. Street, Wiltshire farmer, broadcaster, author and journalist makes a somewhat scathing reference to the country week-enders in his writings in the 1930s, recording that they kept villagers awake with noisy partying on Saturday nights and then complained that the church bells woke them on Sunday mornings. Or again, Beverley Nicholls published 'A Thatched Roof' in 1933, which described his cottage in the country, being typical of the younger, well-off generation which the motor car had enabled to enjoy weekending in the country a matter of course.

There was, of course, nothing very new about this in the 1930s, at any rate as far as South Warwickshire was concerned. In the early years of the 20th. century, and even earlier, wooden shacks and bungalows had sprung up along the banks of the Avon. Also 'summer-houses,' some of them of quite elaborate construction with lawns, gardens, a tennis court or bowling green were to be found here and there in the South Warwickshire countryside, notably at Oldberrow, Fulready and Goldicote to quote a few examples, reached by pony and trap or car at week-ends and holiday times. Moreover, the coming of the railway had allowed Bidford-on-Avon to become a popular destination for an outing on a Sunday, summer's day. And at Welford some villagers supplemented their incomes by taking in holiday guests, who may well have come by train to either Binton or Milcots stations. Indeed, a Sunday morning train stopping at the latter became known as the 'Fisherman's Special,' whose passengers thought nothing of walking to the banks of the Avon at Welford or Weston for a day's sport.

By the end of the 1930s many outsiders had taken up permanent residence in some of the villages in South Warwickshire. It is probably true that the process of gentrification started in Welford-on-Avon sooner than in many other villages, indeed before WWI. For it is an attractive village with its wide grass verges along the High Street, its black and white timbered framed houses and cottages, topped with grey thatch or mellow tile. Comparatively early, several of the larger farmhouses had become residences. Cleavers, The Ashes (its land sold off its land before the end of the 19th. century) and Manor Farm would be three examples. And in later years others were to follow, Weston Sands, Welford Hill and Welford Pastures to name three. And it must be remembered that dwellings, which we now refer to as cottages, had been, in fact, the smaller farmhouses with fewer acres to sustain them than those mentioned above.

In spite of these developments in the 1920s, 1930s and before, Welford was still a village of market gardens and smallholdings into the 1940s and early 1950s. Today it is a different tale. The process of suburbanisation is complete, the vast majority of the population either retired, or urban based, commuting daily. And it is much the same story elsewhere in South Warwickshire.

In passing, an event took place in Welford recently which was the occasion of a quiet chuckle on the part of residents of half a century or more, survivors of those who had worked their orchards and small plots, either full-time or part-time in days gone by. Several villages in the county undertook a study to produce a development plan, which sought to 'preserve the character of the village' and to 'protect its most sensitive areas' in the jargon of the planners. The necessary survey was duly carried out in Welford, entirely by incomers who had not been in the village any significant length of time, a report was prepared and discussed at great length in the village hall.

As a resident of well over fifty summers, I did point out to several of those taking part in this exercise that as far as preserving the true character of the village was concerned they were well over forty years too late. Moreover, had they lived in the village all those years ago, they would not have liked its character one little bit. For many a house, cottage or smallholding had its pigsty or hen house; at first light cocks would be crowing and, as already mentioned, the din of bird scaring at cherry ripening time would have made further sleep impossible. Fortunately then there were no Environmental Health Officers to harass the natives about their business at the behest of incomers.

Much the same sort of story has been repeated time and again in most villages in South Warwickshire. In short, their populations are no longer predominantly agrarian, deriving their livings either directly, or indirectly from the land, but overwhelmingly urban in character. In other words living in the country but not of it.

Over the years, and as a result of economic pressures, farm amalgamations leading to fewer holdings, and also the mechanisation of so many farming operations, has meant that the number of farmers and those who work for them has fallen substantially, year on year, for forty years. Farmhouses and workers dwellings have become redundant, having been sold or let as the case may be.

There are numerous examples of this in South Warwickshire. For instance, less than five miles as the crow flies from where I am now writing, five farms, varying in size from under 100 acres to one of over 400, have been amalgamated over a period of years to make one 1,000 acre holding.

Also, as a matter of policy dictated by the former workings of the Agriculture Holdings Acts and for fiscal reasons, estate owners have taken tenanted land in hand as it became vacant. The Ragley and Weston Park estates are prime examples of this trend, leading to fewer and larger farms. Amalgamations can, of course, also take place by purchase by existing owner/occupiers or others from outside agriculture; again there are many examples in South Warwickshire.

Agriculture in this country has been given no credit for releasing a substantial stock of housing for occupation by urbans. In fact the latter are quite capable of bemoaning the passing of so many 'small, family farms' and then being only too happy to move into the farmhouse originally serving such a holding. Also, of course, the conversion into dwellings of barns and other farm buildings has gone on apace from the 1980s onwards. Traditional farmsteads have, in consequence, been disappearing at a rapid pace in the last thirty years or so.

But, in many cases, this has been no bad thing. The sale of village farmsteads for development has enabled new sets of buildings to be erected, often on a more convenient site, and usually a new farmhouse as well. Not only has this enabled modernisation to be completed at a stroke, replacing structures which were originally designed and built in the 'wheelbarrow and horse-and-cart' age, but has also removed the farming operations from within the confines of the village, thus relieving the social tensions between urban incomers and those who earn a living from the land, of which more later. There are numerous examples in South Warwickshire of this process, notably in the parishes of Haselor, Aston Cantlow, Newbold-on-Stour, Ilmington, Long Compton and Brailes to name but a few.

Nor has the influx of urban incomers into villages been a bad thing, although, only too often it has a downside. The alternative is not attractive. For a number of years I was a consultant to a farming company in East Suffolk. Incidentally, its 2, 000 acres originally consisted of some five separate farms and two parcels of land without houses or buildings, but that is by the way.

This was in the days before so much of East Anglia had been discovered and colonised by Londoners or those from the East Midlands. In consequence some of the villages were a sorry sight. One in particular remains in my memory. The village school boarded up, the shop long since closed, the pub down-at-heel and obviously on its last legs, with one ot two cottages unoccupied; in short a scene of near dereliction, for reasons which have already been stated.

The 'new countrymen' have breathed life into communities, which would otherwise have suffered the same fate, albeit temporarily, of that village in East Suffolk. They have taken over the Parish Council, the running of the village hall, the organisation of the village fete and so on. Naturally enough the indigenous population, so often now largely confined to the council houses, have resented this to a greater or lesser degree. Not least because their own sons, daughters and grandchildren have been priced out of the housing market and, with no properties to rent at reasonable figures, have had to leave the village.

Incomers, both working and retired, have the time, knowledge and expertise to resist further undesirable development in the form of new dwellings. They, to a man or woman, always want their house to be the last built in the parish. It can be argued that this is desirable. But, as mentioned above, there is a downside. They are equally determined that any development deemed to be detrimental to the rural calm, which they regard as their right, should be resisted; even when it involves real country people – farmers, growers and so on – about their business.

In such cases, the volume and vehemence of complaint is always in inverse proportion to the period of residence. A classic example is a riverside village near Stratford-upon-Avon. The 'action group' formed to resist any development, albeit land-based, on the adjacent farm land, consists of residents of less than twenty years standing; indeed only one member has lived in the village that long.

While lip service is paid by planners, and others, to the principle of creating jobs in the countryside to give employment to the rural population, the new countrymen can be relied upon to object to any such project. On occasion the conversion of farm buildings into offices or workshops will be resisted, as will the erection of co-operative grain stores or packing stations for fruit and vegetables, while a proposal to extract sand and gravel will drive incomers into a frenzy. This latter is even the case when the same incomers are, simultaneously, campaigning for a by-pass for their village. Apparently some other parish has got to be dug up to provide the necessary sand and gravel. There are two villages in South Warwickshire where this has actually happened, and the sad thing is that those concerned do not appear to realise that there is any inconsistency in their actions.

Often the main objection to the developments listed above is an increase in traffic. This is a classic case of the pot calling the kettle black. For every gentrified original village dwelling and every new house generates traffic, probably to the tune of an average of two cars each. The commuting fraternity are certainly guilty, turning country lanes and village streets into race tracks, morning and evening, death traps for the elderly, the very young and the unwary.

Not two hundred yards from where I am now writing is an old Georgian house fronting the High Street. At one time, in the 19th. century, this was the site of a veritable hive of industry. One line of production was the manufacture of winnowing machines, another of papier mâché trays, as just two examples. Today if any attempt was made to establish such an enterprise in the centre of any village there would be uproar. So much for 'preserving the character of the village,' as noted above. There is no doubt that one of the most serious obstacles to establishing units of rural industry to give employment in the countryside is Nimbyism.

As far as village life is concerned 'the old order changeth, giving place to new.' I am grateful to have seen the 'old order,' and indeed to have been part of it.

The Village Inn

Once upon a time, in the 1940s and for many, many years before that, the village pub played a central part in the life of the community. It was a meeting place for those who had spent the day working on the land, or otherwise occupied in the village, and, in season, in the evening in the kitchen garden or on the allotment. Everyday working clothes were the order of the day, a dog often at heel and then quiet talk of farm crops and stock, of the progress of vegetables, fruit and the pig in the sty at the bottom of the garden, not to mention village affairs and gossip.

True, there were those who spent too much time, and money, in the 'local,' as there still are today. But these were certainly the exception rather than the rule.

The landlord very often had a 'day job' of one sort or another, his wife looking after the bar in his absence. In those days it was not expected that a village pub would provide a full time living in many cases. Wartime duties led to my spending several months working in the Dorset countryside. There the village inns were basic by today's standards. There was usually only one bar, uncarpetted and stone flagged, and, against the back wall were timber runners supported on short brick pillars. On these lengths of timber, brown with age, the barrels of cider, which was the usual tipple, and beer were stood, each draped with a freshly laundered and meticulously ironed tea cloth. Pillars and walls, sometimes unplastered, were whitewashed.

Outside the towns, these pubs had no spirit licences. If anyone, unversed in these matters, asked for a whiskey, gin, or whatever, he would be rebuked with 'We don't sell that sort of stuff here.' It was cider 'rough' or 'smooth or sweet' or, occasionally beer 'mild' or 'bitter,' and that was that. No food, of course, except fresh bread, cheese and onion.

There was one such establishment in South Warwickshire, now long since demolished to make room for new houses for incomers, run on similar lines, although I seem to recall it boasted a spirit licence. There was just one bar, a small, cosy room with a welcoming fire, except in high summer. Here the landlord, Billy, held court every evening with his wife serving.

'Rattle the glasses about a bit, missus, we have got enough in now,' Billy used to shout, when the full quorum of locals was present.

Apart from the pub, Billy was a man of many parts. His main occupation was his small farm, with a bit of ploughland, pigs, poultry and a few cattle, but he was always there, and more than ready, to earn the odd quid or two, 'helping out.'

One day, towards the end of a very hot summer's afternoon, I called to see Billy on some matter concerning the farm. Going round to the back, as is the usual custom, all was still and quiet with nobody about, the only sign of activity a steaming copper in the wash house. Shortly, one of the daughters, a strapping girl in her early teens, arrived with a bucket in each hand. She proceeded to fill these from the copper with a baler. 'Is your dad about ?' I asked. 'Oh yes, he is having a bath in the orchard,' came the rather surprising reply. 'In that case I won't bother him now,' I said. 'That'll be alright, follow me.' So I did, wondering what sort of rural vision awaited.

There was Billy, sitting in an old bath, which normally did duty as a cattle trough, attended by his wife and the other children who were providing for his needs in terms of soap and flannel and, no doubt in due course, a towel. In summer you never saw him without his straw hat, the brim of which had parted from the crown both back and front. So there he was, hat on head, enjoying his bath in the dappled shade of the old farm orchard. Perhaps a scene reminiscent of 'The Darling Buds of May,' although that book had yet to be written.

Another village landlord, whom I came to know very well and who became a firm and valued friend, was Spence Edkins of the Kings Head, Aston Cantlow. He was the personification of everything that a village inn-keeper should be, the third generation, if my memory serves me correctly, at the Kings Head. Indeed, there was a large framed photograph of Grandpa Edkins, dressed in the traditional smock, which hung for many years in the lounge bar.

As was usual at the time, the previous generations at the Kings Head had other occupations. Spence's father and grandfather were the local carriers, carrying out their business with horse and wagon.

Spence himself farmed around forty acres, two fields each side of the lane leading from Billesley, taking over the 'Allotment Field' nearer the village after I first knew him. This was in a parlous state, being foul with squitch and I have an abiding memory of Spence dragging this out with a set of harrows behind his one and only horse. When he was not too busy in the bar in a summer's evening, there was nothing he liked better than to slip out and walk his crops and many were the occasions when I accompanied him to inspect the progress, or otherwise, of his corn, his patch of potatoes and fodder roots.

What is now the car park at the back of the pub was, in the 1940s, covered with pigsties of varying sizes constructed, for the most part, with second-hand timber, steel sheets and anything else that came to hand. Where the Jaguars, Bentleys BMWS and 4X4s now stand, sows grunting happily reared their litters, these being taken through to pork or bacon weights. For the Kings Head has not escaped the gentrification which has beset the village pub. Beams, thick with dark varnish have been sandblasted, oak furniture has been replaced with pine and the back room, where the farmers discussion club met for so many years, is now a restaurant

During food rationing in the 1940s a sucking piglet had no official existence until it was weaned, when it had to be recorded in the statutory agricultural returns. Thus Spence instituted his sucking pig suppers, to which a few trusted and discreet friends were invited once a year during the winter. Over the course of years and when rationing had ended, this annual event continued with many more guests than originally and certainly involving more than one piglet.

Spence and Mrs. E. , as his wife was known as, were certainly the pioneers, if not the originators in South Warwickshire, of evening catering in village pubs. Certainly by the 1940s their duck suppers were already renowned. They had realised, and exploited, the demand made possible by widening car ownership in the 1930s for pub meals of a high standard. Also their mixed grills consisting of two eggs, several rashers of bacon, a couple of sausages, kidneys and fried bread, with butter cheese and fresh bread ad lib. , could be had for 3/6, about twenty pence new money.

Today, of course, there are few village inns in South Warwickshire and elsewhere, which do not provide lunches, bar meals and suppers year in, year out. With the coming of the breathalyser few would now be able to exist without virtually turning themselves into rural restaurants, bistros or wine bars. Some, but by no means all, manage to preserve a degree of 'pubiness,' running an establishment where locals can still drop in for a pint or two in the evening without feeling out of place. Some, but again by no means all, still have a public bar for this very purpose.

In consequence, one now has a wide choice of village inns in South Warwickshire where one can lunch, or wine and dine, on the very best fare at any time of the year. One might mourn the passing of the traditional village pub but what has taken its place has a wide appeal. Landlords and their families, and the success of these new-look village inns depends upon their personalities, can now look to their business to provide a full time living. Moreover, these new style village pubs provide some local employment, either full or part-time. As far as the latter is concerned, students either still at school, college or University, often find work in the local inn, providing them with welcome pocket money and, work experience and the confidence that comes with dealing with the customers. Who can cavil at the passing of the old, when the new brings so many benefits ?

The Village Farm

Typically in South Warwickshire, villages are 'nucleated.' That is, since the very earliest time, for centuries in fact, farm buildings with their farmhouses and workers cottages, have been located within the confines of the village, with the fields stretching away to the parish boundaries, sometimes with only a paddock actually adjacent to the farmstead. In fact, if a farmstead stands alone out in its surrounding fields, it is certain that it is either post-enclosure, Crimscote Fields Farm is a prime example of this, or the sole surviving farm buildings and farm house of a now deserted village, Longdon Manor and Billesley Manor Farm are examples amongst many others locally. Or, again, the site of a mill which has land attached to it; Fell Mill at Honington and Talton Mill, Newbold-on-Stour are two such as these.

In spite of many farmsteads being sold for development within villages and new ones being built on green field sites out on the farms themselves, there are still many village farms. For generations these farmsteads have been the hub of the land which went them, outside the confines of the village. In pre-enclosure days the arable land would be held in strips in the great open fields, while there would also be rights on the common land and in the hay meadows. Today the open fields, meadows and common land have been enclosed to give us the countryside of fields of all sizes, hedged and ditched with which we are familiar. But the farmstead remains where it has always been.

For generations these village farmsteads have had cattle wintered in them, treading straw into farmyard manure in the yards which, when winter had ended, were cleaned out and the manure carted through the village and along the lanes to be spread on the fields. For centuries cows have been milked in these village farms, the milk being made into butter or cheese, until the 'town dairies' were decimated by the Rinderpest epidemic of 1865, This instigated the liquid milk market, supplied from country farms and transported by rail into the cities and towns.

In the last century, steam driven threshing machines with their accompanying noise, smoke and smell took the place of the rhythmic thump of the flail on the barn threshing floor. Farmyards, even in those days, could be noisy, smelly places, far removed from the rural idyll, or Arcady, which exists only in the imagination of urbans.

For such as these there can be, sometimes literally, a rude awakening on moving into a newly acquired village property, which would quite likely be a former farmhouse or workers cottage. Exception is taken to the noise and movement of tractors; to the running of grain driers, albeit for only a short time each year and then only in a difficult harvest; to the sound of a circular saw cutting fencing timber, or putting points on stakes; to the journeyings of milk tankers and grain lorries, or those delivering feed, fertilisers of what-have-you; to the stately progress of the milking herd from pasture to parlour and back again; or to the night blarting of a cow deprived of its calf, and so on. In short, to the sounds, to the smells and to the trafficking of the countryside about its business.

Examples of such extraordinary behaviour on the part of newcomers to the countryside would fill a book. But here are some of the choicer gems from South Warwickshire, carefully recorded over the years.

Perhaps pride of place, for sheer ignorance and impertinence, must go to the couple who, on moving into their newly acquired village property, immediately enquired of the Council's Planning and Environmental Health departments what they were going to do about the village farm next door.

Then there was the case of the 'Lady and the Milking Bail' and on this occasion I was the root cause of the trouble, for which I make no apology. Many years ago a farmer friend and client came to me for advice on converting his cowpen into a milking parlour. The farmstead was right in the centre of the village and the herd had to tramp at least half a mile to the nearest pasture. In view of this I suggested the purchase of a Hosier milking bail, sited on a suitable concrete pad in the yard during the winter and on another such pad on the summer site, adjacent to the cow pastures. Two small dairies were built to house the cooler and churns, water being available at both sites, but not electricity at the summer station. So the milking machine was driven by a small, stationery diesel engine, winter and summer.

When the good lady bought her property overlooking the farmyard, she failed to notice the presence of cows in the yard and the bail. She paid for her lack of observation by being woken early on a winter's morning by the thump of the diesel engine and the rattle of churns. She was not well pleased and threatened to take her neighbour to court. But a compromise was reached by her and the farmer buying an electric motor for the bail, each sharing half the cost.

In some instances those with farmsteads in villages can be subjected to what amounts to persecution and harassment by incomers. In one instance, the man concerned reacted by obtaining planning consent for the development of the farmyard for housing, constructing new buildings outside the village. But this did not suit. Incomers with village properties, who had complained about the farm in their midst in the first place, objected to more houses in the village, while those within sight of the new farmstead also took exception on the grounds that the new farmstead 'spoilt their view.' It is almost beyond belief.

In another village one incomer adopted the habit of complaining to the Environmental Health Department of the local council on every possible occasion. The warning bleep of the milk tanker reversing; the storage of fertilisers in an adjacent barn and their loading into the hopper of the spreader; the running of a tractor in the early hours for the morning milking to drive the dairy generator when there was a power cut; pieces of straw blowing about in the village street and tyre marks on the grass verge in front of the cottage were all matters to which offence was taken, amongst others.

There is something very wrong with a state of affairs in which such harassment can be indulged in without any cost to the complainant. Frivolous complaints are time wasters both for the unfortunate official who is obliged to investigate and for the farmer victim who has to meet him. The only solution would be to inform the trouble-maker that, in the event of the complaint being considered unjustified, a charge would be made for the time and travelling expenses of the official concerned.

Another example of misbehaviour took place one summer's afternoon on a lane leading into a small hamlet in the depths of the South Warwickshire claylands, again involving a village farm with a herd of milking cows which had to be walked along this lane four times a day to and from the nearest pasture. On the outskirts of the hamlet a small by-road led off to the main road a mile away. Before and after each milking the senior partner, then well into his seventies, stood in this little lane to stop cows wandering down it instead of continuing on their way to parlour or pasture.

On this particular occasion, when the cows were being brought up for the afternoon milking the old man was in his usual place, talking to a girl with her child in a pushchair. A car came up behind the cows and the driver, instead of slowing down and following the herd to its destination only a couple of hundred yards away, put his hand hard on the horn, kept it there and drove on. Naturally enough the cows panicked and stampeded in all directions, knocking the elderly farmer down, who fortunately fell on the grass verge and was shaken but not hurt; while the girl just managed to pull her child to safety in the nick of time. This appalling behaviour could well have resulted in serious injury or even worse.

The countryside is not, primarily, a pleasant place in which to live, to come home to at the end of the day's work and to enjoy at the week-ends. It is the farmer's place of work on which he and those he employs are dependent for their living. The present generation are the natural successors of those who have tilled the land and tended livestock for many thousands years,

Farmsteads and farmland can be smelly, noisy, dirty and sometimes dangerous places for the ignorant and stupid. Incomers, the new countrymen, who choose to live in the countryside and whose sojourn in it is numbered in tens rather than thousands of years, have to accept that this is so; that livestock will be driven down country lanes as they have been for generations; that tractors and other farm machinery will use these same lanes about the daily business of the farm; and that tractors, combines, grain driers and whatever may well be working before first light and after dusk at certain times of the year.

Fortunately the majority of incomers are good neighbours but a minority are certainly not.

The Village Shop

Fig. 23 Welford-on-Avon village post office in the snow. (Jill Jackson)

Until about the middle of the 18th century, villages were self-sufficient as far as the basic necessities were concerned. Travelling chapmen, later to be more commonly known as pedlars or hawkers, provided the other needs such as cheap crockery, cutlery, cloth and ribbons, ornaments and inexpensive jewellery, amongst many other items. Many walked their rounds, carrying their wares in a pack on their backs, others rode on horse back, while the more fortunate might have had a donkey, or pony, and cart.

Not only would they visit villages and hamlets on their beat, but also weekly markets and the annual fairs, some of which would last for several days, or even longer.

However, by the 1820 - 30s, few villages were without a shop, or shops, including a grocers, bakers, butchers, ironmongers, haberdashers, boot and show makers, repairers, and so on. In the case of bakers, bread would be baked on the premises. Butchers would often kill beef cattle, lambs and pigs in slaughterhouses adjacent to their shops. This is in contrast to village shops today where, in the majority of cases, they obtain their meat from wholesalers, and wrapped bread is now sold in general stores.

Regarding village bakers, it is worth recording a conversation I had with the late Edward Adkins, sometimes towards the close of the 1950s. He was then the principal in the local firm Adkins and Thomas, whose mill was in the South

Warwickshire village of Broom, now demolished to provide the site for a housing estate.

He told me on that occasion that his firm was giving up milling bread flour for the simple reason that their customers, almost exclusively village or small market town bakers, had dwindled in numbers to the extent that supplying the few that remained was no longer a viable proposition. But, of course, his firm continued producing animal feedingstuffs of the highest quality for a number of years after it had ceased to mill bread flour.

At one time there were two bakers in Welford-on-Avon, but by the time I came to live in the village there was only one, the bake house being adjacent to the Shakespeare Inn. The bread was delivered round the village by pony and float, loaves (unwrapped) being thrown in the latter in a heap. During rain or snow, a rather grubby tarpaulin was thrown over the load as some protection against the elements. What present day food inspectors would have thought of this can only be imagined, but nobody came to any harm.

It could be argued that the heyday of the village shop covered some hundred years from, say, 1820 to 1920. After the First World War, the writing was on the wall, for in the 1920s the country bus, operated either by individuals (sometimes formerly the village carrier) or by larger companies, put shops of all kinds in the nearest market town within reach of villagers. These would offer a wider range of goods at lower prices than the local shops. It may well be that those to suffer first from market town competition would have been the more specialised such as ironmongers, haberdashers, cobblers and the like. And not only the country bus but also the bicycle played its part in making the town shops accessible to country people. It is significant that in 1940 some villages are recorded as having cycle repairers or agents.

The network of country bus routes became extensive in the 1920s and 1930s. Services eventually became eclipsed, however, by wider car ownership as so many villages became suburbanised from the 1960s onwards.

The country bus was still very much alive and well patronised up into the 1950s. Those of more mature years and with good memories will recall the bus and coach station at Bridgefoot, Stratford-upon-Avon, up until that time. Early on Tuesday and Friday mornings there would be a number of small village buses already parked, having disgorged their passengers with their various wares. On Fridays, in particular, when the produce markets were held, the carriers on the roofs surrounded by metal lattice sides, would be piled high with bags of potatoes, boxes of vegetables, perhaps a crate of poultry and boxes of eggs. On the return journey these would be replaced with sacks of pig or poultry meal, the odd dustbin and maybe an assortment of farm and garden tools, the handles of which would be virgin white before acquiring the brown patina of daily use.

Childhood memories of holidays in Cornwall include those of journeyings by a little bus, which served the countryside around Bude, that doubled as a mail van.

There was a cage behind the drivers seat with a folding door that could be locked to secure the mail bags, which, in theory, were carried within, and were to be delivered to, or collected from, the post offices en route. In practice, these bags travelled underneath the drivers seat, the cage being convenient for the transport of livestock of various kinds. Perhaps a collie pup on its way to its new home, or a weaner pig, or even a calf, both be-nappied in a sack, having been loaded onto the bus at the end of a farm drive to be collected by new owners at a pre-determined stop.

During the second half of the 20th century, village shops were struggling against increasing car ownership, combined with the opening of supermarkets with their one-stop shopping and ample car parking. One by one they closed and, all too often, the Post Office with them. This left the elderly and not-so-well-off entirely dependent upon the local bus service which was, only too often, under threat as well. Some villages with no bus services can now be very isolated places for the young, the old and the car-less.

The trend is well illustrated by a survey of 59 parishes in South Warwickshire, picked at random, and comparing the situation in 1940 to that of 1994. The information for the former was gleaned from Kelly's Directory for that year and for the latter from a survey conducted by the Warwickshire County Council.

Of these parishes 16 had no shops in 1994 and none in 1940, although they may have had one or more shops prior to 1940. Chesterton, in 1891 for example, had a population of 192 and two shops. By 1931, the population had dwindled to 135 and both the shops had gone. Of the remaining 43, 15 (35%) had lost the shop and with it the Post office and 18 (42%) were without a shop of any kind by 1994. This County Council survey is some seven years out of date at the time of writing and, doubtless, other villages have lost their shop/post offices in this intervening period.

From the 1960s onwards, the process of suburbanisation of so many South Warwickshire villages has proceeded apace. Orchards have been ripped out, with houses replacing trees. Every paddock and other open ground has been built on, and village boundaries extended into open countryside by the construction of new housing estates. This has led to a substantial increase in the population of so many South Warwickshire villages.

One might have thought that this would have given a new lease of life to village shops, post offices, garages and so on, but this has not been so. In the past, urban incomers, while expecting the garage and shop/post office to be there when needed, will patronise the nearest supermarkets, some never making any purchases in their village at all. The slogan 'use it, or lose it' used to fall on deaf ears in many cases. Just as the volume and vehemence of opposition to any new development is usually in inverse proportion to the period of residence in the parish, so those who have never set foot in the village post office will be the first to shout the loudest if it is threatened with closure.

Three incidents involving, in this instance, the village garage, illustrate what was the usual attitude. One customer said that he was settling and then closing his petrol account because he could buy his needs in this respect so much cheaper at the nearest Tesco. In passing, one might have thought that some compromise might have been possible, with the individual concerned continuing to purchase at least a proportion of his petrol in the village against the day when his battery was flat in the morning and he needed a mechanic; a service that Tesco was unlikely to provide.

Not very many weeks later it was rumoured that the garage owner was retiring (which was correct), and that he had sold the garage site for building development (which was not). Nevertheless, his former petrol customer arrived and berated him for depriving the village car owners of an essential service. It is difficult to credit anyone with such cynicism, but this is a true story.

Two further incidents illustrate the same point, again concerning a village garage. This particular one had just closed for the day when a motorist drew up begging for petrol as his tank was all but dry. So the pumps and office were opened up again, such was the good nature of the proprietor, who asked 'How many gallons?'; 'Just one to get me in to Tesco's in Stratford,' came the reply. In that winter when the snowdrifts were deep and the power lines down for days, a woman, a former customer who had not been near the garage for several years, rang and demanded a cylinder of gas to be delivered to her at once. When she was told that the very scarce supplies were being reserved for regular customers, she was furious.

Perhaps it is not too fanciful to suggest that that winter was a turning point in the attitudes of many people towards their village shop and, a few years later, the village garage during the petrol shortage of September 2000. For those who had never used them before descended on them like a swarm of locusts. When the snows had melted and power restored, one village shopkeeper remarked that he had never seen so many strange faces when the village was all but isolated and he did not expect to see them again for many a long day.

As a general observation, he might not have been entirely correct. Of course supermarkets stock a much wider range of goods; of course these are cheaper than in village stores (but not necessarily always so); of course many will rely on them for the bulk of their shopping. There is now a realisation, however, that a proportion of any household's needs should be purchased in the village, that any savings in price are offset, to some extent, by the exorbitant cost of petrol and the time and hassle involved in a trip to the supermarket. 'Use them or lose them' may well be accepted, and acted upon, to a greater degree than hitherto. Personal observation suggests that this is so.

34. CONSERVATION

The Open Fields

There were once brooks sweet whimpering down the vale:
The brooks no more - kingcup and daisy fled;
Their last fall'n tree the naked moors bewail,
And scarce a bush is left to tell the mournful tale.

There once were lanes in nature's freedom dropt,
There once were paths that every valley wound -
Inclosure came and every path was stopt; . .

Things do not change at all. It is all there in these verses – the destruction of valuable habitats and restrictions on access to the countryside in the modern parlance of so-called conservationists and ramblers, or rather those who purport to represent them. These words were written by John Clare in *The Village Minstrel* just about 180 years ago.

He is, in fact, bemoaning the creation of the very landscape of fields and hedges which is now, in the imagination of some, being altered to its detriment by hedge removal and so on. The fact is that the countryside is changing constantly. It is dynamic. It can never be fossilised into the Arcady which exists only in the imagination of the urban critics of modern farming, whose knowledge of the practicalities of making a living from the land is non-existent and, perhaps even more depressing, whose historical perspective is minimal.

In the early years of the 19th century, the appearance of the Feldon was very different from that of today. It was at that time that the first editions of the Ordnance Survey maps of South Warwickshire were published. It would appear from a perusal of these that there were still open fields in many parishes in the Feldon. The lapse of time between then and now, during which the Feldon took on its present appearance, is nothing more than a blink of the eyelid in the history of our countryside.

Elsewhere, it is the same story. John Caird, in his *English Agriculture in 1850-1851*, records the ploughing out and cropping of much downland in Wiltshire and elsewhere during the Napoleonic Wars and after. In the 20th century, history has repeated itself and much downland has, once again, been ploughed and cropped. The ancient, close cropped downland turf, the disappearance of which under the plough is criticised by conservationists is not so ancient as they fondly imagine.

The conservation lobby claims an interest in farmland and the countryside in which it has no equity, an attitude which, in any other sphere, would be considered eccentric at best. For instance, at a meeting of the Warwickshire Grassland Society in Moreton Hall, some years ago, the speaker was a member of the staff of the, then, Countryside Commission, and, I am ashamed to say, a former colleague in ADAS. Addressing a meeting the audience which consisted predominantly of farmers, he came out with the extraordinary statement, 'You may farm the countryside but you do not own it.' There was a stunned silence and you could have cut the atmosphere with a knife. But the speaker was so insensitive, he probably was oblivious of the impression he had created.

At question time, members were too courteous, at first, to make much comment until I observed that this was a peculiar statement as many present had documentation to prove that it was untrue. Moreover, if 'The Good Lord gave the Land to the People' it would be difficult to find a record of the transaction in the Land Register. This did the trick and the discussion took off . The speaker was furious with me, and vowed vengeance on a future occasion; fortunately, we never met again. It does show the trouble one can get into by speaking the truth

Field Size and Shape

Few aspects of farming during the second half of the twentieth century have attracted more adverse comment than hedge removal. This has sometimes been directed, in ignorance, at landscapes where few hedges have ever been planted in the first place; for example the Fens, or, coming nearer home, Crimscote Fields Farm. In the case of the latter, coming from Talton through the farm one is confronted by what appears to be an open, somewhat alien countryside, lacking in hedges. The more observant will see that field boundaries have been provided by rows of iron hurdles at the time of enclosure, and when the Victorian farmhouse and farmstead had been built in what had been the open fields of the manor of Crimscote.

Again the not-so-well-informed, sometimes observing the country scene only from the comfort of a car, can be in error when complaining about a hedge being grubbed out when, in fact, it has been cut to ground level. Those better versed in country matters will know that this a common enough practice when a hedge has got old, gappy, and beyond redemption. Cutting off to ground level will cause fresh shoots to be thrown up from the stowels. These, in the fullness of time, will grow to a height at which the hedge can be laid and a fresh start made.

Power Sources

I have already mentioned that one of the most depressing facts about those who find fault with hedge removal, in particular, is their complete lack of a sense of history. The fact that field size and shape has been determined, to a great extent, by the power source available for cultivation at the time has escaped their notice.

The most primitive plough known is a *crook-ard*, formed originally by a forked tree branch, which provided a long handle and a short, wooden *tine*; this was, in other words, a scratching stick with a long handle, which was pulled through the soil. Motive power was provided by the ploughman unaided, or assisted by The Missus on the end of a rope, or a donkey or mule. There is an old drawing depicting a crook-ard being drawn by a pair of oxen harnessed side by side.

The crook-ard was in use from about 3000 BC, a date established by carbon dating. There is evidence that the method of cultivation was to make a second pass, roughly at right angles to the first, resulting in the end in something like a tilth. Today, it is called *minimal cultivation*. Naturally enough, these Neolithic fields tended to be to be square in shape. The human power available was meagre, and only short bouts possible. Moreover, if a second pass at right angles to the first had to be made to produce a semblance of a seedbed, then a field with sides of roughly equal length was the most practical shape.

By Roman times, all this had changed. A crude version of the mouldboard plough, and a wooden breast (pearwood was favoured for this, due to the slightly twisted grain which allowed better scouring in clay soil), an iron share and coulter, was in use. Oxen were the power source and longer runs were possible. Thus, Roman fields tended to be longer and narrower and, again, there is evidence that it was common practice to demolish the old field boundaries, ploughing over them to make the new fields. Field enlargement has an ancient history!

The next phase in the history of the field is one that has left indelible marks on the Feldon countryside, which are still there for all to see at the present time. Historians discuss at length by whom, how, and exactly when, the manorial system with its great open fields was evolved. Certainly, in South Warwickshire, and elsewhere, it persisted for at least eight hundred years, and possibly longer.

These fields had furrows in the characteristic shape of an inverted *S*. The power source consisted of large, unwieldy, teams of oxen which, subject only to the lie of the land and the need for surface drainage, necessitated long bouts and wide headlands on which to turn.

In the Arden it is a different story. What ridge and furrow still remain have narrower ridges and the furrows are straight – horse work in fact. Such fields were probably later in origin, when horses had begun to replace oxen as the main farm draught animal.

The fields in the Arden are smaller than those in the Feldon, and were created by the gradual, piecemeal, clearance of woodland and scrub. Farms were enlarged by expansion in this way from the original farmsteads grouped in clearings in the forest known as 'greens.' These still exist in place names in Arden such as Danzey Green, Blunts Green and so on. Anyone perusing the 6" Ordnance Survey maps of South Warwickshire published during the first half of the 20th century cannot fail to notice the difference in field size between Arden and Feldon. Part of the explanation lies in the way the Arden fields were created, partly due to the fact that the Arden had been mainly pastoral, and partly due to using horses, rather than oxen, for power,

Oxen

Oxen were the prime power source for arable cultivation in this country for many centuries. The horse, up to the end of the Middle Ages, was not used for farm work but for transport and for war. Oxen were less prone to disease, and hoof and leg troubles, than horses. Nor did they compete with humans for feed, i.e. oats, They could live and work on hay and straw. In 1664, the Royal Society carried out an enquiry into farming practices, from which it was clear that horses had, by then, started to replace oxen in plough teams. They were better suited to the smaller post-enclosure fields, not needing the great, wide headlands demanded by the unwieldy ox teams.

For many years, the relative virtues of oxen and horses for farm work were debated in print, and doubtless elsewhere.

The fact remains that they were still very much in use for ploughing and harrowing in the middle of the 19th century. The following quotations are from *English Agriculture 1850-51 (ibid.).*

> On Lord Leicester's estate at Holkham Park in Norfolk:
> 32 farm horses and 20 working bullocks are the working stock of the farms, the bullocks working in pairs, but changed at each yoking, a fresh pair being taken in the afternoon; four bullocks thus do the work of two horses, either plough or harrow.
>
> On the farm of Mr. Hudson of Castleacre, also on Lord Leicester's estate:
> 36 work horses and 16 working bullocks are required for the operation of the farm. The bullocks work in pairs, two in a plough, the same as horses and walk quite as quickly, and either in plough or harrow, get over as much ground as the horses.
>
> On Lord Hatherton's farm near Cannock Chase in Staffordshire
> 14 pairs of horses are kept for work on the farm and plantations and 14 working Devon bullocks are bought in February every year, worked during the spring and summer on the turnip land, assist in getting in

> wheat and are fattened and sold to the butcher in the course of the winter.

It should be noted that the Holkham estate was considered amongst the best run in the country, and Lord Hatherton's was probably in the same class. So, as late as the 1850s, oxen were still being used for farm work, along, of course, with horses even on the most progressive estates. These farms would have been already enclosed. So, while oxen formed the size and shape of the great Feldon fields, they were also worked on enclosed farms at a much later date. No doubt lighter, improved, ploughs enabled a pair of oxen to do work that formerly needed four, or even six.

Finally, a quotation from *The Agricultural Revolution 1750-1850* by Chambers and Mingay:

> In Gloucestershire, teams of oxen driven by labourers of legendary lethargy, took a seven-hour day to plough 3/4 of an acre, or even less; indeed the progress was so stately as one observer said 'Many times I have been compelled to look at some tree at a distance to ascertain whether or not the plough teams were moving.'

Obviously not in the same class as the farms mentioned above!

Steam Power

The next power source to come onto the farming scene was steam. For many years, possibly, the main function of the steam engine was to power threshing drums, and these were in common use well into the 1940s. But we are concerned here with the steam engine used in ploughing and other cultivations. In terms of the history of farming in these Islands, the reign of steam cultivation was short lived, but in isolated areas it had an influence on field shape and size. In essence, steam cultivation was carried out by two engines stationed on opposite headlands. A plough, cultivator, and other implements, being drawn across the field on steel cables, first by one engine and then by the other. In one way it was an ideal method of working land because, unlike the present day tractor, the weight of the power source was never borne by the soil being ploughed or cultivated. It hardly needs pointing out that the ideal field shape for steam cultivation was rectangular. Long headlands meant uninterrupted runs for the engines. Cable length obviously put a limit on field width.

Without any doubt, the pioneer of steam cultivation in South Warwickshire and adjoining counties was Benjamin Bomford of Pitchill, Salford Priors. He bought his first steam tackle in about 1864. The Savory engines were made at Gloucester and were of unorthodox design, having the cable drum encasing the boiler. Later designs invariably carried a horizontal cable drum slung underneath the boiler.

Fig. 24 The last set of steam tackle to be operated in South Warwickshire by the late Phil Newbery, The Mill, Hampton Lucy. Breaking out stubble with a cultivator. Note the elm trees and the spire of Tredington Church in the distance. (John Newbery, Darlingscott, 1940s)

Incidentally, Benjamin Bomford was the grandfather of Ernest Bomford, who has already featured more than once in these pages. In 1867, J. M. Jenkins, at the time Secretary of the Royal Agricultural Society of England, made a special report on Benjamin's farming. He records that a great deal of hedge grubbing had been going on at Pitchill, 'The large enclosures of twenty to forty acres being thrown almost into one great field.' This was prairie farming over 130 years ago, but there is no record of any protests at the destruction of habitat! Is it just possible that, in those days, folks were too fully occupied about their own business to fret about how others were conducting theirs? In a more robust age, they might well have received short shrift if they had behaved otherwise. This open countryside is still there, stretching from Irons Cross to Bevington Waste, and from Bevington Hall to Pitchill and beyond.

About the same time as Benjamin Bomford bought his first steam tackle, a Hertfordshire farmer, George Prout, took two farms and proceeded to grow continuous corn, which has a modern ring about it, all cultivations being carried out by steam tackle. His writing is informative, and demonstrates how the new power source altered field size and shape. Let him tell the story.

> The two farms, enclosed within one ring fence, I found subdivided into fifty-one enclosures, averaging nine acres each. Straggling internal fences, encumbered with brushwood, pollard trees and other inferior timber, wasting a great proportion of ground, hindered the proper expedition of tillage, harboured weeds, birds, insects and vermin, injuriously shaded both land and crops and would have taken great

> expense to reduce into neat form and to keep trimmed and in repair. In four years, I grubbed out nearly six and a half miles of ancient hedgerow, removed crooked banks and filled in the ditches alongside; throwing the whole area into nine principal fields of nearly fifty acres each.

Nothing very new in hedge removal to accommodate a new power source. But then, of course, the environment and conservation had not been invented.

But back to South Warwickshire and Sweet Knowle Farm, near Preston-on-Stour, belonging in the 1940s to the Spenser Flowers and managed for them by Albert Hall, and now the home of the Teletubbies. On my first visit, many years ago, I noticed a number of fields that were under the plough, had great, wide, grass headlands. These were, I was told, to provide a sound surface for the steam engines and for carting coal and water to them. Grass headlands in those days were for utilitarian purposes, in contrast to the present-day conservation practice

The era of steam cultivation was comparatively short, not much more than one hundred years. Steam tackle was essentially for the bigger arable farm and for the contractor. The last steamers in South Warwickshire were owned by a contractor, Phil Newberry, of The Mill, Hampton Lucy, whose sons still farm in South Warwickshire at Darlingscott and Honington.

Mr. Newberry was still working his steam tackle in the late 1940s, when it was in demand for breaking out leys for autumn drilling in the hot, dry summers of 1947 and 1949, when clayland baked as hard as bricks.

Horse Power

During the eighteenth and nineteenth centuries, and the first half of the twentieth, horses were the main power source on farms for field work of all kinds.

Much care and time were lavished on their health and welfare, for they played the most essential part in the working of any farm. Moreover, they were a source of much pride on the part of the farmer and also for those who worked the teams in the field. For a full, and evocative, description of farm horses, their working, the horsemen whose responsibility they were, the blacksmiths and farriers, the wheelwrights and saddlers, all of whom were essential to the horse culture, one cannot do better than read *The Horse in the Furrow* by George Ewart Evans

The head horseman, or carter, was responsible for the horses in his care and for the quality of the ploughing and other field work. He held head status amongst the farm work force, on par with the shepherd. It was he who led the teams out to work and back home at the end of the day, followed by the second horseman with his team and the improvers bringing up the rear with theirs.

Fig. 25 Horse teams at a ploughing match.

The horse population peaked in the early years of the 20th century. The estimate of numbers in 1901 (Professor F.M.L.Thompson) are as follows:

Horses on farms	1,511,000
Commercial horses	1,166,000
Carriage and riding	600,000

Estimated horse population in the UK for 1901

Note that commercial, or 'town,' horses, and those used for private purposes, outnumbered those at work on farms

To digress, town horses created a substantial market for hay and oats which increased steadily during the second half of the 19th century in step with the rise in the town horse population.

Hay consumption is estimated to have risen from 840,000 tons in the 1830s to 2,640,000 in the 1900s, and oats from 490,000 tons to 1,540, 000 tons. Counties nearest to centres of population benefited most from this trade. In the case of South Warwickshire, Birmingham was the main market. During the 1840s and 1850s, the sale of hay from Kenilworth parish, for example, increased six-fold and, no doubt, this was no exception.

But thirty years, or so, after the numbers of farm horses had peaked, the writing was on the wall. Some tractors had been imported to help with the food production campaign during the First World War, and there is little doubt that their numbers and technical development were much inhibited by the agricultural depression of the inter-war years. Nevertheless, the production of tractors in quantity started in the UK in the early 1930s.

Tractor Power

The development of the farm tractor has been described in Chapter 31 *Mechanisation*, but here we simply note that, in the second half of the 1940s, the average horse power was in the range 25 hp. to 30 hp. By the end of the century this had increased by a factor of ten, the most powerful machines being of the order of 250 hp. to 300 hp.

Thus anyone fondly imagining that a tractor in the 1990s ten times more powerful than one in 1940, could operate economically in fields of the same size, displays a certain ignorance of farming economics and practicalities. This increase in power took place over a period of sixty years and was accompanied by similar developments in the size of combine harvesters, forage harvesting machinery, and trailed or self-propelled sprayers, and so on.

When the *ard* was replaced by the Romans' mould board plough, the almost square Neolithic fields were abandoned or ploughed over and replaced by longer, narrower, enclosures. Similarly, the slow-moving ox teams created the characteristic open fields of the Feldon and elsewhere, but the use of steam power demanded realignment of field boundaries. Thus it is that the bigger, and more powerful, tractors and other field machinery needed larger enclosures in which to operate during the second half of the twentieth century.

The wheel has come in full circle. Just as Clare was bemoaning the enclosure of the old open fields to create the farming landscape with which we are familiar today, so 20th century conservationists complain at great length at the removal of those very hedges the planting of which caused such great concern at the time, roughly two hundred years ago. For nearly five thousand years, the power sources available for cultivation have stamped their identity upon the landscape. Is there any good reason why the second half of the 20th century should be any exception?

Finally, another question. Why is it quite in order to remove hedges to accommodate the internal combustion engine in the form of the motor car or lorry, but not in order to accommodate it in the form of tractors, combine harvesters, or whatever? When other peoples' hedges are ripped out for road construction or widening, or any other development there is comparatively little comment. But when farmers or landowners remove their own hedges in the course of field enlargement, it is a very different matter!

ENVOI

This, then, is the story of the transformations that have taken place on the farms, in the fields and in the villages of South Warwickshire, Shakespeare's countryside. It is a story of very great changes and developments in both arable, grassland and livestock husbandry; and of the suburbanisation of so many villages in both Arden and Feldon. All these things I have tried to record.

But innovations which first saw the light of day in South Warwickshire have had an influence far beyond its boundaries.

Dodwell and Drayton

First, the work at Drayton and Dodwell, in the days when these farms constituted the Grassland Improvement Station under the directorship of Sir George Stapledon, which did so much to establish ley farming in lowland England. Later at the NAAS Experimental Husbandry Farm at Drayton, where developments included the re-introduction of in-wintering ewes, the re-establishment of the bean crop as a break from cereals on the heavier land and, possibly above all, the development of minimal cultivations for the preparation of autumn seedbeds,

Agricultural Co-operation.

In the realm of agricultural co-operation, South Warwickshire farmers have been in the lead. The formation in the early 1900s, of the National Farmers Union Mutual Insurance Society was, arguably, the first step. Then, in the 1920s, the Warwickshire Farmers' Co-operative was formed, later after many mergers with other co-operatives, to become part of Countrywide, now the largest farmers' co-operative in the country. Then, in the post-1945 era came the formation of co-operatives for the marketing and storage of grain, and the marketing of livestock. The co-operative grass drying at Bearley is a further example, and South Warwickshire farmers played their part in the running of the Artificial Insemination Centre at Bromsgrove.

Agricultural Education.

Thirdly, the story of agricultural education in South Warwickshire has been notable by its absence in the above pages, for the very good reason that abler pens than mine, and with first-hand knowledge, have recorded the histories of

Studley College and of the Warwickshire Agricultural College before it became merged with the Further Education College at Leamington.

Nevertheless, two firsts must be noted. Miss Hess, who was the last Principal at Studley College, initiated the first course for Farm Secretaries in the country. George Jackson, when he was Principal at the Warwickshire College, at Moreton Morrell, pioneered courses in equine studies. Where Miss Hess and George Jackson had led, others very shortly followed.

Full Bellies Make For Empty Minds.

The tale of how South Warwickshire farmers, and those elsewhere, responded to the need for extra food production in the 1940s, and later, is almost a saga in its own right. But, today, all this is forgotten. A whole generation has grown up which does not know what it is like to go shopping with a ration book in handbag or coat pocket. The lessons of history have been forgotten. There has been much talk of global markets, with supermarkets stocked with imported food, some of it produced under conditions which would not be tolerated in the UK.

Politicians, the media, and the consuming public, are now indifferent to the fate of the farming community. But we have been here before, as A.G.Street so ably described in the 1930s.

It is assumed, without question, that the well-being of the environment and wildlife, as perceived by townies, takes precedence over the interests of those who farm the land or who are employed in the ancillary industries and services. Some green and so-called animal welfare organisations, like the medieval church, do not hesitate to use force against persons and property in an attempt to enforce their dogma. The ways and means by which the medieval church and some such societies fill their coffers, bear a striking similarity, as those readers familiar with the history of nearby Hailes Abbey will appreciate.

We do not know, we cannot tell why, when, and under what circumstances, the urban population of these Islands will have to turn, once again, to our own farmers, fields and farms for a higher proportion of their daily sustenance, a prospect now as remote as it appeared in the early 1900s and in the 1920s.

But it may well be, even in a mainly irreligious society, that the time honoured Grace 'For what we are about to receive may the Lord make us truly thankful' will regain its significance.

INDEX

The Author

Mike Woods graduated from the University of Reading with a BSc. (Agric.) in 1943.

Apart from three years as a crop husbandry specialist in the West Midlands in the early days of the National agricultural Advisory Service, he spent his entire working life as an Agricultural Adviser and Consultant in South Warwickshire. As well as this day job, he was a visiting Lecturer in farm records and accounts and farm business management in what was then the Warwickshire Agricultural College, the Agricultural Department in Banbury and Witney Colleges of Further Education, and at Studley College in the last two years prior to its closure. He also wrote a weekly farming column in the Stratford-upon-Avon Herald for thirty-nine years, and for a few years in the Birmingham Post and the former Coventry Evening Telegraph.

In January 1992, the Council of the National Farmers' Union elected him an Honorary Life Member of the Warwickshire Branch of the NFU in recognition of his services to Agriculture and the National Farmers' Union.